LOCOMOTIVE ENGINEERS OF THE LMS

and its major English constituent companies

Denis Griffiths

CEng, BEng, MSc, FIMarE

PSL

Patrick Stephens Limited

Dedication
For Elizabeth E. Griffiths,
my mother, with love and thanks

First published in 1991

British Library Cataloguing in Publication Data
Griffiths, Denis, *1943–*
    Locomotive engineers of the LMS and its major
    English constituent companies
    1. Great Britain. Railway services. London, Midland
    and Scottish Railway. Railway engineers, history
I. Title
    625.100922
    ISBN 1-85260-142-6

Front endpaper *The paint shop at Derby Works circa 1890.* (G. Charles collection)

Title page *'Dreadnought' compound* Marchioness of Stafford. (G. Charles collection)

Rear endpaper *Streamlined 'Pacific' No. 6220 under construction at Crewe.* (LMS official)

Patrick Stephens Limited, a member of the Haynes Publishing Group, has published authoritative, quality books for enthusiasts for more than twenty years. During that time the company has established a reputation as one of the world's leading publishers of books on aviation, maritime, military, model-making, motor cycling, motoring, motor racing, railway and railway modelling subjects. Readers or authors with suggestions for books they would like to see published are invited to write to:
The Editorial Director, Patrick Stephens Limited, Sparkford, Nr Yeovil, Somerset, BA22 7JJ.

Printed in Great Britain by J.H. Haynes & Co Ltd

10   9   8   7   6   5   4   3   2   1

Contents

Acknowledgements

A work of this nature requires access to a considerable amount of literature which can only be found in libraries. Unknown staff of various libraries have provided considerable help and to these the author offers grateful thanks. These libraries include: National Railway Museum, Institution of Mechanical Engineers, Institution of Civil Engineers, Borough of Crewe, City of Derby, Borough of Bolton, and City of Liverpool. Individuals include Dr Stan Utting, a former Crewe apprentice, John Banks and Frank Smith. Geoff Johnson provided considerable help although he was not always aware of it. Photographic sources, where they are not the author's, are individually credited.

The individuals, most long deceased, who wrote the technical papers or made contributions to the discussion of these papers, have provided valuable material for the author and other researchers. The same is true for those who wrote articles and books on the subject of railway engineering. Throughout the text and in the reference section these sources have been acknowledged.

The author is grateful to the secretary of the Institution of Mechanical Engineers for permission to quote from papers of that learned society and from the Journal of the Institution of Locomotive Engineers. Thanks are also due to the secretary of the Institution of Civil Engineers for permission to quote from the Institution's proceedings. The editors of the *Engineer* and *Engineering* have also given permission for extracts from those journals to be used. Gratitude is also due to Keith Wilkinson and Karen Shepherd for their photographic help and advice.

Introduction

It is a fact that the London Midland & Scottish Railway was the largest of the four companies formed at the grouping in 1923, but apart from William Stanier, and to a lesser degree J. A. F. Aspinall, none of the Chief Mechanical Engineers have been afforded a biography. In the context of railway history that is a serious omission, even if the average railway enthusiast only seems to be interested in pictures of their locomotive products. The LMS cannot be treated in isolation from its pre-grouping constituents, so it is also necessary to consider the Chief Mechanical Engineers of those concerns. That, however, presents problems. Not only did the LMS have more CMEs than the other railways, six in its short history compared with only two for the Southern, for example, but it was also formed from a great number of small and large railway companies, and a work of considerable magnitude would be necessary to cover the lives of all the CMEs. So to keep this volume within reasonable limits its extent has been restricted.

Only the three main pre-grouping companies in England, the Lancashire & Yorkshire, London & North Western and Midland Railways, will be considered, Scottish engineers being left to a later work. Even then it is necessary to define starting points. These have been chosen at different times for each of the railways concerned in order to suit the arrival in office of the engineer whose influence marked a change in the affairs of that company. An introductory chapter will describe the basic situation up to those starting points. Aspinall will mark the beginning for the Lancashire & Yorkshire, as his arrival coincided with operations at Horwich, Ramsbottom for the London & North Western, with centralization at Crewe, and Kirtley for the Midland, from its incorporation.

This restricted view will none the less show how some of the major railway Mechanical Engineers operated and will give insights into the lives of a number of famous men, at least in railway terms; some might argue 'infamous' in certain cases, but much that has been written about these engineers is but hearsay without any real evidence. Reference has been made to papers presented at learned societies and contemporary railway and engineering literature, as well as books and articles by people who knew these engineers at first hand. As a group, the men under consideration were responsible for more papers to learned societies than probably all other British railway Mechanical Engineers taken together. The outputs of J. A. F. Aspinall and Henry Fowler were prodigious and both were highly respected members of the engineering community.

Fowler has received much criticism in less well informed books and sections of the popular railway press without any real evidence to back up such criticism or even explain it. Those responsible have not understood the role of a Chief Mechanical Engineer and have relied upon the ignorance of the reader to bolster their own ignorance or prejudice, or both. One criticism often aimed at Fowler is that he did not design the locomotives produced during his tenure in office.

To make such a statement is to totally misunderstand the work of a CME. These men were heads of very large and important departments, but they were employed to serve the railway and provide it with locomotives, rolling-stock and other mechanical services—they did not dictate policy, nor was the railway operated for their benefit. Just like the drivers and porters, they were company servants, important servants but servants nonetheless.

The CME had a large staff under his control, and one section was devoted to the production of locomotives and keeping them at work. Maintenance of locomotives was, in effect, a larger part of the job than design or construction. The CME would no more be expected to retube a boiler or scrape in a white metal bearing than he would be expected to sit at a drawing-board all day producing new design. Detail design work is time-consuming, and large armies of draughtsmen were employed, under a Chief Draughtsman, to do all of that design work. A CME might outline the general scheme for the locomotive to the Chief Draughtsmen or he might simply indicate the need for a locomotive for a particular duty, but it was the Chief Draughtsman who would then see that the work was done, reporting back to the CME at particular stages or to obtain certain approval. That was the job for which he was paid and the CME was paid to ensure effective operation of the entire department.

The fact that some CMEs took a more active interest in design work than others does not indicate greater knowledge, devotion to duty or even ability as an engineer; it simply indicates a preference, but other branches of their duties would have had to be delegated to other members of their staff. Of course any new design would have to be submitted to the CME for inspection and, if the drawings were passed, his signature, or that of a deputy, would appear upon it. But the fact that a CME signed a particular drawing did not mean that he actually sat at a drawing-board and produced it, any more may the signature of the Chief Cashier on a banknote means that he has printed it.

During the Fowler regime, a number of good designs were developed for particular duties and several designs were produced which others on the railway blocked from going into production. Fowler worked within the very narrow limits imposed by his masters and it was the imposition of those restrictions which acted against the LMS. He was as much a victim of internal politics and misguided ideals as the railway itself. Stanier, however, does not receive the same sort of criticism in relation to his 'Duchess' 'Pacifics', the credit for which should really go to his Chief Draughtsman T.F. Coleman. It was he who masterminded the detail design work whilst Stanier was in India.

In order to reach the position of Chief Mechanical Engineer, any individual had to have a good grasp of engineering but, certainly during the twentieth century, a major part of his job concerned management of plant and individuals. Little management training was ever given; in fact, it has only recently become an essential part of a professional engineer's training programme. All people have preferences in their work, and the CMEs of railway companies were no exception. It was understandable that each individual would tend to show more interest in the topic which taxed his skills and proved most satisfying. Design, manufacture, materials, testing and operation all fell in the general area under the control of the CME. In order to do his job satisfactorily he had to ensure that all areas functioned as he required. He did not, however, need to tend to each duty himself, but had to exercise correct control over those to whom he delegated the work. That some individuals preferred to concentrate their particular efforts in a certain area does not mean that other duties were neglected. Delegation is the key to effective management, and CMEs were managers as well as engineers.

All railways required sufficient locomotives of the correct type and power in order to operate their trains, that being their function. Railway management had to be effective in order to ensure that all branches of its operation were working together, but unfortunately that did not always happen. A change in train services, in terms of load or speed, could cause havoc unless the CME had been informed well in advance of what was required. Over-optimistic planners and less than well-organized management could leave a railway dramatically short of power for operating its intended services. No railway could afford to have its mechanical engineering department so extensive that locomotives, and rolling-stock, could be designed and produced at short notice; this would mean people and equipment lying idle for long periods waiting for the next management dictate. Private locomotive manufacturers could react to sudden orders because their business was organized along those lines, but not so a railway company. Unrealistic demands imposed burdens on some CMEs that they should never have been expected to carry.

Restrictions with respect to loading gauge and weight limitation differed with company and route. The attitude of management to the type of service it wished to operate also imposed restrictions and dictated the size and power of locomotives required. Over such matters the CME generally had no control.

This book is not, however, about locomotives, but is about people. The fact that it must deal with locomotives is inevitable since they were the main product of the Chief Mechanical Engineer's efforts. Their design, construction and maintenance were all part of his responsibilities and all must be considered if a complete picture of the individual CME at work is to be obtained. But that is not all, for each of the men had to relate to his assistants and the workforce in general. How each did that is a reflection of his character.

Where appropriate the engineers will speak for themselves through papers presented before learned societies or in contributions to the discussion of other papers. When presenting a paper or taking part in a discussion with his peers, each man could be himself, an engineer amongst engineers. His statements might reflect the situation which existed upon the railway he served, but he expressed his own opinions and accurately gave the results of his own experiments. No good engineer would attempt to deceive his fellow engineers, for he knew that he would soon be found out and exposed. Where information might be selectively published for general, or even management consumption, that which was divulged to fellow engineers was the complete truth. Views expressed were firmly and honestly held.

Published works of those who knew the engineers personally have been consulted. Such people include R. C. Bond, a pupil of Fowler and a senior LMS engineer, and E. S. Cox, a premium apprentice at Horwich and also part of the LMS engineering team. Their recent works add to the knowledge of some of the men under consideration. That respected railway journalist, C. S. Lake, knew personally a number of the engineers who form the subject matter of this book and his opinions are worthy of repetition. Unfortunately this is not the case with many other statements which have been made with reference to a number of the engineers. Innuendo, myth and opinion have frequently been quoted as fact without any attempt to produce the evidence. This will not be repeated in the present work.

By rights, each of the engineers discussed deserves a full biography, and hopefully one day they will be afforded that recognition. This work aims to look at their engineering lives in the context of the railways they served, and will avoid considering purely personal matters or those which were the concern of employers other than the LMS, L&YR, L&NWR, and Midland railways.

1. The Early Years

Early railway history abounds with the formation of numerous small lines which either grew bigger or were merged to form larger conglomerates. Each of these railways was initially formed in order to serve a particular region, but as the advantages of long-distance rail transportation became evident such lines were extended, merged with neighbouring lines or reached agreements with them for running powers. That allowed traffic to operate over longer distances than had been originally envisaged and also caused an increase in the size of loads carried because the ability to transport goods economically and quicker over such long distances produced a general increase in trade.

The small low-powered locomotives which had been suitable for a railway's original traffic were no longer suitable to meet the ever-increasing demands, and more powerful machines had to be produced. Large numbers were also needed in order to operate the enhanced services demanded, and these all had to be maintained even if, at that time, a particular railway did not manufacture its own locomotives. As larger railway combines emerged, the role of the Locomotive Superintendent became more critical, for on his shoulders rested the railway's ability to operate its services.

Mergers meant that one man took charge of the stock produced for a number of smaller railways. A wide variety of designs, frequently produced by many different builders, would then be available to operate throughout the enlarged railway's system, but the maintenance of 'foreign' locomotives could present difficulties if they were moved to other areas. It is fortunate that the increasing demands of traffic required older engines to be displaced by newer, more powerful machines, so the problem of how to cope with a varied and odd assortment never really taxed the early locomotive engineers — they simply scrapped and replaced. That policy of standardization, even if the term was not specifically used, was followed by all railways right through to nationalization.

The Lancashire and Yorkshire Railway

The Manchester & Leeds Railway formed the nucleus of the Lancashire & Yorkshire Railway. Although a line between those two cities had been suggested in 1825, it was not until the beginning of the next decade that any concrete proposals were produced and action taken. The first stage between Manchester and Littleborough opened in 1839 with completion taking a further two years. The final 9.5 miles between Normanton and Leeds was actually run over North Midland Railway metals. Locomotives and rolling-stock were supplied by contractors although maintenance work was carried out by the company at its Miles Platting works.

In 1839, the Directors decided to appoint a Locomotive Superintendent to deal with all matters appertaining to motive power, and in April selected John Todd. He evidently could not get on with the General Superintendent of the line and resigned just over a year later. The next incumbent, James Fenton, served slightly longer, resigning in January 1845. A period of stability arrived with the third holder of the post, William Jenkins.

Jenkins was the son of a millwright and had served part of his engineering apprenticeship with his father before completing it with the firm Wren & Hughes in Manchester. He later served under Jesse Hartley in charge of engines and machinery in the Liverpool dock system. Railway experience was also gained under Hartley, who had been appointed engineer to the Manchester & Bolton Railway. Eventually, in 1838, Jenkins was appointed to superintend the locomotive stock on that line and served in that capacity until taking up the similar position on the Manchester & Leeds Railway. When, in 1846, these two railways amalgamated, Jenkins retained responsibility only for the Manchester & Leeds stock, with his successor on the Manchester & Bolton Railway, William Hurst, retaining control of that line's motive power centred on the shed at Salford.

Upon appointment, Jenkins took responsibility for the fitting out of the workshops at Miles Platting, then being constructed under the supervision of John Hawkshaw. As Hawkshaw had also served under Hartley on the Liverpool dock system and on the Manchester & Bolton Railway, it is likely that he came to know Jenkins during that period and helped gain him the appointment on the Manchester & Leeds Railway when it became vacant. Early in 1846 the Miles Platting workshops were sufficiently well equipped not only for repairs but also for locomotive construction. Six locomotives were immediately ordered, these being of 2-2-2 form to a design by Jenkins but based on earlier machines delivered by outside contractors. The Manchester & Leeds Railway became the first railway in Britain to adopt the practice of constructing its own locomotives, although others obviously had plans to do so.[1]

The Lancashire & Yorkshire Railway formally came into being in 1847 when the amalgamated lines adopted that title. Over a number of years other lines also joined the combine, but as this is a book concerning Locomotive Engineers rather than railway development, there is no real need to consider these amalgamations apart from where they affected the mechanical engineering side. In 1849 it was decided to combine the two locomotive departments of the former Manchester & Leeds and Manchester & Bolton railways, with Jenkins as the Indoor Superintendent and Hurst as Outdoor Superintendent. Jenkins thus had control of design and construction whilst Hurst dealt with running and day-to-day operations.

Jenkins remained in command at Miles Platting, adding a variety of locomotives to the L&YR stock in order to meet the demands of its developing services. Goods engines of the 0-6-0 type commenced production in 1854, but two years later a number of 0-6-0 tank locomotives were produced for passenger work on the severely graded Oldham branch. These were the first six-coupled engines designed specifically for passenger work. Weighing some 30 tons and with two 15 in x 24 in inside cylinders coupled to 5 ft diameter driving wheels, they proved suitable for the work involved and a total of 26 were constructed, the final one in 1871.[2]

At this time coke was the main fuel for locomotives, but growth of the railway system resulted in a shortage. The combustion of coal not only resulted in the production of smoke and the risk of prosecution, but it also burned badly in the existing fireboxes causing poor steaming. Many engineers engaged themselves in developing a suitable locomotive firebox which would burn coal effectively. Jenkins was one of these. He produced an enlarged firebox with tubular stays at the front for support and introduced a hook-shaped cast iron arch positioned where the brick arch was placed in later fireboxes.[3] Unfortunately no further details are available, nor are there any notes relating to his reasoning behind such a fitment, but he was obviously working along the correct lines in attempting to allow for better mixing of air and volatile gases from the coal.

Like most other railways of the period, the L&YR suffered from financial restrictions and, naturally, the locomotive department had to be restrained. Older lcomotives had to contend with operating enhanced services which then suffered as a result of their run-down condition. The loco-motives designed by Jenkins were certainly effective for their day but development of railway services progressed at a greater rate than the locomotive stock. This does not indicate that Jenkins was not an effective engineer, but illustrates that a limited budget results in a less effective product. A locomotive department uses funds, it never creates any. Directors wishing to cut costs in order to help the dividend looked to the high-spending departments, so accordingly the locomotive department suffered. That situation existed on all railways, and not only during the mid-nineteenth century.

Due to ill health, Jenkins was granted leave during August 1867 and he died on 20 November. For the next eight years the locomotive stock of the Lancashire & Yorkshire Railway became the responsibility of a quartet of engineers. In January 1868 William Yates became Indoor Superintendent at Miles Platting, so was responsible for design. William Hurst once more became Outdoor Superintendent following a spell as Locomotive Superintendent on the North British Railway. He left that post, occupied since January 1855, under somewhat of a cloud following allegations of financial impropriety, returning to the L&YR as Indoor Superintendent at Bury. The workshops there belonged to the East Lancashire Railway which amalgamated with the L&YR in 1859, becoming the East Lancashire Division. Locomotives were repaired at Bury but construction only commenced after amalgamation.

John Jacques became Indoor Superintendent at Bury in 1865 following the death of Sylvester Lees who had held the post since the locomotive department was formed in 1848. Outdoor Superintendent alongside Jacques was R. Mason, who died in 1873 to be succeeded by George Roberts. The Outdoor Superintendent had no real influence on design and Jacques himself exercised very little with Bury engines being basic-ally the same as those produced by outside contractors. Only Yates seems to have had any influence on locomotive design, but the divided command structure and use of different workshop sites certainly restricted development.[4]

The already over-stretched Miles Platting works suffered a serious fire in 1873 and the L&YR Directors were forced to purchase a number of 2-4-0 and 0-6-0 Ramsbottom-designed locomotives from Crewe. This resulted in private locomotive builders taking out an injunction against the London & North Western Railway, preventing it from constructing locomotives for other railways, but it also brought home to the L&YR Directors the deplorable state of its own locomotive stock.

In July 1875 the Board decided that indoor and outdoor functions at both sites would in future be under the control of a single person, and immediately advertised the post.

The man appointed to take sole charge of the Lancashire & Yorkshire Railway's locomotive fleet was William Barton Wright. Designated Chief Locomotive Superintendent, Wright commenced service on 1 November 1875, and the previous four incumbent engineers were told to regard him as their senior. Yates remained at Miles Platting as Works Manager and Roberts occupied the same post at Bury, but the other two left L&YR service, Hurst retiring and Jacques moving to pastures new. Wright thought as little of the locomotive stock as the Directors, and immediately set about rectifying matters, at least as best as he could. In deciding to appoint a single engineer to head the locomotive department, the Directors also seemed moved to furnish additional money for renewals, money which if supplied earlier might have prevented such a run-down situation from existing in the first place.

William Barton Wright.

It has been said that during his first month in office, Wright called for the scrapping of 12 locomotives from one shed alone because they were completely unfit for further service. [5] That story may not be strictly accurate in terms of numbers, but it does illustrate the effect Wright must have had. However, scrapping locomotives was no solution unless replacements could be obtained, but the works at Miles Platting and Bury were already stretched to the limit. Wright had no time to organize the design of his own locomotives and was prepared to deal with trusted private locomotive builders. His previous experience was along those lines anyway for he had been Locomotive Superintendent to the Madras Railway in India from 1855 until his appointment to the L&YR. In that post he had to deal with locomotives supplied from Britain and so knew reasonably well which manufacturers he could trust. An order for 22 0-6-0 goods engines therefore went to Kitson & Co., these being to an almost identical design to those being built by Kitson for the Taff Vale Railway.

John Hawkshaw was consulting engineer to the Madras Railway as well as the L&YR and it is obvious that he was well aware of the attributes of Wright. Such a voice at court cannot have been amiss when the selection for the Lancashire & Yorkshire position had been made. Wright, like so many of the early railway engineers, came from the North East, having been born at North Shields on 13 November 1828. The family had moved to London when he was 11 years old and in 1845, at the age of 17 years, he had commenced an apprenticeship at Swindon under Daniel Gooch. Family connections probably helped in securing that apprenticeship for an aunt on his father's side had married into the family of Anna Longridge, Gooch's mother. Upon completion of his apprenticeship and following a short spell as assistant to the Works Manager at Swindon, Archibald Sturrock, Wright had taken charge of the locomotive depot at Paddington and had remained there until he joined the Madras Railway.[6]

The chronic shortage of space at Miles Platting was relieved somewhat when carriage production shifted to the new works at Newton Heath in 1877. This allowed building to commence of 40 0-6-0 locomotives of the same class that had been constructed by Kitson, and these turned out to be the last locomotives actually built at Miles Platting. So useful were these locomotives that production of the class continued until 1887 with Sharp Stewart, Beyer Peacock and the Vulcan Foundry also receiving orders. In its original

Wright's 0-6-0 locomotive based on the Kitson design. No 975 was built by Beyer, Peacock in 1887.

form it was not exactly a Wright design, but the modifications sought by Wright from the initial constructors, Kitson & Co, and the gradual changes which came about with each batch made it one. Aspinall, who succeeded Wright, continued production and also converted many of the class into saddle tanks. In that form a large proportion of them served until after nationalization, and what had essentially been produced as an urgent replacement for worn-out stock served the L&YR, the LMSR and BR as a useful shunting engine. The last survived until 1964 with 87 years of service to its credit. Wright may not have had time to indulge in much design work, but he knew a lasting product when he saw one. Fortunately an example of each form has been preserved.

The locomotives introduced during Wright's tenure in office cannot really be described as his designs, and it is highly unlikely that he ever claimed them to be so. Orders placed with private locomotive builders were frequently to a design that was already under construction, but Wright knew what would suit his operations and did not appear to be concerned about developing a reputation as a designer. Others were employed to do that and he was content to make use of the expertise offered by the private builders. Certainly if an existing design required modification in order to suit it to L&YR requirements, these were ordered by Wright, but he left the basic design to the manu-

facturer. He was also not reluctant to use the locomotive designs which had been developed for other railways if they suited the purpose. The Taff Vale 0-6-0 has already been considered but that was quickly followed by eight 0-4-2 locomotives from Sharp Stewart to a design by Patrick Stirling for the Great Northern Railway. Nobody could accuse Wright of being on a designer's 'ego-trip'!

Wright's role should not, however, be misunderstood. He was a good engineer who could make rational choices as to which locomotives suited his requirements and would indulge in rebuilding of older stock if that was considered to be necessary. The 4-4-0 passenger tender engines introduced in 1880 can reasonably be ascribed to Wright himself although, again, none were built by the L&YR; Kitson, Sharp Stewart, Neilson and the Vulcan Foundry provided batches between that date and 1887. The final 16 were actually ordered after Wright left office, and had a boiler pressure 20 psi higher than the 140 psi of the earlier locomotives. The other major difference introduced by Aspinall was an American swinging link bogie with 3 ft wheels instead of the Adams sliding centre type with 3 ft 7.5 in wheels. Driving wheels remained the same at 6 ft diameter. Because the existing L&YR turntables were rather short, the original batch of 4-4-0s had to be fitted with short four-wheeled tenders, but these were transferred to the GNR-design 0-4-2s when turntable alterations had been made.[7]

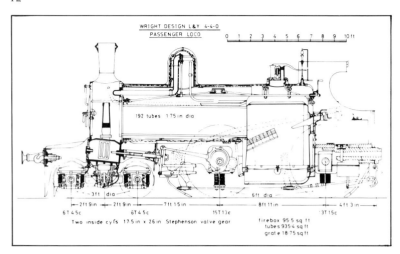

WRIGHT DESIGN L&Y 4-4-0
PASSENGER LOCO

Left *Wright's 4-4-0 passenger locomotive of 1880.*

Below right *4-4-0 No 866, formerly* Princess of Wales, *built by Kitson in 1898.* (National Railway Museum, York)

The L&YR had a separate superintendent to deal with carriage and wagon matters but Wright took an interest, especially with regard to continuous braking. He was a member of the Institution of Mechanical Engineers and of the Institution of Civil Engineers, but his only direct contribution to either professional body was on the matter of braking, during the discussion of a paper entitled 'On Continuous Brakes for Railway Trains' by R. D. Sanders. The Lancashire & Yorkshire had been a pioneer in the adoption of continuous brakes with systems by James Newall and Charles Fay being tried during the 1850s. These were screw-operated brakes and still found use on that railway in 1878 when the paper was presented. Wright considered that the arrangement was not good enough for trains of the period and advocated an automatic type of brake, particularly on lines which were steeply graded like the Lancashire & Yorkshire. He further intimated that he was conducting trials with an automatic pressure system and an automatic vacuum system, but refused to give details.[8]

The fact that Wright rather than F. Attock, the Carriage & Wagon Superintendent, took part in the discussion is interesting and probably indicates that he was the senior man who made the major decisions as far as mechanical engineering matters were concerned. As a result of these and other brake trials a decision was made to adopt the automatic vacuum brake. By May 1888 all passenger stock had been provided with vacuum brakes and even in 1887 it had been decided to fit 100 goods locomotives with automatic vacuum brakes. Continuous brakes for goods trains was not addressed, but at least the goods engines could work passenger stock if required.[9]

Despite improvements to the locomotive works at Miles Platting it became evident during the early 1880s that not even repairs, let alone construction, could any longer be carried out there with satisfaction. Space was not available for expansion and the growing fleet of Lancashire & Yorkshire locomotives did require periodic attention. Security around the Miles Platting site also left much to be desired, with the theft of non-ferrous parts from parked locomotives being common. Ahrons even recounts the tale of a locomotive which was stripped down to its frame, the entire boiler disappearing.[10] New works were essential if the railway was to maintain its engine stock in reasonable condition and once more construct the majority of its own locomotives.

John Ramsbottom, then consulting engineer to the L&YR (see chapter 3), advised the Board on this matter and agreement was reached that a new works should be constructed. Ramsbottom and Wright were told to inspect various sites and report back on the most suitable, and Wright was also asked to find out about the wage rates paid at workshops throughout the country. None of the sites initially inspected proved ideal, but in May 1884 it became known that a 350-acre estate at Horwich would soon be sold by auction. Again Ramsbottom and Wright were requested to make an inspection. This indicated that the site was ideal and authority was given to purchase it. The price paid, £36,000, was just over half of what had been set aside for the purchase, but the sale of leases on 200 acres not required for the works covered the price paid and a substantial amount of the costs involved in erecting the works.[11]

Wright played his part in organizing the layout of shops and the purchase of equipment, but one of his prime concerns was that of accommodation for workers. Probably as a result of his insistence, a housing estate was laid out with streets being named after famous engineers including Brunel, Gooch, Ramsbottom and Webb. Like other engineers of the period, Wright was a hard taskmaster and required his workforce to thoroughly earn their money. The growing awareness of many workers that they were being exploited did show itself from time to time and the use of a hard hand did not generally help matters. Unfair treatment caused resentment, and Wright could be unfair as is shown by an example involving engine cleaners at Newton Heath. A strike followed the raising of working hours without any increase in pay, and the dispute grew to encompass other grievances including the amount of waste issued for engine cleaning and the lack of any allowance for firing turns. Wright refused to discuss the matter with any of the strikers and summarily dismissed them.[12] It is hard to imagine Joseph Armstrong on the GWR treating his men with such callous disregard, but that was the general attitude of the time.

Wright did not remain with the Lancashire & Yorkshire long enough to see the fruits of his labours regarding Horwich for he resigned in June 1886. His reasons were personal and he simply informed the Board that it was desirable that he should remove himself to London before the end of the year. The Board accepted his resignation and agreed to pay him the sum of £1,000 to cover any services they might require from him until the end of the year. In addition, and probably on the advice of Ramsbottom who had been elected a Director in 1885, they ordered that an advertisement be placed inviting applications for the post of Chief Mechanical Engineer of the company.[13] Wright had simply been the Locomotive Superintendent. He subsequently carried out work as a consultant and involved himself again with the railways of India, eventually retiring from active duties in 1892.

Wright's departure from the L&YR heralded a new era, but his efforts should not be looked upon as without consequence. He worked hard to bring that railway up to the standard required to operate an efficient service. During his ten years in office he renewed almost the entire locomotive stock as well as increasing its total number. New sheds and improved workshops were provided or put in hand so his successor could, at least, start from a better position than that which Wright had inherited.

The London & North Western Railway

The London & North Western Railway came into being on 16 July 1846 with the amalgamation of the Grand Junction Railway, the Manchester & Birmingham Railway and the London & Birmingham Railway. A number of smaller lines had also been swallowed up by or merged with these railways before that date, the most notable being the amalgamation of the Liverpool & Manchester Railway and the Grand Junction Railway in 1845. The names indicate the basic operating areas except for the Grand Junction which formed the link between the Liverpool & Manchester at Newton, and Birmingham.

Each of those three main railways had its own locomotive department and it seemed reasonable for the LNWR to operate along similar lines. Three divisions were established corresponding to the former constituent company areas. The Northern Division, based at Crewe and under the supervision of Francis Trevithick, covered the former Grand Junction system; the North Eastern Division, based at Longsight, Manchester, dealt with the Manchester & Birmingham routes; and the Southern Division, based at Wolverton and under the control of James Edward McConnell, was established to encompass the London & Birmingham Railway area. John Ramsbottom was in charge at Longsight but his sphere of operation was smaller than the other two and the North Eastern Division was something of a subdivision of that based at Crewe. Things changed, however, but as the life and works of Ramsbottom will receive attention in Chapter 3, only passing mention will be made here.

Joseph Locke was the engineer responsible for the Grand Junction Railway and, like the Stephensons and Brunel, was in complete control of all engineering matters including locomotives. When the line became operational it became obvious that a full-time locomotive superintendent was required. Locke remembered William Barber Buddicom, one of his assistants, who took over responsibility for the locomotive department in January 1840. At the time his base was at Edge Hill, Liverpool, and he appointed Alexander Allan as foreman in charge of the workshops. Locomotive stock was not in the best condition with the 22 Stephenson 'Patentee' 2-2-2s suffering from a spate of broken crank axles, not unusual for the time, nor in later years.

Buddicom set about trying to rectify matters with newer designs, and eventually a proposal was worked out for an outside-cylinder 2-2-2. This formed the basis of what later became known as the 'Crewe-type' locomotive over which much controversy raged regarding its originator. Buddicom resigned and Francis Trevithick, third son of the famous Richard Trevithick, was appointed to the post of Locomotive Superintendent with effect from 1 September 1841. [14]

The positioning of the locomotive works at Edge Hill, some 15 miles from GJR tracks, caused considerable inconvenience, and a decision was made to seek a more suitable and central location. Locke investigated several sites but the location at what was to become Crewe offered considerable possibilities. Land was acquired and tenders placed for construction of a workshop as well as housing for the workers. By May 1843 transfer to Crewe was complete with Trevithick the Locomotive Superintendent and Allan his assistant, (basically he was the foreman in charge of the locomotive works). Locomotive construction commenced at Crewe almost as soon as the works became operational and by the end of that first year three outside-cylinder 2-2-2 locomotives had been built. Gradually production increased and a different wheel arrangement was produced, 2-4-0, but still of the basic 'Crewe-type'. These 2-2-2 and 2-4-0 designs effectively became standards and little else was produced over the next few years. Improvements by way of Stephenson valve gear and longer boilers were made but the design remained fundamentally the same.

As mentioned above, responsibility for the design of the 'Crewe-type' has been the subject of some discussion, and Allan made claims to be its originator [15], but few real facts exist to support his case. In fact, before he made his claim the only other source to indicate that Allan was responsible for the design was D. K. Clark in his 1855 volume *Railway Machinery*. Trevithick was in charge at Crewe and, therefore, responsible for design and construction. He made the decisions and must have received advice and assistance from a number of people. The original concept was schemed when Buddicom was in charge and was developed by him for use elsewhere. From this it is reasonable to assume that no single individual was responsible for the design but a number of people were influential in its production. The same was true, in most cases, throughout the steam era.

Trevithick was a rather quiet man who appears to have been too easy-going and allowed his authority to slip. He was not a man to court publicity and for that reason his achievements seem to have gone unrecognized. He was extremely popular with the workers, a popularity probably helped by his unwillingness to see anybody hurt or placed in a position of discomfort. The growing scale of operations at Crewe obviously caused him problems and he became unable to exercise proper control. Dissatisfaction with Trevithick's management, or rather lack of it, increased after Richard Moon became a member of the Board in 1851, and by 1856 he was calling for the Northern and North Eastern Divisions to be merged under Ramsbottom. That move was defeated, but in 1857 he had his way and Trevithick was dismissed. Even Moon admitted that Trevithick was clever and honest, but his lack of strength when it came to management just would not do. [16]

At the time the LNWR was passing through a difficult period and, in his letter of resignation of August 1857, Trevithick blamed the problem on poor relations between Directors and Managers. The fact that Trevithick wrote a letter of resignation does not mean that he was not dismissed; such a means allowed an individual to move on without future questions as to the reason. Even Trevithick recognized that he was being dismissed, but he blamed it on disagreements over expenditure rather than his own lack of control.[17]

Trevithick returned to Cornwall but he left pleasant memories at Crewe where he had been popular; the nature of his dismissal, however, left a bitter taste, even Joseph Locke protesting about it. Crewe had become an established town during his stewardship and the LNWR was able to build upon that; unfortunately the locomotive stock was not ideal for the future comprising mainly small engines. The new man would need to produce a more powerful fleet, and money would be required.

The fact that Alexander Allan was part of the early Crewe scene warrants his inclusion here even though he was by no means Locomotive Superintendent. His initial locomotive training was obtained at the works of Robert Stephenson & Co in Newcastle following an apprenticeship as a millwright in his native Scotland. Subsequent experience was gained at Forrester's in Liverpool, with service in Ireland when Forrester's were awarded the contract for maintenance of the locomotives belonging to the Dublin & Kingstown Railway. Upon his return from Ireland in 1835 Allan became manager of the Grand Junction's works at Edge Hill.[18]

Three years later he moved to Crewe as Works Manager under Trevithick, the official title being 'chief foreman of locomotives'. It is almost certain that he was more of a disciplinarian than Trevithick and that matter probably lead to disagreement between the two, although Trevithick would certainly have tried to avoid any real conflict. As has already been noted the influence Allan had on the design of the 'Crewe-type' locomotives has been overstated with a number of people giving him more credit than was deserved. As Works Manager he must have had some form of influence upon production and would certainly have offered advice; how much was taken is not possible to say, but it is likely to have been less than that for which he claimed credit. Forrester's made use of outside cylinders for many locomotives and it is likely that Allan became enthusiastic about the advantages of such positioning, but he was not the originator of any Forrester

design. Therefore the fact that the 'Crewe-type' locomotives had outside cylinders is no reason for believing that Allan had anything to do with the design, which evolved through the efforts of Buddicom, Locke and Trevithick. Allan was a good engineer, but his presence at Crewe was not as influential as certain histories have indicated. A number of railway-based inventions do, however, stand to his credit, the most noteworthy being that of the straight link valve gear of 1855 which was fitted in a great many locomotives and stationary steam engines.

Allan proved to be very effective at managing the works at Crewe and at intervals over the years his salary was increased until in 1852 he earned £500 per annum. Minutes of the LNWR Crewe Committee indicate that Allan was not in agreement with the easy way in which Trevithick controlled his empire and a certain amount of antagonism must have built up resulting in the normally mild Trevithick becoming enraged. He withdrew permission for Allan to grant free travel passes to the workmen. Allan responded by taking up the matter with the Crewe Committee which backed Trevithick. Irritated, Allan then removed the copy of Trevithick's original letter from the letter book and that did displease the Committee. At the Committee meeting on 23 August 1853, when the matter was discussed, Allan's resignation was accepted.[19]

Allan obviously realized that he had gone too far but he was not without employment for long as almost immediately he became Locomotive Superintendent of the Scottish Central Railway. It may well be that the Scottish post was already his before that Committee meeting took place, for he commenced employment there in September 1853. The situation at Crewe may have deteriorated to such an extent that both Trevithick and Allan were of the same mind with respect to the other, 'either he goes or I go'. The fact that both applied for the post on the Scottish Central Railway and both were short-listed leads to that conclusion; that Crewe Committee meeting of 23 August 1853 was therefore probably something of a postscript.[20]

The Southern Division was always the sole domain of J. E. McConnell, and it ceased to exist with his departure. Of Irish origin, McConnell served his apprenticeship at the Glasgow engineering firm of Claude Girdwood & Co before becoming a foreman at Bury, Curtis & Kennedy in Liverpool, where he received his introduction to locomotive construction and also to Edward Bury who, in 1837, became the first Locomotive

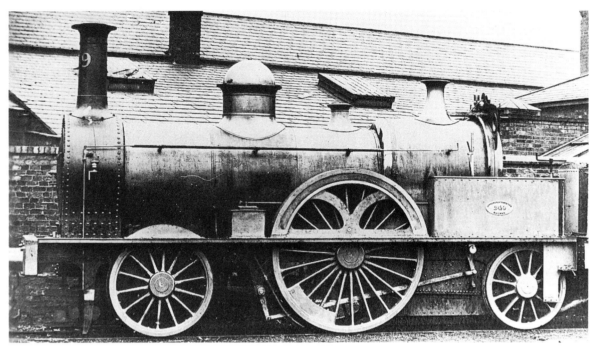

Engineer of the London & Birmingham Railway. Following a short period with Vernon & Co, also in Liverpool, he acted as manager at a machine shop in Manchester. Such widespread experience proved valuable and in 1842, at the age of 27, he was appointed Locomotive Superintendent on the Birmingham & Gloucester Railway.[21]

As a partner in a locomotive construction firm and engineer to a railway company, Bury was in an unusual, but lucrative, position. Locomotives orders went to his engineering firm, the railway not being then in a position to build engines at its Wolverton works. He was a great advocate of four-wheeled locomotives and the use of inside cylinders. His use of bar frames for the locomotives he designed set him somewhat apart from the general plate frame form of construction adopted by British manufacturers. With only four-wheeled locomotives available, the London & Birmingham found itself short of hauling power and multiple heading became common for some trains. Following the formation of the LNWR it was necessary for some locomotives to be loaned to the Southern Division, which the London & Birmingham had become, in order to meet traffic requirements. The pressures resulting from these increased traffic demands and the new regime of the General Manager, Mark Huish, were not to Bury's liking and he resigned his post. That situation would probably have come about in any case

as there was an increasing role for him to play at his engineering firm in Liverpool.

McConnell was appointed to succeed Bury but things remained much the same as no new locomotives could be constructed immediately. There was an order for six locomotives already with Bury's firm, these being of 2-2-2 form and designed by the builders. This order had been placed by the Chester & Holyhead Railway, but when that concern became part of an enlarging LNWR prior to its opening, the locomotives were diverted to Wolverton in order to meet the motive power shortage there. They arrived between June and September 1848 and could be classed as the parents of what were later to be called the 'Bloomers'.

Shortly after McConnell's arrival at Wolverton he set about constructing a large and powerful machine which he claimed would be capable of operating a two-hour service between London and Birmingham. After initial trials on the line at the end of 1848 it was put into store and proclaimed a failure. This 2-2-2 bore little relationship to either the Bury engines or the later 'Bloomer' Class which has often been credited to McConnell. With outside cylinders, outside frames and coil springs it became known as 'Mac's Mangle' and its excessive width resulted in platforms having to be cut back in order to allow trial running.[22]

The Bury 2-2-2 locomotives were still a success and McConnell was ordered to obtain more of a similar type but with greater power. The order for ten engines went to Sharp Brothers, later to become Sharp, Stewart & Co, and the design must essentially be attributed to C.F. Beyer of that firm (Beyer later went on to found the famous engine-building concern of Beyer, Peacock & Co). It is highly unlikely that McConnell had much to do with the basic design of the locomotives built by Sharp; private firms at that time built engines to their own designs following a loose customer specification. In any event, the ten-week interval between the contract and the quoted delivery time of the first locomotive would not have allowed detailed discussion as to design between builder and customer. McConnell did, however, insist upon certain changes including a bigger firebox and transverse midfeather. In basic terms, however, these locomotives, the first 'Bloomers', were not a McConnell design. The same could be said for subsequent orders from Sharp's, but McConnell was planning what he saw as improvements and that came about with his 'Improved Bloomers' or 'Patent' Class introduced at the end of 1852; the initial batch of Sharp 'Bloomers' was delivered during 1851 and the second set a year later.

The 'Patents' were based upon the 'Bloomers' but incorporated several features which McConnell had devised including a steam drier in the smokebox, wrought iron pistons with special types of rings, hollow axles and an indented boiler. The latter was designed as a means whereby the centre-line height of the boiler might be reduced and so avoid the locomotives being 'top heavy'. At the time there was still concern that at high speeds a locomotive would topple over if it had a high centre of gravity. The indentation in the underside of the boiler allowed it to be placed lower down without fouling the axle; however, deposits must have formed in the bottom of each of the sections.

Another boiler feature was that of the extended smokebox. This was essentially a combustion chamber provided between the firebox and rear tubeplate and was intended to promote better combustion. McConnell was intent on using coal instead of coke and the extended firebox together with the use of a longitudinal firebox midfeather were features he considered to be essential. This arrangement was not a success as far as the combustion of coal was concerned, but then neither were most such systems devised by other locomotive engineers. The surprising thing is that this unproven arrangement was fitted to the entire group of 12 'Patent Bloomers'.

McConnell had many patents to his name although most were not taken up to any extent; but such is the case with the majority of patents. He had ideas for multiple blast pipes, tubular stays which could be used for supplying air to the firebox, tubular wheel spokes and hollow buffers through which chains would pass allowing communication between carriages. Together with S. Thornton he devised an arrangement which allowed the coupling and uncoupling of carriages from the side, the idea being to avoid injury to people trapped between vehicles. Many of the patents were registered as 'improvements' and so could not be considered as innovative ideas. 'Steeling', the application of a layer of steel over the base iron, was not a new process but McConnell patented its application to axle journals. The indented boiler was actually a development of an idea by Stubbs and Grylls patented in 1846, and his steam-operated sledge brake patent of 1857 was almost a copy of the 1852 Fitzpatrick

Above left *'Bloomer' No 249, built by Sharp & Co in 1851.* (G. Charles collection)

Right *A drawing of McConnell's 'Patent Bloomer'.*

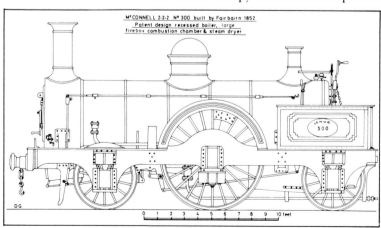

McCONNELL 2-2-2 No 300 built by Fairbairn 1852
Patent design recessed boiler, large firebox combustion chamber & steam dryer

LNWR 300

0 1 2 3 4 5 6 7 8 9 10 feet

'Patent Bloomer' No 300 under construction.

patent. It is not likely that McConnell set out to copy other ideas — he just did not know that they had already been patented. Infringement of patents did occur regularly as many patented ideas were not taken up with the result that they were 're-invented'. McConnell would appear to have been more of a development engineer than an original thinker.

As with most engineers from time to time, McConnell was a little lax with the obvious. David Joy quotes a case when he outwitted 'Mac' regarding a locomotive boiler pressure test. With respect to negotiations concerning operation of the Oxford, Worcester & Wolverhampton Railway by the LNWR, McConnell was requested to inspect the locomotives. One of these he considered to have a burnt firebox crown and insisted upon a hydraulic pressure test with cold water. A measuring gauge was positioned in the firebox and pressure increased to 220 psi, by means of the axle-driven pump. As soon as the pumping stopped, pressure immediately fell due to numerous leaks which McConnell had not noticed but Joy had. When the firebox was inspected the crown showed no deflection as the pressure had by then fallen to a lower value. Joy reported that he 'grinned behind Mac'. [23] Such a situation was possible because pressure gauges were not then fitted, the required pressure being obtained by screwing down the safety valves to the desired

value, water leaking from them when the desired pressure was reached.

McConnell's designs to allow the burning of coal would have improved the operating economics of his engines, but he was also willing to try other schemes. One of these was the use of a contract system for paying enginemen, payment being made for operating a service with the enginemen being responsible for all costs. [24] The idea did not prove a success and was disliked by a number of Directors as it appeared to lead to accidents due to enginemen having to work long hours in order to maintain a reasonable income. Despite such schemes for economic working, McConnell appears to have been rather extravagant and came in for much criticism, especially from Moon. The Board of Directors called for a report on locomotives and operating boundaries during 1859 and McConnell proposed that the Southern Division be expanded. Using very favourable statistical figures he indicated that substantial savings could be made if the border was moved north. McConnell got his expanded division but a number of people queried how he had arrived at his figures.

Moon had no confidence in McConnell and doubted his truthfulness, such misgivings being expressed in a letter to the Chairman, the Marquis of Chandos. [25] By 1861 it was apparent that Moon was correct and that McConnell's figures were, to put it mildly, speculative. His expenditure exceeded target by £44,275 whilst none of the expected savings of some £12,000 per year had been realized. In January 1862 the General Stores and Locomotive Expenditure Committee passed a motion to the effect that its confidence in McConnell was severely shaken. McConnell resigned.

Extravagance may well have related to the 'Patents' for they were essentially unsuccessful, all but three being scrapped in 1864, and they probably required considerable work in order to be kept in service. Improved services of the early 1860s necessitated more locomotives, and additional 'Bloomers' were built during 1861 by Sharp, Stewart & Co and also by Kitson. During 1862 Wolverton turned out ten 'Bloomers', all of these later locomotives being essentially the same as the 1851 versions. McConnell produced plans for much larger locomotives, known as the 'H' Class or 'extra-large Bloomers', but the Board would not allow construction of the ten he wanted, only five being sanctioned. In the end only three were built, probably due to the excessive cost.

The 'H' Class engines had 7 ft 8 in diameter driving wheels, 18 in by 24 in cylinders and weighed 32 tons. They were enlarged versions of the 'Bloomers' but incorporated more of McConnell's patented devices. With a view to burning coal, the firebox contained a longitudinal midfeather and was extended in order to provide a combustion chamber. At its lower part it was extended forwards in order to increase the grate area. A thorough system of staying made the boiler capable of working to a pressure of 150 psi but it is unlikely that such high pressure was actually used in service, that for the 'Bloomers' normally being 120 psi. Rather than crank-driven pumps, two Giffard injectors were used to supply water to the boiler. One of these locomotives was exhibited at the 1862 Great Exhibition in London.[26] It might be argued that McConnell's position as member for railway matters on the Jury for that exhibition, rather than the merits of the locomotive, caused it to be displayed. In view of his known characteristic for self-publicity that is not impossible. As a result of his involvement with the Exhibition, he was called upon to provide a report on the locomotives exhibited. This was written in conjunction with W. J. Macquorn Rankine, Professor of Civil Engineering and Mechanics at the University of Glasgow, and appeared in the Practical Mechanics Journal Record of the Great Exhibition, 1862.[28]

It should not be thought that McConnell only built passenger engines. Goods engines were also required during his time at Wolverton, but these came from private manufacturers and were, in general, designed by those concerns. The 0-6-0 type predominated and in 1854 the 'Wolverton Goods' engine appeared with a boiler showing its relation to the 'Bloomers' but an overall design similar to the Sharp, Roberts & Co 'Sphinx'-type goods engine. In total, between introduction and 1863 some 106 were built, all but 11 coming from Wolverton.[27]

Apart from his designs which made use of too many patent features, McConnell left the Southern Division well provided with locomotive power and his departure allowed the LNWR locomotive department to be unified under a single superintendent, John Ramsbottom. McConnell was a useful engineer and very keen on engineering development, although his enthusiasm appears to have been at the expense of financial logic. He was a founder member of the Institution of Mechanical Engineers and was responsible for proposing David Joy for membership of that body.[29] Following his resignation from the LNWR he practised as a consulting engineer and represented the British Government on railway matters at the 1867 Paris Exhibition. He died on 11 June 1883.[30]

The Midland Railway

Compared with the two pre-grouping companies discussed above, the locomotive department of the Midland Railway had a relatively easy birth. The Midland essentially grew out of three railways centred on Derby and it was in that city that the main locomotive works was developed. During the 1830s many railway schemes were proposed, some never getting further than the initial planning stages. The Derby, Leicester and Nottingham area generated a number of such proposals mainly due to the presence of coal in the region. Eventually three lines were proposed at about the same time with ideas that they would be interlinked in some way.

During 1834 a scheme was proposed by the embryo Midland Counties Railway to build a line connecting Derby with the London & Birmingham Railway, then under construction, but it was a rival line which had its plans passed. The Birmingham & Derby Junction Railway received approval for its link between those cities, and was to connect with the North Midland's line from Derby to Nottingham. The Midland Counties Railway was then left to concentrate upon routes between Derby, Nottingham and Leicester. That was the basic arrangement although a number of smaller lines were absorbed over the years.

Unlike other railway schemes with common areas of operation, these railway companies appear to have been on very good terms and could see the mutual benefits of co-operation, not least in development of a joint station in Derby. The Derby to Nottingham section of the Midland Counties opened in June 1839, the Birmingham & Derby Junction in August the same year and the North Midland as far as Masborough a year later. Although these lines made use of the same station at Derby they had different locomotives and operated different maintenance facilities.

The B&DJR locomotive stock came from outside contractors, as did the locomotives on the other two lines, with examples from Tayleur of Newton-le-Willows, Mather Dixon, and Sharps. They were not exceptional, generally being standard 2-2-2 products of Stephenson form. The Midland Counties favoured smaller four-wheeled locomotives and its collection included examples from Edward Bury, Nasmyth Gaskell, and William Fairbairn. North Midland locomotives also tended towards the larger Stephenson six-wheeled type, although other arrangements were used for particular purposes. This is mentioned because none of these railways was in a position to manufacture its own locomotives, nor did any seem to have aspirations to do so. Near the common station in Derby each railway had its own locomotive depot, although that of the North Midland was much larger than the other two put together.

As was common at the time, the engineer in charge of the railway had initial responsibility for the locomotives but that subsequently changed. The North Midland was a Robert Stephenson railway and under himself as Locomotive Superintendent he appointed William Prime Marshall. Stephenson relinquished his post of overall command of locomotive power during 1842 and Marshall resigned a year later. Thomas Kirtley was appointed Locomotive Superintendent to succeed Marshall, and received a salary of £250 per annum. Kirtley had been born at Tanfield, County Durham, and was the eldest boy in his family. Following a period of driving on the Liverpool & Manchester Railway he founded his own firm of locomotive builders, Thomas Kirtley & Co of Warrington. That concern failed in 1841 and he went to the North Midland.

The Midland Counties line had Josiah Kearsley as its Locomotive Superintendent, whilst on the relatively small Birmingham & Derby Junction Railway, Matthew Kirtley, brother of Thomas, ruled over the locomotives. The lines all operated effectively but without much in the way of locomotive development taking place. One of the reasons was a shortage of money, but their relatively short routes were easily satisfied by the locomotive stock. One ever-present problem was that of coke shortage, or at least the relatively high price of coke compared with coal. During the early 1840s Samuel Hall of Nottingham persuaded the Midland Counties Directors to allow him to carry out experiments on one of its locomotives with a view to burning coal. A small 2-2-0 outside-cylinder locomotive was fitted with Hall's device which consisted of forward-facing bell-mouthed tubes inserted into holes cut in the front of the firebox immediately above the fire. When the locomotive operated, air was forced into the tubes and so provided a form of forced draught for the fire. A brick arch also assisted in mixing the combustible gases and air draught.[31] The experiment was eventually abandoned, but the experience gained was not.

In May 1844 the three companies adopted the logical step and merged to become the Midland Railway. It was a very amicable merger with all parties appearing to be happy with the outcome, all parties, that is, except those whose livelihood or status was threatened. With three companies suddenly becoming one it was obvious that only one chief of any department would be required, and that situation existed for the locomotive department as for others. To the surprise of many, including the individual himself, Matthew Kirtley was selected to be superintendent of the locomotive and carriage departments in preference to Kearsley and his own brother Thomas. Thomas accepted the situation and remained to serve Matthew as an inspector, but Kearsley would not stay and went elsewhere.

Thus the Midland Railway came into being with its locomotive department under a single head and its main works located at Derby. Such a settled beginning so early on had its advantages, but a major disadvantage concerned the fact that the 90-strong locomotive fleet was a mixed bag of generally outdated machines from a variety of builders. Kirtley's prime task was to achieve some order from the chaos and build a stock of fairly standard engines which could be maintained readily at the company's workshops. Outside contractors would still do the supplying until those workshops were equipped for manufacturing purposes.

2. Lancashire & Yorkshire Railway Locomotive Engineers

John Audley Frederick Aspinall

Any appointment involving senior personnel can present problems within any organization for there is never any certainty that the individual will have the desired effect. Some people turn out to be unsuitable whilst others just manage to keep their particular departments functioning without producing any real signs of advancement. If the choice of those on the selection panel has been wise then the department can flourish and become a hive of progressive ideas.

In its choices of personnel to oversee its locomotive department, the Lancashire & Yorkshire Railway Directors proved themselves to be makers of wise decisions and their selection of one man in particular was positively inspired. Over the years, John Audley Frederick Aspinall demonstrated that he was not only a brilliant engineer, in the complete sense, but was also an equally exceptional manager.

J.A.F. Aspinall was born in Liverpool on 25 August 1851, his father being a member of the legal profession who became Recorder of Liverpool in 1861. A family move to London in 1864 caused problems with respect to schooling, and the young Aspinall was sent to Beaumont College in old Windsor. The family home at Kensal Green allowed ready access to the developing railways of north London, and it is probable that Aspinall developed his interest from such sights for by the time his schooling finished he had made up his mind to become a railway engineer. At that time railways were still too new for there to have been any family tradition in that field, but neither had there been a family tradition in any branch of engineering. Although Aspinall progressed through life by his own efforts, at the age of 17 he had very little influence, but his family connections must have been of great assistance in his being accepted by John Ramsbottom as a pupil to start in December 1868.[1] Aspinall was to be one of the first, but by no means last, of the great Crewe-trained locomotive engineers.

As was usual for a pupil, Aspinall served in most of the departments at Crewe works and also had a spell on the footplate as fireman. Such work illustrated the practical problems involved in working a locomotive — design could not be pure theory, but had to consider practicalities. During that period of training Aspinall gained first-hand experience of the more hazardous aspects of railway operation when he observed the procedure for detaching the pilot from the Crewe to London train at Tring. Once past the top of the incline, the pilot would be uncoupled without stopping and the driver would take his locomotive ahead, past a set of points which were then reset; he would then reverse over the points to the adjacent line, and then the points would be reset once more for the oncoming train.[2] A risky business indeed, but it saved time.

A little later the same sort of incident was encountered during a trip to America, and no matter how hair-raising it may have been it was experience. As far as Aspinall was concerned, all experience was education and all education was worthwhile, for even the less acceptable parts had

John Audley Frederick Aspinall.

D. Griffiths
1988.

a point and provided knowledge upon which to base future practice. It will certainly have been part of his nature to consider education as an invaluable prize, but his early experiences must have shaped his attitude. He always encouraged engineers to obtain the best training they could and would endeavour to ensure that educational facilities were available to all who sought knowledge. One of his early steps upon becoming CME at Horwich was to seek funding and space for a Mechanics' Institute. Money was forthcoming from the Directors, but the largest amount was pledged by Mrs Fielden, the widow of a former Director. In addition to the Institute itself, money was also provided for the fitting out of a gymnasium.[3]

In one of its famous interviews, *The Railway Magazine* reported Aspinall's pride in the achievements of the Institute. Classes commenced in 1887 as soon as the first block was erected and at the end of the first year over 700 individual students were attending a total of 45 different classes each week. By the turn of the century the Institute boasted a library in excess of 10,000 volumes as well as rooms equipped for the teaching of metallurgy and chemistry.[4] Aspinall could not have accomplished all of that himself, but his encouragement and drive certainly helped.

During his years in command at Horwich, and later as General Manager, Aspinall was always willing to offer help and encouragement to aspiring engineers and his involvement in the affairs of the Institution of Mechanical Engineers of which he was a member illustrates his love of engineering and his firm belief in the status of the engineer. He took pride in membership of engineering institutions both large and small. Upon being elected President of the Liverpool Engineering Society in 1900 his address opened with the words, 'I have to thank you for electing me your President. I appreciate the honour, and feel proud of being placed at the head of the leading Northern Engineering Society'.[5] These were not hollow words, for Aspinall took his position seriously and occupied the chair regularly during his term of office. In 1881, during the second year of that society's existence, he presented a paper on vacuum and automatic brakes.

His Presidential Address to the Institution of Mechanical Engineers left no doubt as to his views on the status of engineers nor his pride in being elected President. By this time Aspinall was General Manager of the L&YR and no longer its CME, but he was still very much an engineer at heart and knew the value of sound practical experience. 'The success of the engineer undoubtedly depends upon his being connected with works which have a commercial value, and his avoiding those which, though they may give him some temporary employment, are destined to be pointed to in the future as failures due to the product of a too speculative brain. No engineering subject requires more thoughtful care than the mechanical and electrical working of a railway.'[6]

His feeling had not changed when he delivered his Presidential Address to the Institution of Civil Engineers in 1918. The First World War had just ended and he spoke well of the role played by engineers in that conflict, but was not so kind in his remarks regarding the Government which used unqualified personnel to head engineering projects. He said ' . . . it is not unreasonable to suppose that where works constructed under Government auspices have not been successful, better results would have been obtained had more attention been paid to the selection of men who were properly qualified to direct them'.[7] His remarks were cutting, but Aspinall was held in high regard and a year later he was appointed as Consulting Engineer to the Ministry of Transport. At this appointment he resigned as General Manager of the L&YR and so ceased to have any direct control over railway matters, but he never lost interest.

Whilst at Crewe as a pupil, Aspinall struck up a friendship with Henry Ivatt and that friendship lasted for life. The two friends shared a house together rather than suffer the tribulations of lodgings. During those days at Crewe there was a pioneering spirit abroad, for Ramsbottom was in charge and he was never short of new ideas. Pupils were taken on in order that they might receive a training at the feet of the 'master', but Ramsbottom was not prepared to spend too much of his valuable time actually teaching. Experience was the best teacher and pupils were assigned to different tasks throughout the works and out on the line. One such task given to Aspinall by Ramsbottom was to assist in running trials of his new design of displacement lubricator.[8] Drawing office training was useful, but if the product wasn't right trials out on the road could quickly become unpleasant.

Ramsbottom retired in September 1871 and all of his pupils were transferred to the care of F.W. Webb. The new man obviously thought highly of Aspinall, for the following year he was selected to make a trip to America. It was not a holiday but part of the education process, and Webb already had plans for his return. One purpose of the trip was to investigate the latest American railway practice, but the other, and probably the more important, was to observe the recent improvements made in steel making. In December 1872 Aspinall completed his time as a pupil and was officially designated as a draughtsman, but Webb appointed him as Assistant Manager at the Crewe Steel Works.[9] Development of the Steel Works will be considered in the section concerning Webb and need not be dealt with here apart from mentioning that Aspinall had a hand in that work and his experience proved valuable in later years.

A further piece of work with which Aspinall was involved at the same time involved the making of bricks. Such a simple job description did not mean that the individual was solely concerned with that area — adaptability and versatility were key words at Crewe in those days. Two large kilns were erected and Aspinall mechanized the loading and unloading procedures which reduced the price of bricks by 4 shillings (20 pence) to 15 shillings (75 pence) per 1,000. Such economy interested Webb and Aspinall's salary was doubled to £3 per week.[10]

Keen engineer though he was, Aspinall still found time for romance, and a young lady, Gertrude Schrader, was very much to his liking. Prospects were reasonable and a long courtship seemed to be in the offing when Gertrude's mother died suddenly during 1874. Her father had died some years before and there was now nothing to prevent a quick marriage, which both parties wanted. The wedding took place at St Anne's church, Edge Hill, on 2 September 1874; the groom was 23 years old and Gertrude 20, but they were destined for a long and happy married life which started at the house in Crewe which Aspinall had shared with his friend Ivatt — the latter naturally moved out.

It was common for the smaller railways, and many overseas, to approach the larger British companies whenever positions of responsibility had to be filled. British companies always trained more pupils and apprentices than they could absorb and experience elsewhere was always valuable if that individual was ever required in the future. Crewe had a fine reputation for producing men of quality and Aspinall certainly fitted that bill. During January 1875 Webb was approached by the Great Southern & Western Railway of Ireland to suggest a suitable person to fill the post of manager at its Inchicore works near Dublin. With Webb's recommendation, Aspinall's trip to Dublin for an interview was something of a formality and in March he made a return trip in order to take up the position.

Life in Ireland suited Aspinall and his young wife but he was there to work. The railways of Ireland had a deserved reputation for 'completing' the training of engineers, and they served as a sort of finishing school for many well-respected Chief Mechanical Engineers of British main lines. The Great Southern & Western was no exception and as *The Engineer* stated in Aspinall's obituary, 'No man ever went into Inchicore and came out of it without being the better, and there is never an Inchicore man who does not cherish an affection for it.'[11]

This book is not really concerned with Aspinall's work whilst in Ireland, but that part of his life was formative and he gained in experience as well as stature working under Alexander McDonnell, the Locomotive Superintendent. Whilst there Aspinall took out a number of patents concerning vacuum brakes and became very interested in the subject of stopping passenger trains safely. His first major technical paper was, as has been already mentioned, on the vacuum brake, and was delivered to the Liverpool Engineering Society in February 1881. Dublin was not that far from Liverpool, a short overnight ferry journey, and it was possible for the Aspinalls to maintain family and professional contacts with that city. As a firm believer in education and the transmission of knowledge to like-minded people, Aspinall joined the Institution of Civil Engineers of Ireland shortly after his arrival on Irish shores and during 1881 he obtained associate membership of both the Institution of Civil Engineers and the Institution of Mechanical Engineers on the mainland.

McDonnell and Aspinall worked very well together and the former certainly knew the worth of the latter, for when he resigned in 1882 in order to become CME on the North Eastern Railway, he had no hesitation in suggesting that Aspinall was the only person the Board need consider as his successor. The advice was taken and J.A.F. Aspinall became Locomotive Superintendent to the Great Southern & Western Railway at the age of 32 years. Age and religion (he was a Catholic) might have conspired against him, for although Ireland was a devoutly Catholic country its 'establishment' was fervently Protestant and religion played an important part in decisions of that sort. However, not for the first or last time, Aspinall's undoubted qualities as an engineer and a manager were decisive.

One of his first decisions was to make Ivatt his deputy and manager of the works at Inchicore. The bonds that had grown at Crewe were strengthened at Inchicore and both men gained much from having the other close at hand. In his new post Aspinall was able to travel more widely and meet other Locomotive Superintendents on an equal footing, or nearly so. Trips to Crewe must have been regular and meetings with Webb both interesting and valuable. It is highly likely that Webb found great satisfaction in seeing one of his former pupils obtain a position as Locomotive Superintendent, and it is equally as likely that Aspinall was certainly proud of being a 'graduate' of Crewe, and during one of his visits there suggested to Webb that it would be interesting to organize a reunion of Crewe 'old boys' on an annual basis. Webb was enthusiastic and the first of the Crewe dinners took place at the Criterion Restaurant, Piccadilly Circus, in February 1884. Webb, naturally, took the chair, and Aspinall acted as secretary. These dinners, later attended by many other famous engineers, were a part of Aspinall's life and he relished meeting fellow engineers who all had that one thing in common, a Crewe training.[12]

In locomotive terms, Aspinall saw no reason to change matters as the McDonnell engines were capable of performing most of the work required of them. If improvements were necessary they could be carried out on existing designs. That does not mean that Aspinall was idle and spent his time touring Britain to meet old friends — the job of Locomotive Superintendent was more than design. The Carriage and Wagon department also came under Aspinall's control and efforts were made to improve the stock, especially in terms of wagon capacity as will be considered later.

Professionally, although relatively young Aspinall was amongst the top rank of railway engineers and his standing increased when in November 1885, at the age of 34 years, he became President of the Institution of Civil Engineers in Ireland. His address covered a wide range of railway topics from standardization to education and the burning of turf in locomotive fireboxes, a matter of considerable importance to Irish railways due to the need to import coal.

The Crewe influence did not leave him and he was always willing to make use of practical ideas from there, or anywhere else for that matter, but some of Webb's passions, such as compounding, never did find favour with Aspinall. The cast wheel became one of Aspinall's early import ideas from Crewe, whilst some years later he had no hesitation in making use of steel plate for boiler construction. One of the lasting lessons learned at Crewe and a subject for which Crewe remained famous was that of experimentation. The pursuit of knowledge through trial was not exactly an obsession with Aspinall, but he thoroughly indulged himself in it whenever he considered

that benefit might accrue.

Slide valves were always a problem as far as any steam locomotive, or steam engine for that matter, was concerned. Most engineers had ideas as to the design which would minimize the work involved in moving such valves; they were essential to the operation of an engine, but produced no useful work, only used it. Whilst at Inchicore Aspinall devised a rig which could be used to determine the work absorbed by particular slide valves under certain load and operating conditions. The apparatus consisted of a hydraulic cylinder interposed between the valves and its operating link, motion from the link to the valve being transmitted through the oil in that cylinder. As the force increased to move the valve, so the pressure increased and this caused the pencil on a normal steam cylinder indicator to be raised. Movement of the indicator drum represented actual valve movement. With this apparatus a diagram of the force required to actually move the valve could be obtained; another produced an equivalent diagram for steam pressure variation in the valve chest.

During 1885 and 1886 a series of tests was conducted with two different engine types, a four-coupled passenger type and a six-coupled goods. From the results of these trials, Aspinall obtained values for resistance offered by the slide valves under different conditions. It is not necessary to discuss the results in detail, but the basic conclusion drawn was that the work lost in moving the slide valves and operating the valve gear was about the same as that needed to haul $2\frac{1}{2}$ 10-ton wagons. Experiments and results were detailed in a paper Aspinall read before the Institution of Civil Engineers in London on 18 December 1888, and in that paper he acknowledged the help given by Mr R. Coey, a young assistant at Inchicore.

In order to present the experiments and results in a paper of reasonable length it was necessary to abridge the detail somewhat, but the audience, containing some distinguished engineers, found much of interest to discuss. William Stroudley considered the results to be of considerable importance and congratulated Aspinall on his work.[13] It was obvious that Aspinall's first paper read at the premier English engineering institution was a great success and it served to further increase his stock amongst fellow engineers.

This was not the end of Aspinall's investigations into the frictional losses involved with slide valves, but between carrying out the experiments and presenting the paper an upwards move in his career took place. With the resignation of Wright,

Aspinall's equipment for determining friction in slide valves.

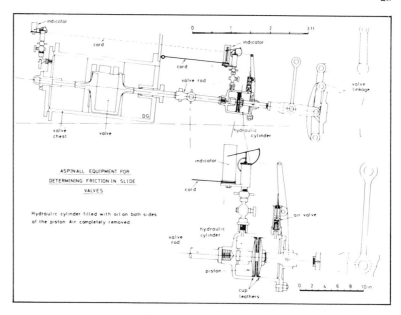

the L&YR Board suddenly found itself requiring a new superintendent for its locomotive department and nobody from inside was suitable for promotion. The post was advertised and a number of applications were received, one from J.A.F. Aspinall. What form the selection procedure took is not known but it appears that Aspinall headed the list and was the only one called for interview. Minutes of the Board Meeting for 14 July 1886 indicate that Aspinall alone was called before the Board which unanimously agreed that he should be appointed Chief Mechanical Engineer at a salary of £1,500 per annum. It is likely that Webb and Ramsbottom, then a Director of the L&YR, were asked for their opinions and made strong recommendations. The GS&WR of Ireland lost a valuable engineer when Aspinall took up his appointment at Horwich on 1 October 1886 but the loss was made easier when, on his recommendation, H.A. Ivatt succeeded to the post of Locomotive Superintendent at Inchicore.

Aspinall found no real need to design new locomotives when he arrived at Horwich, so his time could be profitably spent developing the locomotive works at that site. In fact, that was his priority. Wright had organized the general arrangement of the works and had even decided upon movement of machinery from different workshops to Horwich, but Aspinall was faced with implementing most of the changes and getting the works into full production. He superintended the erection of workshops and the machinery arrangement in those shops.[14] By June

1887 the move to Horwich was basically complete. Such a simple sentence indicates completion of the first stage in the development of Horwich workshops, but it by no means illustrates the work involved.

Over the succeeding years the works expanded to meet demand for the construction and maintenance of locomotives, but it also expanded in order to suit a policy directed by Aspinall. From his experiences at Crewe, Aspinall understood the advantages to be gained by production of steel on site rather than importing such an essential material. During November 1886 he was asked by the Directors to report on the progress of work at Horwich and on other work he considered essential. That document, presented the following month, related the actual construction and installation which had taken place or was planned, but it also outlined some of Aspinall's proposals, neatly phrased in the form of recommendations.

There had already been some thought given to the production of steel at Horwich, but nothing definite had been settled and the new CME put the matter firmly back in the Directors' court by telling them that no progress on the installation of the forge could be made until the matter of steel production had been settled. He then went on to detail the reasons for internal steel making, stating that it was just as easy to make castings from steel manufactured on site as it was to melt and cast bought-in pig iron. His managerial talent, and financial acumen, were evident by the

way in which he emphasized the points in favour of steel making. Knowing full well that Directors were reluctant to part with any money without good cause as far as they could see it, Aspinall impressed upon them the simple theory of stock-keeping and costing.

Good stocks of plates, axles, tyres and other steel components had to be kept if delays in repair or construction were to be avoided. Such was evident to all, but Aspinall hammered home his point by stating that this stock just lay about for long periods tying up valuable capital. If these steel components were manufactured on site, it was only necessary to keep a stock of raw material which could then be used to form any of the items in question. As a *coup de grâce* he mentioned that all scrap material generated in the workshops and by scrapping old locomotives could be recycled.[15] Needless to say Aspinall got his steel foundry. He had originally estimated that a capability of 10 tons of steel per day would be required, but within ten years Horwich had one 20-ton and two 10-ton Siemens-Marten regenerative furnaces with direct connection of the steel foundry to the iron foundry by means of an overhead tramway.

A short paper to the 'Civils' during the 1886-7 session outlined the workshops at Horwich as they stood a decade after construction began.[16] It was not a controversial paper and did not produce any printed discussion, but as a document of fact it provides an insight into what Aspinall had been able to achieve in a relatively short period and with cash severely limited. His powers of persuasion and managerial talent are well demonstrated by these achievements, for in addition to the expected premises of boiler shop, forge, wheel shop, smithy, fitting shop, etc there were other features which illustrate Aspinall's views and talents. At the beginning of the paper he makes mention of a physical laboratory, chemical laboratory and a test room, illustrating his demand for information. The test room contained a 100-ton tensile testing machine as well as a spring testing machine.

The testing section took on a very important role during those formative years at Horwich, and provided much useful information for Aspinall which was used in the development of locomotive designs and constructional procedures. Aspinall was never reluctant to divulge such information and his output of papers to learned societies was prodigious. Like many in his position he was not able to conduct every aspect of an investigation, nor draw up tables of results, but he relied upon a small team of trusted people whose efforts would always be acknowledged in his papers. That was the way of things and still is. The level of scientific investigation he engendered attracted many young engineers willing to learn and keen on the pursuit of knowledge. These included George Hughes, Nigel Gresley, and Henry Fowler, all of whom were involved in aspects of testing materials and locomotives during their early years at Horwich. It is a measure of the status of Aspinall and his training, as well as of the quality of the individuals, that they all became CMEs in their own right. The same is true of R.E.L. Maunsell, who came from Inchicore to finish his training as a Horwich pupil. At the grouping in 1923, three of the four CMEs were Horwich-trained men. Aspinall's status in the engineering world ensured that such brilliant individuals were keen to make the move to Horwich. Hughes came from Crewe in 1887; Gresley, who decided to finish his time as a pupil under Aspinall rather than Webb, arrived at Horwich from Crewe in 1898.

Experiments continued into the work required to move slide valves, although this was now applied to L&YR locomotives. The original apparatus employed for his investigations in Ireland had proved itself to be satisfactory, so the same sort of arrangement was adopted with but simple modifications. Again, the results were presented to his fellow engineers in a paper read before the Institution of Civil Engineers on the same evening, 8 February 1898, as one on locomotive fireboxes by William Throw, and the meeting attracted an audience of distinguished engineers including F.W. Webb and Alexander McDonnell. Aspinall's experimental work included friction tests on plain and balanced slide valves as well as valves made from cast iron and phosphor bronze. The results indicated that friction was slightly less for valves placed against a vertical face rather than one which was horizontal, and the unbalanced valves required more effort to operate them than the balanced valves. Webb complimented Aspinall on his paper and agreed with him as to the advantages of balanced valves which he had noticed from practice.[17]

As part of Aspinall's data-gathering exercise related to locomotive design, a series of tests were carried out on the strength of draught at differ-

ent locations in the boiler. A 4-4-0 of Wright design was fitted with vacuum pipe connections at four points in the smokebox and chimney, whilst another pressure-measuring connection was provided above the brick arch in the firebox, and two more in the ashpan. Operating the locomotive between Manchester and Southport, a series of readings were taken as to the draught effect at each of these points. In his 1893 paper on the subject[18], Aspinall simply presented the results without comment as to their usefulness in design work, but he must have been storing up a mine of valuable data.

A major paper on train resistance appeared in 1901 and was the first paper presented to a learned society on that topic for a great many years.[19] Taking an active part in the discussion was the redoubtable F.W. Webb, who was referrred to directly by Aspinall as 'his friend Mr Webb', the respect for his old chief still being strong. Aspinall had made use of the four-wheeled Horwich dynamometer car for his experiments and Webb could not resist a playful dig at his former pupil

Above left *Horwich locomotive works with the Erecting Shop on the right. In the centre is Aspinall's dynamometer car and behind that is a Hughes rail car.* (G. Charles collection)

Right *An Aspinall-designed 0–6–0 based the Wright 0–6–0 Preserved No 1300 built in 1896*

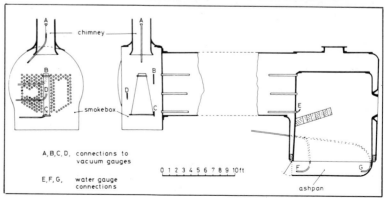

A,B,C,D, connections to vacuum gauges

E,F,G, water gauge connections

Right *Diagram showing the positions of gauge connections for draught tests.*

by stating that the L&NWR dynamometer car was a six-wheeled affair, the centre set of wheels carrying little load and being used mainly to drive the recording instruments. The Aspinall dynamometer car took the instrument drive from one of the main axles.

An initial set of experiments was conducted during 1898-9, but Aspinall was dissatisfied with the recording arrangements and organized a second set of experiments to be carried out between June 1899 and January 1900. The reason for dissatisfaction related to the effects of wind resistance which had not been addressed. Aspinall considered the matter of vital importance and rearranged the experiments to take account of that matter as far as he was able. Up to that time, few investigators had ever dealt with the matter.

Wind gauges were provided in order to measure wind strengths at various locations around the car. There were eight sampling points at each end of the car with measurements also being taken at least 3 feet above the car and 3 feet from the sides. A measurement of wind strength was also taken below the car; Aspinall was nothing if not thorough when it came to gathering data and nothing which could be of use was neglected. Observers were also positioned along the route in order to measure wind strength and direction from a static location. In order to observe the effect of wind eddies around the sides and ends of the dynamometer car and trailing coaches, Aspinall arranged for scraps of paper to be fed out from a number of points on the car. Conscious that he might be accused of creating litter, the CME only allowed such trials to be conducted on certain occasions; at other times water

droplets were used, or the wind effect was judged by the action of fine muslin attached to the windows.

By comparison, the basic data such as speed and drawbar pull were pretty mundane. The test train comprised five bogie coaches with oil-lubricated bearings and the dynamometer car with grease-lubricated bearings. Testing took place on the 5-mile section between Burscough Bridge and St Luke's Road, Southport, that section being fairly level and straight.

Experiments were carried out at different locomotive operating conditions and indicator diagrams were taken as necessary. It is unnecessary to detail these experiments or results, but interested readers can refer to the paper presented on the matter. As well as the main tests with the set train composition, other tests were carried out using trains comprising 10, 15, 20, 25 and 29 bogie coaches in addition to the dynamometer car. Graphs of resistance against speed were drawn in each case and an equation derived to fit each curve. A general equation for all cases was obtained, this being:

$$\text{Resistance (lbs per ton drawn)} = 2.5 + \frac{V^{1.667}}{50.8 + 0.0278L}$$

where   V = velocity in miles per hour
             L = length of train over coach bodies (feet)

The paper contained an appendix giving some 50 train resistance equations derived by others, and that provides some indication as to the thoroughness with which Aspinall approached his experimental work.

By any accounts the paper, for which its author

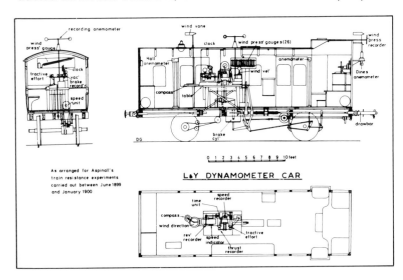

Drawing of Aspinall's dynamometer car.

Inside view of Aspinall's dynamometer car.

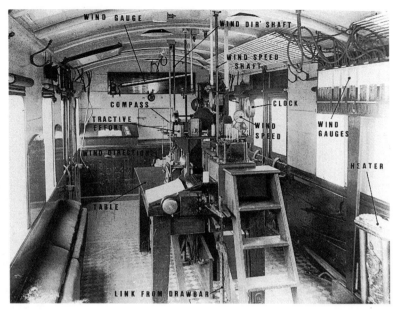

was awarded the Institute's 1902 Watt medal, was a brilliant piece of work and marked an advance in train testing. However, Aspinall was under no illusion that everybody would agree with his results and conclusions. He pointedly remarked that publication of all the main details of the experiments was made in order that the results might be criticized and checked by others so as to eliminate any inaccuracies.

As a follow-up, a paper on the tractive resistance of loaded wagons appeared two years later. Test runs were carried out on the same section of track using trains made up from varying numbers of 10-ton, 20-ton and 30-ton wagons together with the dynamometer car. In plotting the results it was found that considerable variation existed for the same speed, but when wind resistance was taken into account a more acceptable comparison could be made.[20] With these tests Aspinall had forcibly brought the effects of wind resistance on moving bodies to the attention of the engineering fraternity in general.

The meticulous way in which he approached his experimental work mirrored the way in which he dealt with all matters, and he expected the same from his staff and workforce. E.S. Cox, an apprentice at Horwich immediately before the grouping, relates the tales told by the older draughtsmen whilst he was in training. Their accounts indicate the worry Aspinall's visits to the drawing office engendered, for each man feared for his job should his work or general attitude give cause for offence.[21] As with all such stories

there is likely to have been some exaggeration, but they do give an insight into the Aspinall character.

The papers on resistance were actually presented after Aspinall's duties as CME ceased, for at the end of May 1899 Aspinall was appointed General Manager of the L&YR. Engineers tend to stay in their own field rather than go into management in general, although many have been exceptionally good managers of their engineering plants. In this case there was no doubt that the man chosen by the Board was a good engineer and few would have argued that he could not do the job expected of him. This proved to be the case, and the railway developed.

This might be a suitable point to close discussion of Aspinall's work, but a move to the post of General Manager did not mean a loss of interest in engineering matters. Membership of the Association of Locomotive Engineers was open to CMEs and other heads of railway engineering departments, but not to General Managers. It is evident that Aspinall considered himself to be an engineer who was also a General Manager, and he lobbied to retain membership of that organization. A rule change allowed him to do so but he could not maintain as active an interest as he had in the past — his other duties simply did not allow time. He was later asked to become Vice President of the association, but declined indicating that somebody more closely in touch should hold the position.[22]

Although others now directly managed the

The CME's coupé in LMS days. Powered by Ramsbottom 'DX' No 731, it was built at Crewe in 1873. (National Railway Museum, York)

locomotive department, this former CME retained a strong interest in engineering developments and it is probably that interest and understanding which helped the L&YR to progress at such a rapid rate during his period as General Manager. Perhaps the single most important change during that period related to electrification. In this matter Aspinall was an enthusiastic pioneer who fought for development of the railways in a most realistic and economical way. It may come as a shock to the steam enthusiast that all CMEs were not solely devoted to steam traction; they were employed to do a job and that concerned the economic operation of their railways' service by whatever means possible.

As far as electrification was concerned, it was the most suitable means of traction for certain situations; speedy services could be operated with fewer units of propulsion or carriages, and that in turn allowed a deferment of an increase in the capacity of terminals. More frequent trains had advantages for the public as well. In Aspinall's mind electrification had been introduced 'not to save money but to make money'.[23] This was the positive attitude which characterized his life. He also did not consider the railway in isolation, but took account of other factors, especially competitive forms of transport. The L&YR was not a major trunk route but had a considerable route mileage which could be classed as suburban, and that was what he sought to develop. His view, expressed in 1909, was that people should be encouraged to live way outside the towns and use the railways to take them in, thus increasing the overall average fare; short-distance traffic could be left to municipal tramways.[24]

At the turn of the century, and even before, it had become obvious to Aspinall that short-distance haulage by railway was not an economical proposition, but he did not envisage road trans-

port completely replacing railways, especially for intermediate and long-distance work. At least, that was his opinion with respect to the road haulage vehicles as they existed in 1900, although one wonders how he would have viewed British inland transportation of the 1980s or 1990s. In order to check on all possibilities, a Thornycroft steam wagon had been purchased in December 1899 and used for deliveries in the streets of Salford and later in Liverpool. At an Institution of Mechanical Engineers meeting in April 1900 to discuss the paper on 'Road Locomotion' by Professor Hele-Shaw, one of Aspinall's close friends, the new L&YR General Manager was asked to comment on its operation. He stated that it was better than horses for some work but not as good for other, and went on to add that, 'from the results of the L&YR trials there was no possibility of such lorries being capable of competing with the railway between Liverpool and Manchester.'[25]

Despite his joy at being able to defend the railway and at being able to issue a mild rebuke to his friend, Aspinall had no desire to retain old ways just for the sake of nostalgia. His views that machinery had to be kept well up to date were evident from his works, and he was never reluctant to tell others. 'A Railway is not a museum for retention of old machinery, but a highly organized implement of commerce and to be efficient must progress'.[26] J.A.F. Aspinall was one of the most progressive engineers, or managers, of his day, probably because he was an engineer who was also a manager.

As General Manager Aspinall had more to concern him than purely mechanical engineering matters, but he retained that interest and continued to pursue experimental work as far as he was able. Because he had selected his successors from within the ranks of those already at Horwich and had been instrumental in developing their talents as engineers, that road was so much easier. Both Hoy and Hughes appeared to be content with the situation and there is no evidence to suggest that Aspinall interfered to any great extent. Although, as will be seen later, Hoy resigned after a short period in command at Horwich, no mention was ever made that it came about because he was unable to carry out his role in the way he wished. Aspinall was too busy running the railway as a complete unit to spend undue time on locomotive matters; however, in certain respects he did take an active and natural interest.

The pursuit of knowledge had always been a prime concern and that continued, especially under Hughes, but not in the active way that it had in former years. Certainly the new CMEs would have had little difficulty in obtaining the General Manager's support for experimental work or innovation. As we have seen, electrification was a project close to his heart for he saw this as a means of expanding the work of the railway as indicated by the statement in his Presidential Address before the 'Mechanicals'. In the discussion on a paper concerning the electric lighting of trains two years later, Aspinall reiterated his point of view by stating how desirable it would be to have all railways electrified, but added that they could hardly be electrified simply for the sake of easier lighting of coaches. He further added that, 'Electric light was charming, and everyone would be delighted to have it; but it was far too costly'. However, his views on the ultimate solution for electric lighting of coaches were a little away from that eventually adopted. He did not believe that each coach should be its own generating station but felt that the solution lay in the carrying of a bank of batteries which could be charged at a centre where electric energy was available at a reasonably low cost.[27]

It is probable that the manager in him rather than the engineer was speaking, for his analysis was based on cost rather than engineering reasoning, but that does not negate the analysis which was sound as far as it went. Engineers unfortunately often fail to see the cost implications of ideal solutions to a particular problem, and railways, after all, were in the business of making money, not spending it. At the time, 1911, a considerable amount of money was invested in gas lighting of vehicles and to refit these with electric generating sets was not an economic possibility. Aspinall considered that the cost of equipment had to be reduced considerably before all stock would be fitted with electric lighting; even then he appeared to be intent on backing the wrong horse.

Despite now being primarily a manager, his unceasing work for the Mechanicals and Civils was much appreciated and both bodies elected him to the high honour of President. Having been elected a Member of the Institution of Mechanical Engineers in 1881, Aspinall served on the council from 1892 until 1928 when he was elected an Honorary Life Member. In 1900 he became a Vice President and served as President during the 1909-10 session. His love for the Institute was well known and he continued to attend council meetings right up to his death in 1937. The highly decorative Presidential Chair was a gift from him to the Institution in 1929, but an award to him by the Institution failed to be presented due to his death three days earlier.

In order to mark the James Watt Bicentenary, the Institution of Mechanical Engineers sponsored the James Watt International Medal to be awarded to engineers who had received international recognition for their work. At the council meeting on 20 November 1936, with the President, Sir Nigel Gresley, in the chair, it was unanimously agreed to award the first medal to Aspinall. The man himself was actually attending the council meeting and had to be requested to wait outside whilst the vote was taken. The Duke of York never had a chance to present the medal, for on 19 January 1937 J.A.F. Aspinall died peacefully at his Woking home, aged 85.[28]

Presidency of the Institution of Civil Engineers was conferred in 1918. He had joined that body as an Associate Member in 1881, becoming a full member in 1887, a Member of the Council in 1907 and Vice President in 1916.[29]

Aspinall received many honours during his lifetime, but as an enthusiastic engineer it is likely that Presidency of these Institutions was the most valued. Close behind would, however, have been the knighthood conferred in the Birthday Honours List of 1917. With the establishment of the Faculty of Engineering at Liverpool University in 1903, he was appointed an Associate Professor in Railway Engineering, an honour he again took to his heart due to his love of education, engineering and his home town of Liverpool. Although not directly concerned with teaching, Aspinall used the role to assist the University in the gathering of finance for building works. In 1908 he became Chairman of the Engineering Faculty, retaining that position until 1915, and during that period succeeded in raising over £35,000 from Liverpool shipowners and businessmen for the erection and equipping of the large Harrison-Hughes engineering laboratory. In May 1922, as recognition for his work, the

University awarded Aspinall the honorary degree of Doctor of Engineering.[30]

Aspinall enjoyed a happy married life but the death of his wife in 1921 dealt him a severe blow. However, he decided that work was the best way to get over his grief and indulged in even greater activity.

As an engineer Aspinall had few equals and the same can be said of him as a manager. His talents were wide and deep but he was always willing to share his knowledge and help as best he could whether it be through papers to learned societies, in the training of pupils, or in his work for educational institutions like the Horwich Mechanics' Institute and Liverpool University. Engineers rarely cross that apparent gulf into general management and that may be why British industry suffers compared with its European competitors. Aspinall proved that the engineer can be a first-class manager but, unfortunately, nobody had faith enough to follow the lead. His works are obvious but he does not seem to be given the credit that later locomotive engineers have received despite the fact that he was a much better all-round engineer and manager. So long as the railway enthusiast takes the blinkered view of seeing only powerful express locomotives as a sign of excellence and engineering achievement, that situation will remain. As far as engineering is concerned, however, Aspinall is at the top of the list with the very best.

Henry Albert Hoy

Upon becoming General Manager it was natural that Aspinall should have wished for some form of continuity within the mechanical engineering department. Few were surprised, therefore, when H.A. Hoy, then Works Manager at Horwich, was appointed as the new Chief Mechanical Engineer. As we have seen, Aspinall had no desire to sever his links with that side of the railway's affairs and an internal appointment of somebody he trusted and knew was logical. It might also appear that he wished to remain in control of the mechanical engineering side with Hoy as its titular head only. His statement at the 1899 winter meeting of the Assocation of Railway Locomotive Engineers certainly gives that impression, for he told the assembled body that in future he would be so closely connected with the mechanical engineering side of the railway that it could hardly be said that he had left the department.[31]At the time sentiment certainly coloured his statement, for he had no wish to end the friendship and comradeship he enjoyed with his fellow engineers, but the nature of his new role left him little time to dabble in the affairs of just one of the departments under his overall control, even if he did have great personal interest in its workings.

Hoy's work obviously satisfied Aspinall and the two certainly got on well together for they collaborated on a number of experiments including that of train signalling. However, being Chief Mechanical Engineer was very different from being Works Manager, and Aspinall was a hard act to follow. For Hoy there was the added burden that the previous act was now directing the show and, it would appear, retained a wish to perform. It says much for Hoy's character that he took to the job with enthusiasm and little upheaval resulted. Credit for that must also go to Aspinall, for his organization and skills and the family atmosphere which he had built up at Horwich. There was never any intention of bringing in outsiders to fill the top mechanical engineering posts; people already at Horwich had been groomed for such roles. It is always the sign of a good manager that he has a replacement ready trained to step in should he depart, for whatever reason.

Not surprisingly, Hoy had received his initial training at Crewe, being apprenticed under Webb in 1872. Born in London on 13 January 1855, he received his early education at King Edward VI Grammar School, St Albans, and later at St John's College, Liverpool. He made his mark at Crewe when, in 1877, following a fatal rail accident at Wigan, he constructed a model of the permanent way in the vicinity for use at the inquest. As a result of the incident he devised a mechanism which would effectively lock facing points and so prevent accidents of the same type. These model-making and inventive skills interested Webb, and Hoy found himself performing similar duties for his CME; for example, he produced the working models for Webb's interlocking signal and point lever frame. In 1878 a transfer to the drawing office was obtained, and there he worked on plans for continuous brakes, mechanical and fluid, and also carried out experiments with them.[32] During his final years at Crewe, Hoy was engaged upon design work for the second series of Webb compound engines and such work must have provided valuable experience.[33] A Crewe training was always thorough but some learned more than others, and Hoy appeared to be in the former category.

A change came in 1884 when he was appointed to the outdoor locomotive staff of the L&YR under W.B. Wright. Eighteen months later he was promoted to manage the workshops at Miles Platting, and as soon as the new works at Horwich

Henry Albert Hoy.

were ready he took over as manager. Such rapid progress was the result of hard work and ability, but Hoy did not rest and over the following years did much to develop the workshops for the manufacturing of most items required by the railway. Although Aspinall was in overall command, he needed a good works manager at Horwich, and it was Hoy who set in motion schemes to manufacture electrical apparatus there; he also played a leading part in plans for the electrification of the Liverpool to Southport line.

Although a member of both major engineering Institutions, 'Civils' and 'Mechanicals', Hoy did not take an active part in their affairs. His only contribution to any paper appears to have been the appendix concerning the operation of the L&YR's Thornycroft steam wagon which appeared with Hele-Shaw's paper, 'Road Locomotion'.[34] Even with this contribution, Hoy took no other part in the discussion and it is unlikely that he actually attended many meetings of either Institution. The appendix does, however, illustrate the thoroughness with which he approached the gathering of information, for it contained details of loads as well as fuel and water

consumption over a complete week of trials during February and March 1900. He even made allowance for the fact that inexperienced drivers had charge of the vehicle on its first days in both Liverpool and Manchester.

Not wishing to take an active part in the running of learned societies or even in the discussion of their papers does not make for a bad or disinterested engineer; Hoy was certainly keen on the pursuit of knowledge, although somewhat less active than Aspinall. The fact that he did not publish the results of his experiments directly does not indicate that he was not involved in the gathering of information. As an inventor he was very active and many of those inventions had direct application to the job with which he was currently occupied. Mention has already been made of the electrical apparatus for signalling and point interlocks, but he was also responsible for the steam dynamos fitted in the works at Horwich.

Efficient production of electricity required the dynamo to be driven at fairly high speed, and that usually implied some form of belt drive in order to bring about a speed increase. Directly coupled high-speed engines were more advantageous not only in the fact that there was no belt drive to cause trouble, but also due to their more compact size. Hoy set about designing such a machine and it turned out to be very effective. His experience with Webb compounds at Crewe must have been useful, for the engine was of single acting tandem compound form with two sets of cylinder units, the high-pressure being of 10 in diameter, the low-pressure of 14 in diameter and the stroke 6 in. The high operational speed of 460 rpm allowed for direct connection to a dynamo, and with steam supplied at 160 psi the unit could develop some 100 ihp (74.6 kw).

High-speed operation required effective distribution of steam, so Hoy employed piston valves but positioned them in rather a strange manner. Instead of being placed alongside the cylinders, the valves actually directed steam via ports in the cylinder heads; because the engines were single acting, ports were only required above the pistons. Two eccentrics operated the valve spindles, one steam inlet and the other exhaust, for each in-line set of cylinders, and to save space the spindles actually passed through the pistons. In order to obtain maximum work, the space below the LP piston was kept under vacuum conditions, the 18 in vacuum being maintained by exhaust steam from the cylinder acting in an ejector.

For accurate production, Hoy arranged for the manufacture of jigs and templates with their assembly, by just one man, taking place well away

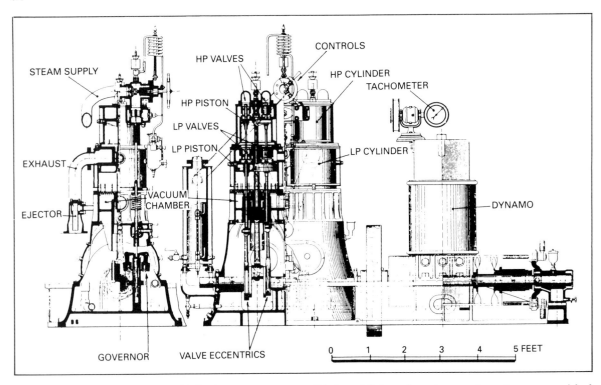

from the machine shops in which the parts were made. In all ways the engines were identical, but the person charged with assembly could build them up with the operating valves on the left- or right-hand side according to requirements. Design and production of such engines illustrates Hoy's capabilities not just as a designer but also a manufacturing engineer. They became the standard power unit in the shops at Horwich where, coupled to Hoy-designed dynamos, they supplied the electrical requirements; they were also used as the power source for other purposes.[35]

A number of other items of plant were designed by him during that period as Works Manager and most were directly related to the requirements of the works rather than being speculative inventions. Hoy's policy seems to have been that if it is needed and does not already exist, then design it. Horwich works gradually became equipped with a variety of devices to the design of its Works Manager including electrically-powered cranes and capstans for the movement of components. The workshops were even illuminated by arc lamps to his design.[36] Made at Horwich, these lamps found application in large numbers throughout the plant; boiler shop, 28; machine & fitting shop, 40; heavy machine shop, 15; iron & steel foundry, 31; and erecting shop,

74. In addition, four inverted arc lamps provided reflected light for the drawing office in order to supplement that supplied by incandescent lamps.[37]

With Aspinall's appointment as General Manager in 1899, Hoy took over as CME and George Hughes replaced him as Works Manager at Horwich. As already discussed, the change was not a major upheaval and all of the major players remained on the scene, but Hoy now had greater responsibility and authority. Electricity or its use figured in many of Hoy's designs and he must have been one of the first CMEs or Works Managers to fully appreciate its advantages and implications. Proposed electrification of the Liverpool-Southport line obviously delighted him and he was charged with the responsibility for the design of much of the equipment to be used. That which was not designed under him had to meet with his approval. Contractors Dick, Kerr & Co had responsibility for the entire work except rolling-stock design, which was carried out at Horwich. For the power cars, Hoy himself designed the bogies which incorporated a much simpler system of springing than had previously been employed. This replaced the earlier 'swan neck' compensating bars, thus producing a lighter bogie on which wheel or electric motor changes would also be much easier.[38]

As Works Manager at Horwich, Hoy was responsible for the implementation of many of Aspinall's schemes, but much of the credit for the way in which the workshops developed is due to him. Obviously the CME had the responsibility and final say in what did or did not take place, within the limits of finance and Directors' support, but his faith in Hoy must have been considerable. Managerial skills developed during that period were to prove of use in later years when his experience as a manager was sought by an outside concern.

As Chief Mechanical Engineer of the L&YR, Hoy's locomotive policy seems to have been to follow the Aspinall lead. It is highly unlikely that he would have received backing for widespread construction of new designs anyway as the railway was reasonably well equipped with locomotives. There is, however, no evidence to suggest that Hoy had any desire to adopt such a policy; he appears to have been content to modify existing designs and introduce experimental ideas with individual locomotives, and Aspinall had left him a number of existing projects to be getting on with. Matters relating to locomotives will be discussed in a later chapter, but the subject has been raised here to indicate that the new CME was not inactive during his period in office.

That period was short, and it came as a surprise to a number of observers when Hoy resigned in 1904 to become General Manager of the locomotive builders Beyer, Peacock & Co of Gorton. That post suited him well as he was called upon to reorganize the workshops and promote better production methods. As an incentive, his £2,000 per annum salary was to be supplemented by a 2.5 per cent commission on the net profits; that sort of incentive was not offered at Horwich.[39] His relatively short period as CME might suggest that he

was unable to operate under the conditions which existed with Aspinall apparently unwilling to relinquish command. Certainly the former CME took an active interest in mechanical, and electrical, engineering matters and still supervised some experimental work, as his papers to learned societies show, but there is no evidence at all that Hoy was dissatisfied. The reason for the move was simply that it was a better job, more challenging and more highly paid, his salary as CME having been £1,500 per annum.

Hoy's reign at Beyer, Peacock was also short for he died, following a brief illness, on 24 May 1910 at the age of 55 years. A quiet man who had few other interests apart from his family, Hoy was highly respected by the workforce at Gorton and townspeople of Horwich where he had occupied a seat on the District Council. His managerial skills were highly regarded amongst the engineering community and he would certainly have served the L&YR well had Beyer, Peacock not secured his talents. At the time of his death he was President of the Manchester District Engineering Trades Employers' Association and in addition to membership of both major engineering institutions he also held membership of the Iron & Steel Institute.[40]

George Hughes

It is almost unnecessary to say but George Hughes was also Crewe-trained. Born in Norfolk on 9 October 1865, he received his early education at the Norfolk County School before becoming a premium apprentice under Webb in 1882. As usual, the training would have been thorough and in 1887 he moved to Horwich, no doubt attracted by both the idea of working at the new establishment being constructed there and the apparent lack of promotion prospects on the LNWR. During his first year of employment with

Above left *Hoy's high-speed compound dynamo engine.*

Right *L&YR steel-ended electric motor car No 3037, built in 1906.* (National Railway Museum, York)

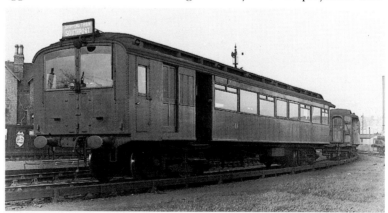

George Hughes

experience. In 1894 he became assistant to the Outdoor Locomotive Superintendent, and after a very short period was given charge of the gas works at Horwich as well as responsibility for gas lighting throughout the whole railway system. Today that may not seem very important but at that time the post held considerable responsibility, for much of the works, almost all stations and practically the entire coaching stock was illuminated by means of gas. Production and consumption of gas came within this area of responsibility, but safety was absolutely important, especially with regard to carriages. Hughes was a firm advocate of gas lighting for railway carriages even as late as 1906, despite a number of railway accidents where fire had taken place following the incident. After examining reports of 1,427 accidents over the previous 26 years, he found that in only 14 cases was the wreckage involved in fire, and only four of these could be attributed to gas. At the time, 1906, gas was cheaper than and superior to other forms of lighting and Hughes concluded that engineers should concentrate on preventing accidents in the first place, and the risk of fire would then take care of itself.[42]

In 1895, Aspinall became a true Chief Mechanical Engineer when the Board of Directors put the Carriage and Wagon department under his control, the previous incumbent, F. Attock, having resigned due to ill health. Hughes was immediately appointed Assistant Carriage and Wagon Superintendent, effectively in charge of that section, as Aspinall concentrated on the locomotive and administration side. Henry Fowler took over responsibility for the gas works. That appointment put Hughes in the top rank of L&YR engineering managers — at the Newton Heath works he had some 3,500 men under his control — and set him up as an eventual CME.

When Hoy became Chief Mechanical Engineer of the L&YR, Hughes was appointed as his principal assistant and manager of the locomotive works. The way was now open for full responsibility and that came in March 1904 when he became CME on Hoy's resignation. Again there was no major upheaval and matters progressed steadily as before — the mould had not been broken, just recast with new names.

In terms of his character, George Hughes was very much a quiet and retiring man, but that did not mean that he was soft or would tolerate slackness. According to E.S. Cox, Hughes also had a strong personality and could exercise command without appearing to exert any real effort or coercion. He always came straight to the point regard-

the L&YR, Hughes was engaged upon fitting work in the millwright and erecting shops, but his potential must have been quickly recognized for soon afterwards he was put in charge of the testing department, and also had responsibility for the inspection of purchased materials. Under Hughes, but obviously at the instigation of Aspinall, the testing department flourished as additional laboratories were added for chemical and physical testing of materials.[41]

Work in the testing department under Aspinall must have been interesting and exciting, but Hughes was not just acting at the behest of his CME; he also carried out work on his own initiative, especially in the development of alloys. This interest in metallurgy remained with him in later years, for he fully appreciated the important fact that any machine was only as good as the materials from which it was constructed. An essential part of the Hughes philosophy was to ensure that materials were always available to do the job.

It is fairly certain that early in his career on the L&YR Hughes was singled out for greater things, as can be witnessed by his progression through the more important departments in order to gain ing any matter with which he was concerned and would not indulge in unnecessary small-talk. Despite this he was willing to share a joke or indulge in witty repartee, his nasal manner of speaking making imitation of such almost compulsory.

On a railway as compact as the Lancashire & Yorkshire, it is understandable that its senior officers were well known to the workforce, and Hughes always made his presence felt about the system as well as at Horwich. He obviously had an affinity for the place as could be witnessed by his lack of interest in moving to one of the larger sites following the grouping. Cox also states that Hughes was well liked by close colleagues and assistants as well as by the factory workmen. In a leader, who could also ensure that the work was performed effectively and economically, that was, and still is, a rare quality. Hughes had a keen interest in the welfare of the employees both on the L&YR and on the enlarged LMS system, having special regard for the workings of the various Mechanics' Institutes. Although not one to force himself on others, he did play his part in the Horwich works social life and seems to have been well respected because of that.[43]

Upon retiring from the post of CME of the London Midland & Scottish Railway in 1925 Hughes expressed the desire that that no formal presentation of a retirement gift be made. A considerable amount of money had already been donated for such a presentation and much more pledged, but Hughes asked that the money be devoted to the foundation of an annual prize in his name at the Mechanics' Institute. That was done, but his friends and colleagues at Horwich were not to be denied some form of presentation and one was arranged when the cheque for such a prize could be passed to the retiring CME. Some

of the money was kept back, however, for the purchase of a bracelet watch which was presented to his wife in gratitude for the work she had carried out amongst the staff at Horwich.[44] A wife was often required to perform functions arising from the position held by her husband, and a caring considerate wife was an asset.

The Railway Gazette, obviously echoing the views of its management, was forthright in its praise, declaring that Hughes was 'recognized in railway mechanical engineering circles as an authority' who would 'be reluctant to express publicly any opinion to which he had not given mature thought beforehand'. In addition, that journal stated that 'His utterances on any phase of the locomotive engineering subject have always been listened to with attention'.[45]

In its obituary notice, *The Engineer* referred to Hughes as a very lovable, cheerful man, the obituarist being of the opinion that he never received the recognition due to him because he never put on any real display about his works but simply got on with the job. The notice finishes with the simple statement 'Dear George Hughes', which indicates the affection with which he was held by the engineering community in general.[46]

The association between that journal and Hughes actually went back more than half a century, for in the early 1890s *The Engineer* had published a series of articles by him on the construction of a locomotive. This was no historical description of the steam locomotive's development nor a glamorous account of operation, but was a detailed record of the building of an Aspinall 0-6-0 tender engine. For the modern enthusiast the articles might seem dull and lack the fire and sparkle associated with late twentieth century railway writings, but they accurately detail all steps of construction from raw material to final

Aspinall 0–6–0 No 52455, formerly L&YR No 873. The construction of this type of engine was described in George Hughes' book. (D. K. Jones collection)

assembly. The articles were intended to educate those with an interest in locomotive construction, and so well were they received that they were later compiled to form a book. Published by Spon in 1894, *The Construction of the Modern Locomotive* would serve as a very useful reference work for any present-day enthusiast wishing to understand how locomotives were built during the late Victorian period, or any period for that matter, for steam locomotive construction varied very little during its history.

Hughes possessed many of the qualities of Aspinall and one of these was the desire to gather and pass on knowledge whenever possible. Less prolific in terms of papers to learned societies than his notable predecessor, Hughes did, however, provide a number of very useful papers to the 'Civils' and 'Mechanicals', as well as to the Institute of Metals. Of these bodies, as well as of the Iron and Steel Institute, Hughes was a member and would frequently take part in the discussion of papers.

An appreciation of metals is an essential requirement for any mechanical engineer, and Hughes kept himself abreast of developments in that field, even adding to the knowledge. Over the years he amassed considerable data relating to ferrous and non-ferrous metals, gathered from experimental work and operating experience. This information was not obtained just for the sake of knowledge but for good commercial reasons, and Hughes never forgot that he was part of an enterprise whose purpose was to make money. During the latter part of the nineteenth and early part of the twentieth centuries, economic operation was as important as it is today, and locomotive construction at the least cost conducive with safety had to be the aim. Copper and brass were more expensive than steel or iron and Hughes always aimed at using the minimum amount of such materials wherever possible. That was his stated aim in the paper prepared for the Institute of Metals in 1911.[47]

The paper, presented at a meeting in Newcastle, was well received by an audience bristling with eminent scholars and engineers, but Hughes could not be present himself for he was preoccupied with a strike at Horwich. *Engineering* reported that he had been threatened with rough treatment by the strikers, and that the respected metallurgist Sir Gerald Muntz had advised him to go to Newcastle for his own safety.[48] That he did not, but stayed where he was needed until the dispute was solved, says much for his character. The paper was detailed in every respect and covered all aspects of the use of non-ferrous metals for construction and repair. Details of various alloys were given as were methods of manufacture and the repair of such items as fireboxes. It is unnecessary to go into details as to the contents of the paper here, but a few comments from those taking part in the discussion are worthy of repetition. Muntz considered it to be a most useful paper and one of the clearest he had read for some time, whilst Dr Cecil Desch considered it to the most valuable yet to be brought before the Institute.

Praise from such notable worthies indicates the strength of the paper and also the care with which Hughes gathered and presented his information. A paper such as that considerably enhanced his reputation in the engineering and scientific world. A good Chief Mechanical Engineer was more than just an introducer of locomotive designs, and Hughes had proved himself before his peers to be a very good engineer.

The gathering of useful information was not confined to the environs of Horwich, and Hughes would seek knowledge wherever he could. In 1905 he accompanied Aspinall to America nominally to attend the International Railway Congress being held in Washington. During the trip, Hughes took the opportunity to visit several railway workshops including those of the Pennsylvania Railroad and the Canadian Pacific Railway. Upon his return he described the trip in his Presidential Address to the newly formed Engineering and Scientific Club at the Horwich Mechanics' Institute.[49]

In international terms Hughes was also recognized, and was asked to present the report on locomotive bogies, axles and springs at the 1922 meeting of the International Railway Association. That report covered British and overseas locomotives indicating that he was at least well read on the subject, but his coverage of American practice indicates deeper knowledge, probably gathered from more intimate contact.[50]

Hughes would often accompany Aspinall to meetings at the 'Civils' and 'Mechanicals', of which he was a member of council, and at times they would both take part in the discussion of a paper. Such strength from the L&YR must have been feared by many authors, both men always always appearing eager to promote the practice on that railway.

An example of this is the 1910 'Civils' paper, 'Suburban System of the LB&SC Railway' by P. Dawson. Aspinall's comments covered electrified railway systems in general, but covered the Liverpool-Southport line in some detail before going on to discuss the relative merits of direct current (dc) compared with alternating current (ac) electrical supply. He finished by emphasizing that the dc-powered Liverpool-Southport line was doing very well both electrically and mechanically and that the author had not convinced him that any other system was more suitable.

Hughes continued the attack with detailed facts and figures of L&YR electrical operations, especially regarding the contentious issue of operating costs. The paper's author had quoted favourable figures regarding cost per ton mile, but Hughes countered with better figures related to cost per seat mile, and as these were passenger routes his basis for costing would seem to be the more realistic. He then went on to add that the power consumption per ton mile was in any case subservient to the operating requirements — high power was needed for a fast service, but such a service allowed more passengers to be carried thus giving a greater load factor for the line.[51] Both men seemed to relish the occasion and provided a formidable double act.

Sometimes the onslaught was in two stages if either could not attend the initial presentation. Such was the case with the paper 'Railway-motor-car Traffic' by T.H. Riches and S.B. Haslam, read at a 'Mechanicals' meeting in Cardiff during August 1906 when Aspinall was in the chair. Hughes could not attend but made his presence felt at the October discussion when he presented the advantages of his own design of steam railcar as opposed to the Taff Vale variety. He did, however, pay tribute to the cars designed by Riches and acknowledged that fact that the L&YR had had two cars to his design built by Kerr, Stewart & Co. Hughes concluded his contribution by consider-

ing the desirable feature of such vehicles in general. He held the view that the railways should give the public plentiful opportunities to travel by means of a fast and frequent service, and the railcar could provide that service. He was also of the opinion that an individual was willing to allow about 30 minutes for travel to his place of work, and that if a fast service could be provided suburbs could be further opened up, thus increasing railway traffic.[52] There was more to Hughes than just engineering — he obviously had a keen business sense.

Even when going solo, Hughes was ready with figures to back his statements and would always defend his own railway. During the discussion of a paper concerned with stock for heavy gradients, Hughes provided the meeting with a detailed account of Lancashire & Yorkshire locomotives for such working and, as usual, backed his claims with facts. These were drawn from experiments he had conducted with goods locomotives on heavy gradients, and he then emphasized the strength of his own case by producing graphs which compared his results with those of the author. Naturally, the L&YR locomotives were shown to have greater hauling capacity.[53] This was not arrogance, but was part of the Hughes character — he always insisted upon accuracy and had pride in the achievements of the railway he served.

If he was rigorous when discussing the papers of others, he was absolutely meticulous about his own. Two papers before the Institution of Mechanical Engineers during Aspinall's term as President were of a nature and class which set them apart from most others. The first concerned

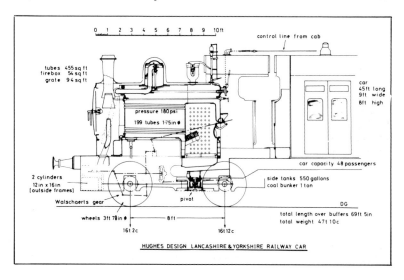

A drawing of the Hughes-designed Railcar.

locomotives designed and built at Horwich, whilst the second dealt with the contentious issues of compounding and superheating. In terms of their detailed content these papers were masterpieces of engineering literature and well deserved the praise heaped upon them. Of the first, T.H. Riches, a Past President of the Mechanicals, considered it to be a most complete and useful paper which would be appreciated by the younger members because the detail of experience it contained would save them years of worry. Henry Fowler was no less glowing in his praise, especially with regard to the reports of failures of built-up crankshafts, mention of such failures, he considered, being a rare thing to find in papers read before institutions and societies.[54]

The 1910 paper 'Compounding and Superheating' was just as detailed, Hughes being one of the few locomotive engineers with any real experience of these features which were claimed to reduce operating costs. Results of trials concerning both were presented in detail and G.J. Churchward opened the discussion of the paper with a tribute thanking the author for actually providing such results. After commenting on the careful way in which the figures had been presented, he went on to add: 'There are very few people in this country who had the opportunity of arriving at such a mass of figures and results, and he feared that there were still fewer who, when they did arrive at them, presented them free to the Institution for consideration and assistance to the members'.[55] This was praise indeed from one of the few engineers who did have an opportunity of gathering such data and had done so.

C.J.B. Cooke of the LNWR also offered thanks for the mass of useful information provided and considered that all locomotive engineers in the country were indebted to the author. Shortly before he died, Cooke again offered praise to the L&YR engineer during discussion of the paper 'Electrical and Mechanical Equipment for All-metal Cars on the L&YR', read before the Institution of Civil Engineers during 1921 and for which Hughes was awarded the Telford Gold Medal. 'Mr Hughes' Paper was not only excellent from an engineering and scientific point of view — his Papers were always above praise in that respect — but for the very useful information of a commercial character which would be invaluable to those interested in the construction of electric railways with either wood or steel coaches'.[56] It is little wonder that *The Railway Gazette*'s obituary notice stated that his utterances on locomotive matters were always listened to with attention.

These papers were obviously extremely valu-

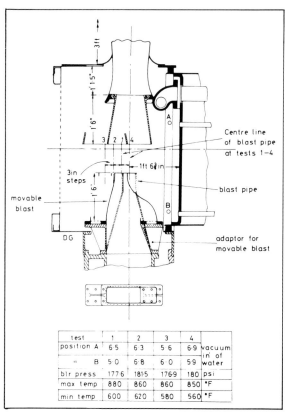

Variable position blast pipe arrangements.

test position A	1	2	3	4	
position A	6·5	6·3	5·6	6·9	vacuum in of water
" B	5·0	6·8	6·0	5·9	
blr press	177·6	181·5	176·9	180	psi
max temp	880	860	860	850	°F
min temp	600	620	580	560	°F

able in their day, but even now the wealth of information they contain is worth reading. As documents of historical fact they have few equals in railway mechanical engineering. Not only do they contain details of construction, but they also give information regarding the experimental work carried out by Hughes. In many respects he was as avid a searcher after truth as was Aspinall, and it seems highly likely that both men enthused over current experimental work whenever they got the chance.

Following on from Aspinall's earlier work on boiler draughts, Hughes conducted similar experiments using long and short smokeboxes and concluded that an extended smokebox was better for maintaining steam pressure. Other experiments were conducted with a radial passenger tank engine fitted with such an extended smokebox in order to determine the best arrangement and size of blast pipe. Investigations then took place regarding the best position for the blast pipe in relation to the tubeplate and to achieve this a moveable blast pipe and chimney were provided on the test locomotive. Several sizes of blast pipe and chimney were used on a whole series of tests over a prolonged period and the results proved to Hughes that it was not possible to standardize the front end as had been attempted by some engineers. Hughes believed that each new design of locomotive required some experimental work in order to optimize the size and position of blast pipe and chimney.[57]

Hughes was no advocate of compounding irrespective of locomotive type, but considered it only suitable for goods engines, with their lower piston speed. Under such conditions a large temperature change would be experienced by the steam during expansion due to heat transfer to piston and cylinder. Drop in temperature caused condensation which resulted in less efficient working. He concluded that the temperature drop in the cylinder during expansion had to be reduced if condensation was to be avoided, and that could be achieved by expanding the steam in two stages rather than one, hence compounding. The situation was not the same for express engines which operated at higher piston speeds because, even with an early cut-off, the steam temperature range was small. Hughes came to the conclusion that there was very little benefit to be obtained from compounding express passenger engines, but that goods engine offered possibilities. This deduction was not based upon pure theory, however, but arose from observations of passenger and goods engines at different speeds and cut-offs.[58]

During 1906 Hughes opened the discussion on Churchward's famous paper, 'Large Locomotive Boilers', and expressed clearly his own views regarding their construction and operation. He also raised the point about compounding and posed the question, 'Why in this country were passenger engines compounded instead of goods engines?' This was obviously aimed at the author of the paper who had been actively engaged in trials with compounding, but for passenger locomotives. Other matters raised by Hughes included water softening, furnace design, heat storage, and piston valves, in fact most aspects concerned with any locomotive boiler. The extent of the points raised and the tone of his remarks, though courteous and friendly, left no doubt that Hughes was a well-informed engineer with a forceful manner.[59] At that time Churchward's stock was high, and Hughes had occupied the CME's chair for less than two years, but such matters were of no consequence and the northern engineer obviously had no feelings of inferiority.

With Aspinall as General Manager, Hughes had an ally in a powerful position and many engineering projects could be undertaken which under different conditions might not have been sanctioned. Without doubt it was a very successful partnership and helped enhance the reputation of the railway in mechanical engineering terms. Horwich Works became one of the most advanced in the country with facilities for complete manufacture from raw material to finished machine. The drawing office was actively engaged

Hughes' proposed 2-10-0 locomotive.

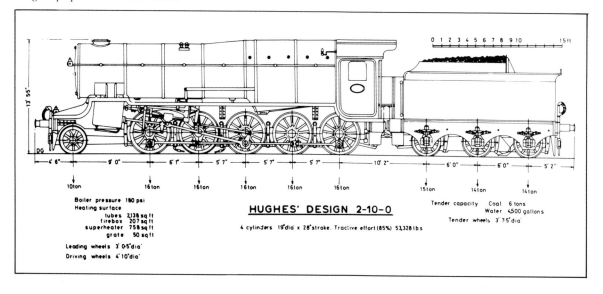

HUGHES' DESIGN 2-10-0

Boiler pressure 180 psi
Heating surface
    tubes 2,138 sq ft
    firebox 207 sq ft
    superheater 758 sq ft
    grate 50 sq ft
Leading wheels 3' 0·5"dia'
Driving wheels 4' 10"dia'

4 cylinders 19"dia' x 28"stroke. Tractive effort (85%) 53,328 lbs

Tender capacity   Coal 6 tons
    Water 4,500 gallons
Tender wheels 3' 7·5"dia'

in new design work, although many schemes never progressed past the initial outline stage. Hughes was not prepared to let matters rest; although he would build on the strong foundations of Aspinall and Hoy, modifying whenever necessary, new designs were considered for changing traffic demands. Increasing freight traffic resulting in heavier trains prompted him to consider a 2-10-0 design which would do the work of two 0-6-0s on the heavily graded L&YR lines. A drawing of this four-cylinder, wide-firebox locomotive was produced in 1913 and was based upon a Belgian 2-10-0 he had seen a few years before.[60]

Nothing came of the proposal either then or in the 1920s when it was raised again as a means of dealing with heavy freight traffic on the Midland section of the LMS. Restrictions imposed by the Civil Engineer's department prevented what would have been a rather impressive locomotive from being constructed, but CMEs were frequently thwarted in their plans by their less ambitious civil colleagues, who always seemed to prefer to say 'no' than to involve themselves in upgrading routes. The design does, however, indicate how active and innovative Hughes was in the locomotive field.

In 1922, when the Lancashire & Yorkshire Railway amalgamated with the London & North Western Railway to form an enlarged LNWR, it was inevitable that Hughes would become CME of that new concern. He had the seniority, status and experience for the post. Some later commentators have argued that the Crewe incumbent, H.P.M. Beames, should have been appointed on the grounds that he was CME of the senior partner in the merger. Crewe loyalties ran deep, and still do, but there was really no competition — Hughes was the better man. Had he not been selected it is certain that the Midland's CME would have been appointed to head the new London Midland & Scottish Railway at the grouping a year later. Nobody, apart from Crewe loyalists, would have considered that the relatively young and inexperienced Beames had the credentials to oversee mechanical engineering on the largest of the grouped railways. Hughes was a well-respected and highly qualified engineer with an engineering pedigree that few others at the time could match.

Over the next few years he must have found life completely different from the times when he could deal with the amiable Aspinall. The Midland-dominated management of the LMS made life difficult, but he still had some control and imposed his will by maintaining his base at Horwich. The days were not all bad and he still managed to produce locomotives to meet traffic demands, but the nature of the large and unwieldy LMS made long-term planning extremely difficult. It is highly unlikely that any engineer would have been able to satisfy himself and the disparate demands of management. As constituted, the Board and management team comprised cliques with an interest only in imposing the regime which they knew and believed to be most suitable. Derby and Crewe factions fought a bloodless civil war much to the detriment of the LMS, and one party had to win otherwise the railway would have died from the effects of the infighting.

That the Midland Railway group became dominant is history, but even had the LNWR faction gained control there would still have been an imposition of will which would not have suited other parties. Nobody really won, but the LMS certainly lost until the old guard was moved on and a management team with purely LMS interests at heart took over.

What effect the infighting of the immediate post-grouping period had on Hughes is unknown — he never made his views public — but the restrictions must have been annoying. However, at Horwich he could still rule his world of sorts, but the paymasters elsewhere curtailed any plans he might have had for larger and more powerful locomotives. By 1925 he decided enough was enough and retired. He was 60 years old and may have considered leaving at that age anyway, but the frustrations of having to deal with a somewhat antagonistic management must have made the parting easier. At that time letters of resignation never included contentious points but simply stated the intention in a courteous manner. Hughes was a courteous man and would never have contemplated saying publicly what he felt.

George Hughes loved locomotives but, apart from retaining membership of learned societies, never took any other part in activities related to his profession. The award of CBE marked his retirement and he took himself off to Cromer in the county of his birth where he served on the Coastal Erosion Committee. In later years he moved to Stamford, Lincolnshire, and occupied his time in the growing of vegetables, a particular speciality being tomatoes. He did not lose touch with friends nor did he lose his sense of humour, the editor of *The Engineer* receiving from him a sketch of one of his locomotives with a plume of tomatoes bursting from its chimney.[61]

George Hughes died at his home in Stamford on 27 October 1945 aged 80 years.

3. London & North Western Railway Locomotive Engineers

John Ramsbottom

In all walks of life there appear periodically individuals whose stars shine brighter than their contemporaries. Their gifts of originality and innovation set them apart. The mechanical engineering profession was blessed with the talents of John Ramsbottom, and it is certain that he would have received a more universal acclaim had he graced the theatrical, musical or literacy professions. His genius is recognized by engineers whilst those with an interest in railway and mechanical matters can appreciate his works even if they do not perceive the intellect which produced them. In the wide world, unfortunately, he receives no acknowledgement. Such, however, is the way of things as far as engineering is concerned.

John Ramsbottom was born in the small town of Todmorden on 11 September 1814, his father being a cotton spinner. There was engineering experience to be gained for the young Ramsbottom when his father became owner of the first steam-driven mill in the valley, and it is clear that he had an aptitude for mechanical matters. Early education came by way of a number of private teachers in his native town, but formal tuition was meagre compared with what life had to offer. It may easily and accurately be said that John Ramsbottom was a self-educated man who attended the 'University of Life'. Todmorden may have been small, but he soaked up all it had to offer and then sought after more.

Aware of his interest in mechanical matters, Ramsbottom's father brought him a 6-inch lathe and provided space for it in his warehouse. Soon the young Ramsbottom was producing model steam engines, including a small working locomotive. It would seem certain that he also manufactured parts for the engine at the mill and some of the mill equipment itself. As his skills increased, so did the scale of his work, and small engines became bigger, culminating in an engine of 4 in bore and 12 in stroke for a confectioner friend. Later he organized the reconstruction and erection of the steam engine in his father's mill, experience of dealing with contractors being gained whilst this work was being undertaken. Into the bargain he also fitted up the mill with coal gas lighting, then a novelty.[1]

Ramsbottom's first 25 years of life were spent in Todmorden with few ventures further afield, but he did take an active interest in the local Mechanics' Institute. In 1839 he obtained a position as a skilled worker at the firm of Sharp, Roberts & Co in Manchester, his practical experience making this possible without the formal apprenticeship normally required. That concern was engaged in the manufacture of a variety of engineering equipment at the time with specific emphasis on locomotives. In addition, cotton spinning machines were also manufactured and that fitted in with Ramsbottom's earlier experience. Whilst engaged in work at his father's mill, he became familiar with machinery for textile manufacture and schemed out various systems for improving production. One of these was the weft stopper which acted on the shuttle of a loom in order to bring it to rest. That device found universal application as it allowed for high-speed power operation of looms. About the same time he also

John Ramsbottom.

devised a machine for the automatic manufacture of nails.[2]

The urge for invention obviously gripped Ramsbottom at an early age, but he was equally adept at organization and the acquisition of new skills. These attributes and an almost unlimited enthusiasm for engineering soon came to the notice of C.F. Beyer, subsequently to co-found the firm of Beyer, Peacock Ltd, but then head of Sharp's locomotive department. At that time it was common practice for railway companies to ask the advice of manufacturers from whom they purchased locomotives whenever an appointment to the railway locomotive department was being made. In 1842 the Directors of the Manchester & Birmingham Railway decided to appoint a Locomotive Superintendent to take charge of its locomotive facility at Longsight, Manchester. Advice was sought from C.F. Beyer, who had no hesitation in recommending that Ramsbottom be appointed.

Such a position obviously suited the enthusiastic and ambitious Ramsbottom who soon got to work dealing with the mixed fleet of locomotives made by Sharp, Roberts & Co and Robert Stephenson & Co. Despite his wide engineering experience, Ramsbottom was completely new to the requirements of working a railway but his capacity for learning soon had him in complete control. However, as traffic increased over the years, it became evident that a foreman would be required to take charge of the running shed. On the recommendation of Isaac Watt Boulton, in 1852 Ramsbottom obtained the services of John Rigg who had gained his operating experience on the Manchester, Sheffield and Lincolnshire Railway. The pair obviously worked well together for Ramsbottom took Rigg to Crewe in later years where he subsequently had charge of the Running Department of the LNWR and acted as Deputy Locomotive Superintendent, taking over during Ramsbottom's spells of illness.

Boulton, writing nearly 50 years later, described the situation in 1852 when Ramsbottom was very concerned about the working of heavy Whitsun week traffic. 'I heard him [Rigg] say to Mr Ramsbottom, "Leave it to me, I feel quite at home with it, and all will come out right." It did, and ever after Mr Ramsbottom had full confidence in Mr Rigg.'[3]

When the Manchester & Birmingham became part of the London & North Western, Ramsbottom remained in charge at Longsight, his area then being designated the North Eastern division. With the dismissal of Trevithick from his post at Crewe in 1857, the Northern and North Eastern divisions were combined under Ramsbottom. A year earlier Ramsbottom had contemplated taking up the position of Locomotive Superintendent on the Eastern Counties Railway, or even of going back into industry. These alternatives he had discussed with the Marquis of Chandos, Chairman of the LNWR[4], but how serious he was is open to speculation. In the light of subsequent events it is possible that Ramsbottom was pushing his case and trying to influence those in command to promote him or lose him. Certainly he was a favourite with the very influential Richard Moon.

Ramsbottom pushed the matter further when he indicated to Moon that he would want a salary of £1,200 per annum if placed in charge of the combined Northern & North Eastern divisions. Again Moon pressed his case but was not immediately successful, for Ramsbottom, upon being appointed to superintend the newly combined

Ramsbottom's coking crane.

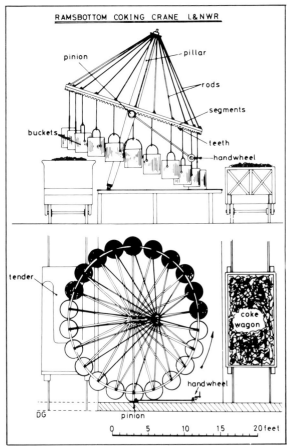

division in August 1857, was granted a salary of £1,000 per annum. McConnell at Wolverton received the same salary and both were awarded a £200 increase soon afterwards.

With the departure of McConnell in 1862, Ramsbottom assumed control of mechanical engineering matters for the entire LNWR system. A degree of rationalization was long overdue and he took steps to deal with the rather unwieldy system which had developed. All locomotive work was centred at Crewe, Wolverton dealt with carriages, whilst wagons were to be built and repaired at Earlestown. Assistants dealt with the day-to-day operation of these out-stations, but Ramsbottom as Locomotive Superintendent and Mechanical Engineer to the London & North Western Railway, had overall control.

Whilst at Longsight Ramsbottom engaged himself in a number of activities which were intended to make operations there more effective and efficient. He devised an improved coking crane for supplying fuel to locomotive tenders with the minimum labour. As with many inventions it was simplicity itself, and consisted of a merry-go-round arrangement of coke buckets, each bucket being capable of holding 3 cwt (153kg) of coke. Twenty-two buckets were supported at the circumference of a wheel, the centre support pillar of which was inclined at an angle. A system of gearing allowed a small handwheel to turn the main wheel and so rotate the buckets, but because the axis was tilted the full buckets would be made to rise by some 6 ft (1.83m) as they turned from the filling platform to the locomotive road. The force needed to raise the buckets was relatively small, and a number of full buckets were always available for the next locomotive.

The device was installed at the LNWR station in Manchester during 1851 and, when described by Ramsbottom in a paper before the infant Institution of Mechanical Engineers in 1853, had been performing perfectly, delivering 21 cwt (1.07 tonnes) of coke in two minutes and reducing the loading crew to two people, half the number formerly required. In the paper Ramsbottom did point out its one drawback, which was that an engine could not run past the crane on account of its chimney coming into contact with the buckets. Ever interested in improvements, he did point out that the crane could be fitted slightly higher with coke being delivered by a moveable chute.[5]

Ramsbottom was a founder member of the Institution of Mechanical Engineers and took an active part in its affairs. Over the years he con-

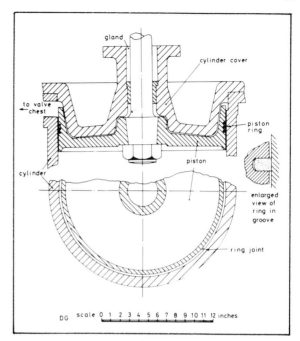

The piston arrangement devised by Ramsbottom.

tributed 13 papers, all describing his own inventions. He served the Institution as a member of council for seven years, then as Vice President for 13 years and finally as President in 1870-1. His earliest paper was presented in 1849 and covered aspects of a design for an improved boiler which had a separate steam chamber, a large-area flue and an even larger heating surface, low weight and simplified construction.

The impact Ramsbottom's inventions had on contemporary engineering is difficult to appreciate today when many of his ideas are taken for granted as basic engineering. A 'Mechanicals' paper in 1854 described the construction of a light and simple piston; today the idea seems obvious but it was a considerable advance on the type then commonly available. A year later a more important invention was described, one which revolutionized the steam engine of the time and is still in general use today for all reciprocating machinery. Few people are unaware of the piston ring as found in motor car or motor cycle engines, but not many appreciate that this is but a small advance on the simple piston packing ring described by Ramsbottom in the mid-nineteenth century.

Steam leakage past a piston reduced the amount of work available and caused a fall in efficiency, but no really satisfactory method had then

46

been devised to seal the piston against the cylinder wall without causing increased friction. Ramsbottom's arrangement comprised of a piston with three grooves 0.25 in (6.35mm) wide, 0.3125 in (7.9mm) deep and 0.25 in (6.35mm) apart cut into the circumference. Packing rings of brass, steel or iron could be inserted into the grooves, but the important aspect was that the rings had to be made such that they would spring outwards by a small amount. It was that spring which caused them to press against the cylinder wall and so effectively seal the piston. Over the intervening years nothing better has been found; although several variations have been developed, they are still fundamentally Ramsbottom rings. The other aspect of the paper covering the use of a recessed piston and covers was overshadowed by the description of the multiple piston rings.

By the time he presented the paper, the first pistons as described had been at work for 16 months without any trouble and 15 other locomotives had been similarly fitted. Ramsbottom considered that a set of rings would last for 3,000 to 4,000 miles and cost 2 shillings and sixpence (12.5p), little more than the cost of the hemp packing then commonly used. He further added that the use of the rings was expected to reduce coal consumption by 5.7 lb/mile (1.6kg/km) compared with hemp-packed pistons on trains undertaking similar duties.[6]

A further innovation of almost equal importance was the tamper-free duplex safety valve. It was not unknown for locomotive drivers to load their safety valves in order to obtain increased boiler pressure so that they could make up lost time. Such practice was dangerous and a number

of boiler explosions were attributed to it. Ramsbottom's safety valve design prevented any loading which would result in an increase of boiler pressure, but did allow pressure to be released by means of a lever which had contact with both valves.[7]

A major innovation was the picking up of water whilst a locomotive was at speed. The LNWR desired to increase the average speed of its boat trains to Holyhead, but a limiting factor was the water capacity of tenders then in use. Increasing the capacity was no solution, as that meant carrying an extra load about unnecessarily. Moreover, tender frames were always made from wood because Ramsbottom considered that the tender should be the weakest part of the train which would break up in the event of a collision and so minimize damage to carriages.[8]

Ramsbottom solved the problem by arranging for locomotives, or rather their tenders, to pick up water between Chester and Holyhead. The system, comprising a water trough laid between the rails at some level part of track and a scoop arrangement fitted in the tender, later became an accepted part of British steam railway practice, but only the LNWR adopted it during the early years. That first system, laid near Conway, allowed services on the line to be accelerated without the introduction of larger tenders than the 1,500- or 2,000-gallon capacity units then in operation. During a run over the troughs it was expected that about 1,000 gallons would be collected, but the locomotive had to be travelling above a certain speed. However, excessive speed also had to be avoided as it caused large water forces to be exerted on the tender tank, but locomotives of the period were not provided with speed measuring devices.

Ramsbottom's solution to that problem was to invent one. It was not particularly accurate nor could it be considered to be ideal as a universal speed measuring device, but it did serve the purpose. In basic terms the unit consisted of a glass cylinder containing oil, the cylinder being rotated by a pulley driven by the engine's rear axle. The rotational speed of the tube was, therefore, proportional to the speed of the engine. The principle of operation was based upon the fact that as fluid in a cylinder is rotated the centre of the fluid is depressed whilst that against the sides rises (the same effect can be observed whilst stirring a cup of tea or coffee). Marks on the outer surface of the cylinder allowed the driver to observe the speed at which he was running and so make any necessary adjustments in order to pick up water.[9]

It might be considered that Ramsbottom's tal-

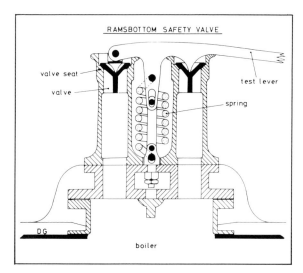
RAMSBOTTOM SAFETY VALVE

Below left *The Ramsbottom safety valve.*

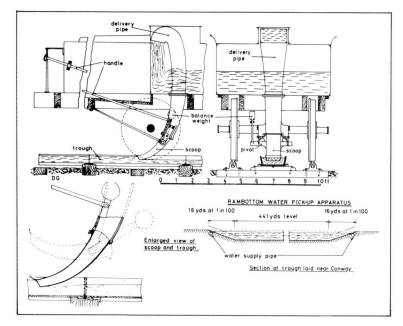

RAMBOTTOM WATER PICK-UP APPARATUS

Enlarged view of scoop and trough,

Section of trough laid near Conway

Right *Ramsbottom's arrangements for picking up water at speed.*

ent for invention was inexhaustible, and it nearly was, for other devices to his credit include a displacement lubricator and a screw reverser. It was not just mechanical devices with which he was involved, for he also devised schemes for overcoming operating problems. One of these concerned the desire to commence locomotive operations from Lime Street Station in Liverpool. Since its opening in 1837, trains leaving Lime Street had been hauled up the gradient of 1 in 97 by means of an endless rope and a pair of winding engines located at the top of the incline. Most of that gradient was through a 2,025-yard (1.85mkm) tunnel, so the use of locomotives for haulage presented some inconvenience with regards to clearing of the exhaust. Ramsbottom's solution was to provide a large exhausting fan near the middle of the tunnel, and it worked, clearing the tunnel in about 8 minutes after a train entered at the lower end.

Details of the installation and its operation were given by the engineer in a paper and supplement to the Institution of Mechanical Engineers during 1871, the year in which he was President.[10] The papers were not a Presidential Address, the practice of printing any address given not then being fully established, but they could have been classed as a farewell performance for in that year Ramsbottom retired as Locomotive Superintendent of the London & North Western Railway due to failing health.

It had been McConnell's dismissal which had

given Ramsbottom his real chance to stamp his mark on the LNWR, especially with relation to manufacturing facilities at Crewe. The works at Crewe had been steadily developing under the stewardship of Trevithick and during the early Ramsbottom years, but centralized manufacture of locomotives there provided opportunities for expansion. It was not only locomotive construction which became centralized, for Ramsbottom also arranged for the manufacture of basic materials, including steel. Steel had actually been manufactured at Crewe during Trevithick's days using the puddling process, but the plant was of limited capacity and the steel produced was of very variable quality. Its use was limited to specific components such as cutting tools.

Ramsbottom had a considerable interest in both the material and its manufacture, but his knowledge was rather restricted. Any invention connected with the production of steel was keenly watched and that eventually moved him in the direction of Henry Bessemer. Bessemer had patented a process for the manufacture of steel from molten iron using an air blast. The basic principle was that oxygen in the air blown through the molten iron combined with carbon, thus reducing the level of carbon in the material to a relatively low value. During a meeting between the pair, Bessemer, much to Ramsbottom's horror, suggested that rails could be made from steel rather than iron. His reply, 'Mr Bessemer, do you wish me to be tried for manslaughter?', is almost folklore.

That reaction was, however, based upon knowledge of the quality of steel produced by the puddling process, and was quite understandable. Such material was too hard and brittle for use as rails and fracture would have quickly resulted, with consequent derailment, injury and death. Bessemer steel, however, had a much lower carbon content, was more ductile, and had considerable hardness, making it ideal for rails. Ramsbottom required some convincing, but remained open-minded on the subject. After seeing samples of Bessmer's product, Ramsbottom requested material for trial purposes: ' . . . let me have 10 tons of this material so that I may torture it to my heart's content'. A steel rail was rolled and was then literally tortured, hot and cold, by twisting and bending into very unusual shapes. Ramsbottom was convinced, and set about doing the same with his Directors.[11]

In 1862 the first steel rail was laid between two adjacent iron rails in Camden goods yard and was still in place in 1864 without having been turned, although the iron rails alongside had been replaced numerous times during that period.[12] With such evidence Ramsbottom was able to persuade his Directors to invest in a number of Bessemer converters for installation at Crewe. Full-scale steel production could then commence, and the use of the material extended to other purposes. One of these was boiler construction, although the first steel boiler had actually been made at Crewe in 1863, a year before the Bessemer converters became operational, steel plate having been obtained from Bessemer's works in Sheffield. The rival Siemens-Marten steel-making process was developed later in the decade, and by 1869 Ramsbottom had a furnace installed at Crewe for making use of the process. The works was, therefore, the first establishment to take up steel-making on a production scale using both processes.[13]

Not content with introducing these processes, Ramsbottom devised means by which the large quantity of steel might be readily dealt with. A powerful cogging mill was developed for the initial rolling of large Bessemer ingots, but it was his duplex steam hammer which attracted attention. Normal steam hammers, as devised by James Nasmyth, were mounted vertically and considerable forces were exerted when the heavy hammer head hit the ingot held on the anvil. This caused vibration which was high for the larger hammers, these also required considerable headroom. Ramsbottom devised a hammer which had two heads running on rails and which were driven towards each other by means of steam cylinders. The work would be positioned between the heads and the force exerted by the hammer heads by this arrangement acted as if the heads were working against an anvil of infinite mass because the forces opposed each other. There was no force downwards, apart from weight, and so foundations could be simply laid.[14]

A further invention which has frequently been credited to Ramsbottom is the reversing rolling

Bessemer converters at Crewe works.
(G. Charles collection)

mill. He certainly devised the machinery but always acknowledged that the idea came from James Nasmyth, and wrote a letter to him indicating as much and thanking him for the idea.[15] The conventional reversing mill employed slow-speed steam engines to drive the rolls, a clutch mechanism being used to disconnect the drive and allow a reverse gearing to be engaged. The Nasmyth/Ramsbottom arrangement employed high-speed engines, without flywheels, directly connected to the rolls, these engines being reversed themselves. The design was much simpler to operate and lasted longer as there was less strain on the parts. For many years plant of this type rolled rails and plate at Crewe Works.

Other developments involving the use of steel concerned locomotive tyres. Steel had long been acknowledged as a much better wearing material than iron and several processes had been patented for the steeling of iron rails and other machinery parts. Steel tyres for locomotives had many advantages, but manufacture of continuous rather than welded tyres presented problems. A weld in a tyre rotating at high speed could fail and lead to a serious accident, and a number of patent fastening devices were developed for holding the tyre on to the wheel in such an event; there was, however, still potential danger from the failed weld. Ramsbottom solved the problem with his development of weldless steel tyres manufactured from ingots initially forged into conical shape and then subsequently rolled.

Portable appliances were devised for boring cylinders and machining valve faces *in situ*, early versions having been introduced at Longsight. For Crewe Works he developed a very useful transportation system making use of aerial and ground level spaces. In addition to the standard gauge railway system in the works an 18 in (0.457m) gauge system was installed throughout the premises which could go where the standard gauge could not. Traversing cranes with cotton rope drives allowed for easy transportation of large and small items.[16] Many other manufacturing establishments installed items of this type but Ramsbottom did it on a grand scale, quickly and often to his own design; if something was needed he did not wait for others, but got on with the job and devised a solution. All of this development was taking place whilst Crewe Works continued the construction and repair of locomotives to meet the developing needs of the LNWR.

It required an extraordinary engineer to achieve so much in so short a space of time, but Ramsbottom's 14 years in charge at Crewe saw major innovations that few others could even dream of matching. He never appeared to seek reward other than his salary and the satisfaction of seeing the job well done, but if he had been in any other profession honours would surely have come his way. Whilst Managers and Directors of the LNWR received knighthoods and other signs of public, or political, recognition, Ramsbottom's efforts went unacknowledged, at least publicly. Some people, however, did recognize his works, and said so.

In 1868, the year he died, Sir Cusack Patrick Roney wrote the following: 'At the head of the mighty establishment at Crewe is one man who, if he had been in Egypt, with works not a quarter of the size and not half so ably carried out, would at least have been a Bey, or more probably a Pacha; in Austria a Count of the Holy Empire; in any country in the world, except England, with crosses and decorations, the ribbons of which would easily make a charming bonnet of existing dimensions. But in England, the earnest, persevering, never tiring JOHN RAMSBOTTOM is — John Ramsbottom'.[17] That situation did not change; few practising engineers have received the same public acknowledgement received by their brothers from the commercial side of industry.

Roney had received his knighthood following service as Secretary to the Dublin Exhibition of 1853, but he did have connections with railway operations. Between 1853 and 1860 he had been Managing Director of the Great Trunk Railway of Canada, and had also been Secretary to the Eastern Counties Railway between 1845 and 1851. It is highly likely that he was a friend, or at least an acquaintance, of Ramsbottom, for the engineer had at one time contemplated employment on the Eastern Counties Railway, although after Roney had left.

Like the majority of Locomotive Superintendents, Ramsbottom had a keen interest in technical education and took an active interest in the Mechanics' Institute at Crewe, including a period as its President. In 1873 he provided money for the foundation of the Ramsbottom Scholarship at the Owens College, Manchester. This scholarship, worth £40 per annum and tenable for two years, was intended for the benefit of young men working in the LNWR's locomotive department. He became a governor of Owens College and donated money for construction of a medical school there.

When ill health forced him to retire from active service at Crewe in 1871, he ceased all activities concerned with engineering. The complete rest restored his health and obviously renewed his interest in engineering matters, for in 1883 he

Left *Outside the CME's official residence. F. W. Webb is on the extreme right, Ramsbottom third from the right.*

Below right *Francis William Webb.*

became a consulting engineer to the Lancashire & Yorkshire Railway and two years later was appointed a Director. A particular part of his consulting duties concerned the building and equipping of the new works at Horwich, which were considered in the previous chapter. One interesting inclusion in the scheme for Horwich was an 18 in narrow gauge railway similar to that employed at Crewe. Ramsbottom had obviously been so impressed with the usefulness of that arrangement that he considered a sister layout to be essential at Horwich.

Additional activities included a directorship of Beyer, Peacock & Co, membership of the Manchester Literary and Philosophical Society and membership of the Institution of Civil Engineers. It is interesting to consider that although he had been a member of that learned society since 1866, all of his papers were read before the 'Mechanicals'. The University of Dublin conferred upon him the honorary degree of Master of Engineering in 1888, the only award he ever received apart from praise from his fellow engineers.

John Ramsbottom died at his home in Alderley Edge on 20 May 1897, aged 82 years. Few people have had such a significant influence on engineering, and by comparison its recognition is trivial.[18]

Francis William Webb

The life and achievements of F.W. Webb have been the subject of more controversial writings than probably all other British locomotive engineers put together. Unfortunately, much of the comment since his death has been based upon myth rather than fact. Ill-informed writings have given a distorted impression of the man and his works, the most disparaging comment only appearing after his death and then by people who did not know him. Much has been written about his notorious compound locomotives, but many of these 'expert' writings are by people who were not even born when those engines were in service. Fiction can so easily become established fact if it is repeated often enough.

It has been said many times that the dictatorial Webb would not suffer any criticism of himself or his locomotives, verbal or in writing. The simple fact that is that nobody in a free society can achieve that sort of control. Even if he did exercise an autocratic rule at Crewe, he would have had no such influence over well-respected journals such as *Engineering*, *The Engineer*, *The Railway Magazine*, and *The Railway Gazette*, or any other part of the general press. Facts which might have been suppressible on railway premises would not have escaped a wider audience as Webb was no hermit of Crewe Works and his locomotives did not run hidden in tunnels. Any of the publications mentioned would have been able to gather information from a multitude of journalists and informants. That none of the tales so freely peddled after his death merited publication during his life by any journal gives reason to doubt their authenticity. The life and work of F.W. Webb can now be discussed without prejudice.

Francis William Webb, the second son of the Rev William Webb, Rector of Tixall, Staffordshire, was born at Tixall Rectory on 21 May 1836. It

appears that he showed early mechanical apti-
tude and was articled as a pupil of Francis
Trevithick, commencing his long association with
Crewe and the LNWR on 11 August 1851. At the
end of his training in 1856 he entered the draw-
ing office and stayed there, becoming Chief
Draughtsman on 1 March 1859. By this time
Ramsbottom had replaced Trevithick and the
works was undergoing considerable expansion.
On 1 September 1861 Webb was promoted to
Works Manager and also became Chief Assistant
to the Locomotive Superintendent.[19]

During those early years as manager of the
works, Webb was involved in the installation of
the Bessemer converters and the commencement
of steel production. Interest in that material
never left him and he became one of its great
advocates. It is highly likely that he instigated its
use for boiler construction. During his five years
as Works Manager, Webb worked closely with
Ramsbottom and became involved with many of
his schemes to develop the works; he must have
gathered much useful information for future use.
In July 1866 Webb resigned in order to take up an

appointment as manager of the Bolton Iron and
Steel Company. Why he should have taken that
step is not easy to discern for he had already been
singled out as the person to take over from
Ramsbottom when the latter retired.

At that time, however, nobody knew that
Ramsbottom was likely to retire early due to ill
health and possibly Webb considered that he
would need to wait a considerable time to suc-
ceeed him. Webb was still only 39 years old and
his advancement to that date had been rather
meteoric; remaining in a position for an
unknown number of years might not have been to
his liking. The Bolton Iron Co was partly owned
by the Hick family, and John Hick became a
Director of the LNWR in later years, Webb subsequently naming a locomotive after him. These are
just connections, and may not have had any bearing on what actually transpired, but the connections were there and when the 'king-maker'
Moon called upon Webb as replacement for
Ramsbottom, Webb made himself available.
Shortly after Ramsbottom gave the expected 12
months notice of resignation in September 1870,
his young assistant and Works Manager Thomas
Stubbs died at the age of 34 years. Ramsbottom
may have had Stubbs lined up for the succession,
but that was no longer possible.

Moon knew the sort of man he wanted and
Webb fitted the bill. Both men could obviously
work together and, although Webb would not
exactly dance to his tune, Moon knew that he had
the same sort of management philosophy as his
own, progressive but economical. Soon after
Ramsbottom gave notice of his resignation, Moon
contacted Webb to see if he would be willing to
return to Crewe and discussions followed as to the
terms. Early in October, Moon wrote to Webb
again informing him that his appointment as
Locomotive Superintendent had been agreed by
the Special Committee set up to deal with the
matter. Salary was to be £2,000 for the first year
and £3,000 thereafter with a 12-month notice of
resignation being required. Webb was further
informed that he could take no more than four
pupils but that he could have use of the house set
aside for the Locomotive Superintendent on the
same terms as Ramsbottom.[20]

The letter also stated that as Webb already knew
the Company's regulations regarding patents,
there was no need to give further details. As was
common with many organizations, the LNWR
expected free use of patents taken out by its
employees whilst in its employ. It became something of a joke that Webb would always modify the
patents of others in some way and then make use

D. Griffiths 1989.

of them. This was not done in order to receive credit, but to avoid the LNWR having to pay royalties.

The only person who received a royalty from the mechanical engineering department whilst Webb was in charge was David Joy for his valve gear. Even then it was a nominal amount as Webb convinced the inventor that the LNWR would be showing the gear off to the world. In May 1879 Joy met Webb at Crewe and later that year struck a bargain. 'In autumn we settled it, and he was at once to start an engine to exploit the plan, and then to allow it every possible publicity. Webb did fairly fulfil his part of the bargain, and it was due to this that the plan was so soon and so prominently brought before the public'.[21]

Webb could not return to Crewe immediately as he was required to give six months notice to the Bolton Iron Co. The state of Ramsbottom's health gave cause for concern and the parties agreed that Webb should take control at Crewe in late June 1871, before Ramsbottom's notice had expired. An improvement in his health allowed the notice to be worked out, so it was decided that Webb should in the meantime make a short tour of the USA in order to study steel-making. Webb officially became Locomotive Superintendent of the LNWR on 1 October 1871, and remained in command for over 30 years.

Webb was a keen engineer who expected those under him to do their jobs effectively and efficiently. It cannot be doubted that he was a very good, even brilliant, engineer, despite the derision which was heaped upon some of his compound locomotive designs, generally unfairly. These machines will be considered in a later

chapter, but even if they were as bad some have claimed, locomotive manufacture was only a small part of Webb's duties. Brunel had many more spectacular failures and is still looked upon as one of the most outstanding engineers of his day. Webb may not have been in the same class as Brunel, but at least he made money for the shareholders whilst Brunel usually lost it.

Being economical was one of the ways in which money could be saved, and Webb would not spend more than he needed, but everything which was done had to be to the highest standards. Minimum cost never meant second best. Modification of other patents certainly avoided having to pay royalties. Webb had some 80 patents to his name, most by his own invention rather than a modification of another's idea. He was a prolific inventor and whilst many found no practical application, a number saved his employers a great deal of money. Those connected with the manufacturing processes at Crewe were certainly advantageous, especially that concerned with centrifugal casting of steel wheel centres. Other patents covered signalling equipment and points, for which he was also responsible, tools, brakes, electrical apparatus and even a foot-warmer. One of the brake patents was actually for a form of vacuum brake, but it is his modification of the Clark brake that is most widely known in that field.

Waste cost money as did unnecessary cosmetic work merely for the sake of appearance. In a 1903 article about the works, C.S. Lake wrote, 'Crewe Works is possessed of a motto. This is short but comprehensive — "Waste not, want not". Nothing indeed is wasted than can possibly be used up in any shape or form.'[22] Webb organized

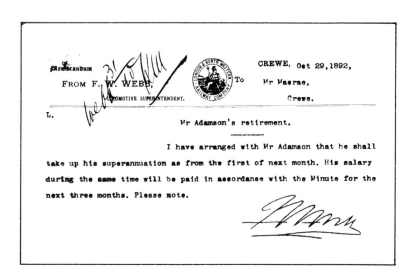

Webb's signature on a personal internal LNWR memo.

the works so that the smallest portion of scrap metal could be recycled, and even old grindstones were used ornamentally as corner pillars for the hospital garden. Enginemen's cloths would be washed to allow for further use. Over 10 million of these and 90 tons of waste were cleansed each year, the grease extracted being made into soap.[23] Washing certainly saved on the purchase of cloths, but over 2 million were still required to be supplied new.

A further example of Webb's seeming obsession with economy revolved around the painting of locomotives. As far as he was concerned paint was simply a protective medium and that which did the job for the lowest cost had to be used. Pigment cost money, thus black paint was the cheapest; hence all LNWR locomotives were painted black. Such views he would admit before his fellow engineers. During the discussion on an Institution of Civil Engineers paper by William Stroudley, he told the audience that he had once been attacked by a member of the Shareholders' Audit Committee for painting the engines black. His reply was that when they paid a dividend of 10 per cent he would line them in gold.[24]

The urge to keep costs as low as possible, without sacrificing quality — for Webb was always a conscientious engineer — almost certainly directed him in the way of compounding. Having carried out early tests with a degree of success, he convinced himself that the compound locomotive was more efficient than the simple. That conviction required clarification, and more factors influenced overall efficiency than the thermodynamic argument.

As Chief Mechanical Engineer, (the title was changed from Locomotive Superintendent shortly after Webb took charge at Crewe), there was much work for him to do regarding the works and also aspects of locomotive design, construction and repair. Webb took a great interest in the education of the workforce and played an active part in ensuring that the Mechanics' Institute functioned without financial constraint. As CME he became President of the Institute and during his earlier years at Crewe had even taught engineering drawing there. Webb took pride in the fact that, both through his own generosity and that of the LNWR, the Institute had an enviable record for the award of Whitworth Scholarships to its students. A chemical laboratory and a mechanics' shop were provided at the Institute with a mechanic on hand to provide practical assistance.[25] Such an arrangement was, however, not completely one-sided, for Webb must have realized that well-trained and educated people were more likely to be of use to him at the works.

As an engineer Webb took a keen interest in both major engineering institutions, but his association with the 'Mechanicals' came to an unfortunate end. His membership had been taken out prior to his move to Bolton and he would attend meetings in London whenever the opportunity arose. His one major paper, 'On Compound Locomotive Engines', was read before the Institution in 1883 and attracted considerable interest. The paper itself dealt with the design, construction and early operation of the 'Experiment' Class locomotives, and they will be discussed in a later chapter; but what is of importance at this stage is that little adverse comment was made by members present. Engineers such as Anatole Mallet, Thomas Crampton, William Stroudley and Alexander McDonnell all commented favourably on the way in which the design and experimental work had been carried out. A number did, however, consider that better results might have been achieved had compounding been first tried with a goods engine.[26]

In June 1879 Webb joined in the discussion of Mallet's paper, 'On Compounding of Locomotive Engines', and expressed the views he then held. One of these was that compounding would be of considerable advantage for working in tunnels as less fuel would need to be consumed. He then went on to mention his experiments in converting an old engine to compound form before stating his belief that ' . . . to get a compound engine which would work steadily and economically at high speeds, it would be necessary to go back very much in form to the engine designed by Robert Stephenson some years ago having three cylinders'. He went on to comment that if he had to build a new engine it would have high-pressure cylinders of the full size and a large low pressure one would be incorporated. Already he had the form of a three-cylinder compound firmly set.[27]

It is to the discussion of George Marie's 1884 paper, 'On the Consumption of Fuel in Locomotives', that Webb made his final published contribution to the affairs of the 'Mechanicals', and even then it was a written one; Webb could not attend on the night of the presentation — but neither could the author. The paper did make some complimentary comments about Webb's compounding experiment and so, in the absence of the paper's author, the discussion turned into one about Webb compounds. McDonnell, Ramsbottom and Aspinall, amongst others, took part and many of the comments were critical. That does seem unfair as the individual concerned was not present to answer his critics nor had he even made any contribution to the paper as presented, apart from giving Marie details of his locomotives.

Webb provided a written contribution which was published along with the paper and discussion, but it was direct and made no reference to his reasons for adopting his particular method of compounding. He commenced by stating that he ' . . . does not purpose answering the objections raised to his method of compounding, as he would prefer to let the continued working of the engines show what they are capable of doing. Their performance continues to give satisfactory results.' He then went on to provide details of that work and concluded with a statement as to the coal and water consumption.[28] That was the last contribution the Institution of Mechanical Engineers received from F.W. Webb.

He obviously felt aggrieved that the President, Sir Lowthian Bell, who was in the chair for the session, should have allowed matters to continue as they did without him being there. Such annoyance is reasonable and any engineer would have felt the same. At the time Webb was a Vice President of the Institution and so was one of its most senior members — in time he may well have become President. The Webb temperament was such that he would not let matters be and considered the matter an affront. What went on behind the scenes is unknown, but Webb's reaction of cutting himself off from the Institution does appear to have been excessive, but such is what he did. That, perhaps, says much for his character: a good engineer, but petulant, unforgiving and even intolerant.

Associate membership of the Institution of Civil Engineers had been taken out in 1865 followed by transfer to full membership in 1872, and from 1884 most of Webb's efforts were directed towards the 'Civils'. He became a member of the Council in 1889 and in 1900 one of its four Vice Presidents, being the most senior when he retired from the Council in 1905. Again, the Presidency of an illustrious organization just eluded him.

Webb presented a number of papers at meetings of the Institution of Civil Engineers, the earliest concerning his design for a standard engine shed. It was a straightforward paper for information rather than discussion, and was published during the 1884-5 session. It was common practice with the 'Civils' to produce many papers in that manner, as that allowed as many members as possible to provide information to others. Design of the shed illustrated the CME's desire to standardise as many things as possible, thereby helping to minimize costs. The system of construction could be extended laterally or longitudinally in order to suit any particular needs.[29]

That, however, was not his first contribution, for he took part in the discussion of Findlay's 1875 paper on railway management. Webb's views regarding operation came across during the discussion and he made the point that a railway must meet demands of the customer rather than impose on him what the railway wished to do. He told the meeting that sufficient lines to meet peak traffic demand had to be provided: 'Goods could not be delivered at midnight, and passengers would not travel just when the company chose to take them'. Within that there may have been the seeds of the discord between him and the traffic department. He had also had a dig at the Board of Trade who had proposed limiting trains to the power of one engine irrespective of other factors. Trains over Shap had long been assisted by a banker, but had comfortably managed other parts of the route unaided. Webb's view of the proposal was that ' . . . those who made it could know but little of railway working'.[30] His opinion would appear to have been that a locomotive should be pushed near the limit for most parts of the run and assistance provided where necessary. There was no point providing a powerful locomotive if that power was only called upon for a short period of known duration and locality where assistance could be made available.

Each year the 'Civils' would organize an Engineering Conference when distinguished engineers from all fields would be asked to prepare papers for presentation at different sessions. Webb's contribution to the Railway Section during the 1897 conference was entitled 'Permanent Way' and it basically described his design using deep fishplates and a type of fishplate chair. This required only three bolts, none of which passed through the rail. In devising the chair he had experimented with lead fishplates in order to obtain the optimum shape to deal with weaknesses in joints.[31]

At the conference two years later it was advertized that Webb would present a paper in the Machinery Section entitled 'Recent Advances in Locomotive Practice'; he actually produced a paper entitled 'Compound Locomotives' and there were complaints that it bore only a remote relationship to the subject as advertised. Webb obviously considered that his compounds, for the paper only dealt with his design, were the main advance in locomotive practice. Despite the disappointment felt by some that the paper was so confined in nature, it was a very good, though somewhat biased, overview of Webb's compound-

'Dreadnought' compound Marchioness of Stafford. (G. Charles collection)

ing developments. At the end of the presentation Webb was able to pronounce that following careful and exhaustive experiments he could claim savings of 19 to 20 per cent. Compared with what he did not say.[32]

During the discussion William Dean said that he had no doubt that the figures given were accurate, but a great deal depended upon the quality of coal used. It is known that compounds were usually supplied with the best screened Welsh coal and Dean was possibly making a mild comment on that. J.A.F. Aspinall also joined in the discussion and compared performances of compound locomotives in America and France, where very good results were being obtained on long runs with heavy loads at high speeds. Without actually criticizing Webb's figures, he did comment that the circumstances of working had to be taken into account. A Mr B.H. Thwaite stated that the Richmond Locomotive Co in America had offered to send one of its compounds, for which savings of 26 per cent had been claimed, to be tried on English lines. Webb quickly countered, saying that he had received drawings of the engine and it would not pass the loading gauge, being unable to get through a single British station, tunnel or bridge. Despite the widespread objections which had been raised to compound locomotives, Webb still stuck to his beliefs. At the end of the formal presentation he stated that he was satisfied that compounding of locomotives had come to stay and would spread universally. He added that he had advised his Director to run heavier trains and ' . . . was prepared to build big engines which he would guarantee to be equal to any in the world for working cheaply and keeping out of the shops'.[33]

It seems that Webb always wished to have the final say on anything with which he was involved, and in this case he certainly did. He had arranged for members attending the conference to pay a visit to Crewe Works on the day after presenting his paper, and had also arranged that one of his four-cylinder compounds, Iron Duke, would haul the train. Needless to say the performance was perfect, although everything had probably been arranged that it should be so with a thoroughly checked locomotive and good quality coal. In that Webb would have been no different from any other locomotive engineer. To invite an august body of engineers for a trip behind one of your latest products and not take steps to ensure reasonable success would have been foolhardy in the extreme, and Webb was certainly no fool. Details of the locomotive, train and performance were published in *Engineering* for 16 June 1899.

Webb appears to have enjoyed his visits to the 'Civils' and would take part in discussions whenever interesting matters were presented. At both conferences mentioned above he involved himself in discussion of other papers. During the 1897 conference he raised the topic of chrome steel and mentioned that it had been used at Crewe to great advantage, all locomotive springs then being made from that material, and old springs scrapped and replaced by chrome steel examples.[34] This indicates the breadth of his interest and experience and illustrates that he was not just obsessed with compound locomotives; in fact, metallurgy was one of his major passions and he probably devoted more time to that than to compounding. Other comments made during that conference, together with his later papers on boiler tubes and firebox stays, serve to illustrate his knowledge of the subject.

Two major papers dealing with metallurgical matters were published by the 'Civils' in the years just prior to Webb's retirement. That delivered in April 1902 concerned firebox stays and was very well received. Webb was too busy a man to actually carry out all of the investigation work himself — nobody in such a position as his could spare the time — but he did instigate and direct the trials and experiments. Results of tests with firebox stays made from various copper-based alloys and steel were gathered over a number of years. The paper was not simply the product of a data-gathering exercise, but was the result of operational experience and a well-organized series of tests on the materials. The words of Professor W.C. Unwin in opening his contribution to the discussion indicate the paper's merit: ' . . . the paper was extremely interesting, and was a typical account of a careful inductive investigation. The experiments were ingenious and conclusive.'[35]

Webb's final contribution to learned discussion came during the 1903-4 session of the 'Civils' and was published as a paper without discussion. Entitled 'Copper Locomotive Boiler Tubes'[36], it extended the work illustrated in the paper on firebox stays and again contained the results of careful investigation over several years. Information presented was extensive and it is a pity that no formal discussion took place, but the circumstances of his departure from Crewe may have prevented that in any case. For publication during the 1903-4 session, it is likely that the paper would have been completed at the end of 1902 or early in 1903. By this time Webb had indicated his wish to retire, but that alone would not have prevented a discussion. Illness certainly would, and

that may have been the reason; or maybe the Institution of Civil Engineers did not intend the paper for formal presentation and discussion. Whatever the reason, it was a fine paper on which to go out and one which illustrates the talents of an exceptional engineer who did much more than merely enthuse about compound locomotives.

A great deal of that 'much more' related to the development of Crewe Works into a major manufacturing establishment capable of producing most of the railway's needs from the raw materials. It is almost certain that no other railway of the period was so independent of outside suppliers. Innovations and extensions at the steel works were regular events; forging and rolling equipment was updated whenever the need arose to suit changed circumstances, and in order to allow production of 60 ft (18.3m) rail lengths the rail mill was altered in 1895. One of the earliest introductions was hydraulic riveting which eased the work and speeded up production. In 1885 Webb informed the audience for Stroudley's paper on 'Locomotive Engines' that ' . . . the day of drifting and 4.5 lb flogging hammers, in his opinion, had gone by'.[37] Hydraulic riveting had been introduced to Crewe just after Webb took control, and soon many portable machines had been provided for boiler construction.

Another source of power Webb took to was electricity. As late as 1901, although he did not believe that electrification of LNWR main lines would be very quick in coming, he did consider that many suburban lines would be worked electrically in the near future. Shunting was a different matter, and he told a 'Civils' audience discussing a paper on 'Electrical Traction' that 'A live rail at ground level would make the yard an

Crewe works at the turn of the century. (G. Charles collection)

exciting place for the shunters to work at night'.[38] Age had not dulled a sense of humour which only infrequently surfaced.

His contribution to the same paper also illustrates an encyclopaedic memory for facts or a degree of preparedness with which few are blessed. Webb commenced his part in the discussion by saying that he would not have spoken but for the expressed desire that somebody should speak concerning the locomotive side of the question. He then went into details of locomotive performance and even produced two small pieces of coal to illustrate the amount of coal his compounds would consume per ton mile. Such organisation and knowledge are not the signs of a demented man. However, the Webb detractors would aver that only the insane would habitually carry small pieces of coal in their pockets!

Electricity for powering portable workshop tools was greeted with enthusiasm, a number of drilling machines of different sizes being made available. A tool much appreciated was the electric tube-cutter which would save much labour in the removal of old tubes and the dressing of holes for the fitting of new. Electricity was also used to power cranes, and Crewe was one of the first places to be provided with electric telephones and electric clocks. Webb enthused about the use he had made of electricity in an interview published in *Cassiers Magazine* during 1897[39], and although he would express a disinterest in such matters he seems to have enjoyed the publicity.

In 1900 *The Railway Magazine* published an interview with him as part of its series of illustrated interviews with famous railway personalities. At the start Webb told the reporter that he had a disinclination to giving interviews but would make an exception if it was thought that anything he had to say would be of interest to the magazine's readership.[40] Reporters from other newspapers and journals, including *The Boy's Own Paper*, were also afforded similar facilities from time to time. Requests for information and pictures from journals like *The Engineer* were always courteously met.[41] Even when no such request came, Webb was not reluctant to make use of the letter pages of such periodicals to publicize the latest Crewe practice or achievement. Built-up crankshafts were given such treatment in 1896 when his letter opened with the words, 'You may think the enclosed photograph of a built-up locomotive crank axle of sufficient interest to your readership to illustrate in your journal.' *The Engineer* duly obliged.[42] The following year a crane safety hook was given similar treatment, but Webb stated that he made no claims to be the originator of the design.[43]

One of the most famous of railway journalists, Charles S. Lake, publicly acknowledged that Webb helped him on his way in journalism and always offered assistance whenever he could. Lake did have an advantage in that he was the son of a partner in the firm which acted as Webb's patent agent, but the CME had no obligation to him. Lake was encouraged to write an article about Crewe locomotive practice under the Webb regime by Webb himself, who then took the trouble to read the manuscript and suggest amendments. Of course, he might have been seeking to remove any uncomplimentary passages, but Lake only states that amendments were suggested, not requested.[44]

Like all engineers, Webb had enthusiasm for certain practices and not others, compounding, of course, being one such. He also had an initial preference for continuous brakes of the chain type rather than air or vacuum types. During the 1870s, the Clark chain brake was superior in some respects to the other forms, especially in terms of power, but the continuous brake trials carried out in 1875 did not prove conclusive for any form. That the Clark chain type, as modified by Webb, found application on the LNWR was preference, not folly; it may have been the wrong choice in terms of what was to become the British standard form, but its low cost and relative simplicity were attractive at the time. In any case, Webb was not an enthusiast of continuous brakes, whatever the type. His view was that drivers could become so reliant upon them that accidents would occur if brakes failed to act correctly when a train approached a station too quickly. LNWR rules insisted that only the tender and guard's brakes were to be used for normal stopping, the chain brake being for emergency only, test application being made but once during each run.[45]

Webb had complete control over his empire at Crewe and he did not like interference from anybody, especially those who knew little about engineering practice. During the time that Moon was Chairman, Webb's rule was never questioned. Moon's departure and that of the General Manager brought a new managerial regime into existence. The new Chairman, Lord Stalbridge, presented no real challenge to Webb's authority but the young and very ambitious Frederick Harrison as General Manager did. Harrison had many ideas with which Webb did not agree, and one of these was that all heads of departments should report not to the Board but to the General Manager. CMEs on other railways had to deal with similar situations, most notably Churchward on

'Large Bloomer' Torch *as modified by Webb, with the chain brake windlass on the cab side.* (LNWR official)

the GWR. Webb, naturally, did not take to the idea, and went his own way at Crewe. In other areas Harrison had more success, particularly with the traffic department. Schedules were suddenly changed and strange rules regarding locomotive loading and delay time reporting were instituted. This had the effect of putting the Webb compounds in a bad light, as these machines were designed for efficient operation close to peak performance; in effect they had little in reserve, but none had been needed when they were originally designed. Webb, it seems, considered that providing extra power capability was a waste of money and resulted in heavy locomotives.

This is not a discussion about Harrison, and the matter has only been raised because he caused Webb considerable aggravation from the middle of the 1890s until Webb's retirement. In many respects Webb was correct in his approach to locomotive design in relation to the conditions they were required to meet. Over-powered locomotives are costly and wasteful, but at least they have something in reserve; however, if no reserve is needed it is simply extra cost. An arbitrary rule dictated that double-heading had to be provided for trains exceeding a set size based upon the number and type of carriages. This made no allowance for the condition of the locomotive, the loading of the carriages or the weather conditions, and Webb felt frustrated that people with no real knowledge were dictating matters. In discussing J.A.F. Aspinall's paper on train resistance, he said, 'Some managers — he hoped that the Author was not one of them — thought it was only necessary, with a certain number of carriages, to use two engines, without any reference to the state of the weather, the direction in which the wind was blowing, or gradient over which the

train ran. That was what managers were coming to in this country, and he thought it was quite good time they learned a little about the effects of wind and of gravity in working the heavy trains of the present day.'[46] The remark was certainly not aimed at Aspinall, and there is little doubt as to whom Webb had in mind.

Webb and Aspinall were, in fact, very good friends. The latter was proud of his early connections with Crewe, and had been instrumental in starting what became a regular event, the famous Crewe dinners. Webb, naturally, was delighted and took the Chair at the inaugural dinner held in London during February 1884. It is also fitting that one of his final public appearances was at the 1903 dinner. Webb did not seek social popularity and only attended those functions with which he had any real interest. Engineering was certainly one of them, and his active dealings with learned societies have already been considered. Although he was friendly with most of his contemporary CMEs, he did not necessarily consider them as friends, despite common interests. It is probably for this reason that he had nothing to do with the Association of Railway Locomotive Engineers which was involved in social activities as well as technical matters. The latter Webb could obtain from learned societies, and the former he would indulge in with people of his own choosing.

People are quick to imply that in choosing not to have many close friends Webb had something seriously wrong with his character. In the same way, his failure to marry is generally looked upon as sinister. Churchward never married and is not criticized for it. Few people who actually knew Webb ever troubled to put their impressions in writing, at the time or later, and so what has developed from hearsay is a total misrepresentation of the man. The ageing process certainly changed him as did the chronic illness, peritonitis, from which he suffered, but many tales which abounded after his death are much closer to fiction than fact. Certainly those in charge at Euston and Crewe did nothing to correct the stories, and that is to their discredit. It is difficult to write anything about Webb without having to first deal with these legends, but that will not be done here. The author has read versions of them but chooses not to use up space with repetition of that which has no credited source. Some may have a spark of truth, and the reader must judge for himself what to believe of those tales which are written elsewhere.

One individual who knew Webb, as already mentioned, was C.S. Lake. Lake always found him to be amiable and courteous but noticed a change in him during a visit towards the end of 1902. He found Webb to be a little less consistent in manner, showing less patience and being more irritable. The fact that he noticed these changes and would comment about them indicates that normally Webb was the opposite. Lake admits that he never had anything to complain about concerning Webb, always finding him helpful and kind. Others he met were not so well disposed, and these he concluded had been subject to Webb's criticism.[47] Webb was a strict disciplinarian — anybody in charge of such a vast organization as Crewe had to be, so he did make enemies. It is not unusual, for example, for the recipient of a reprimand to hold a grudge. He also made enemies at Euston, especially Harrison, and rumours are easily spread but not so easily refuted. Malice can be a difficult thing with which to deal, and its effects know few boundaries.

Discipline is essential to the safe and efficient operation of any workplace and it also ensures that effective control can be achieved. Webb had the works at Crewe organized to perfection and they met all the usual demands and many unexpected ones. Collapse of the Llandulas viaduct in 1879 paralysed the Chester-Holyhead line. On many other railways it would have remained that way for a considerable time, but Webb knew exactly what was required following a visit to the site. A new steel structure was planned and girders rolled at Crewe within a week of the disaster. Webb's properly organized system achieved that, and although he may not have demanded that his staff and workforce put in exactly the same effort as himself, he did, rightly, demand that they 'pulled their weight'. *Engineering*'s obituarist believed him to be a man of remarkable personality who would have risen to the top in whatever profession he chose. His strength of character

compelled him to dominate and not allow any opposition, but his self-reliance and untiring energy were typical of a great commander.[48]

Despite this, Webb was not the straight, hard taskmaster some would like to believe. Given the chance he would enjoy a joke, although his sense of humour appears to have been on the dry side, as indicated by his comment about shunting electrically-powered yards. Letters, signed 'Argus', appeared regularly in issues of *Engineering* during the 1885-6 period, and these set out to denigrate the LNWR compounds. Webb neither answered the criticism nor commented upon it, he simply named one of his compounds *Argus*. That, for those who care to think about it, is probably one of the best put-downs imaginable — there was no possible reply!

With regards to the numerous anecdotes concerning Webb, those provided by J.M. Dunn in *Railway Magazine* for November and December 1961 are probably nearest to the truth. It is not intended to repeat them in detail, but the articles are well worth reading. They were based mainly upon the letters written by W. Noel Davies, one of Webb's final pupils, and deal with some personal recollections and some hearsay.

Most interesting of the anecdotes are those which shed light upon the Webb character. No matter what people might have thought about him as a manager, few would have doubted his honesty. A representative from a firm of brake manufacturers (it is alleged to have been Westinghouse) called upon Webb and demonstrated his company's product. This impressed the LNWR's CME and he agreed that a trial should be organized for the Directors. Instead of leaving the matter there, the representative indicated that Webb would receive a commission of some £20,000 if the brake system was adopted by the railway. An enraged Webb ordered the representative out, and that brake system never stood a chance on the LNWR. Another case concerned repairs to the conservatory heating system at the official CME's residence, for which the CME paid rent. Webb instructed that all time and materials be charged to him and not the company.

When Webb happened upon an illicit barber's shop in the millwrights' shop during one of his late tours of the works, he did not discipline the men involved but let them worry for a while about the possibility of dismissal. Their period of worry probably produced a better result than any dressing-down from the boss. Webb did insist on discipline for safety reasons, and would suspend a driver if any company regulation or his own instruction had been disobeyed. If, however, he considered that a driver had been treated unfairly by a foreman, he was very willing to listen to the argument and rectify the matter should it be necessary. The problem was always a matter of how to get the ear of the 'chief', for he was an extremely busy man. Webb may have been an abrasive character, but he was fair and meted out discipline to anybody irrespective of position. On the other hand he would defend his men against the judgement of those outside his department if he considered that they had been dealt with unfairly.

His sense of humour is evident from the anecdote concerning the porter at Shrewsbury. Webb would habitually tip the old man 2 shillings (10p) for his help, but one day the amount increased to 2s 6d (12.5p). When the money had been pocketed, the CME asked the porter if he knew that accepting a tip from a passenger was breaking company rules. The old porter replied in the affirmative, but added that no such rule applied to gratuities from company employees. Webb enjoyed the joke and the pair continued to meet at Shrewsbury for some time afterwards without any sign of resentment on Webb's part.

Webb ruled Crewe and rarely needed to call upon anybody for assistance. Only in money matters did he seek help from headquarters, but if he could avoid it he would. In terms of engineering he was his own boss and did what he thought fit without consulting his Board. Rosling Bennett, organizer of the 1890 Edinburgh International Exhibition, sought help from a number of Locomotive Superintendents with regards to obtaining locomotive and rolling-stock exhibits. Bennett reported that Webb was 'somewhat sharp of speech and a bit dictatorial', but he was the only Superintendent who would agree to provide exhibits without making the promise subject to the approval of the Directors. Webb ruled at Crewe — and that probably riled some at Euston.

These are just some of the anecdotes related by Dunn[49] and they may have been distorted somewhat with time, but they do illustrate an underlying kindly nature which has been ignored by the more sensation-seeking writers. Webb was certainly hard and insisted upon discipline, but he was no bully. That he liked his own way is not disputed, but in many matters he was correct, especially with regards to manufacture.

The town of Crewe developed because of the works and it was natural that LNWR officials would take a hand in local government. Webb seems to have held the belief that anything which was good for the LNWR was also good for the town, and acted accordingly in town matters. He was appointed as an alderman and then later

became mayor of the town, but politics did not really suit him; the compromise which was required by political discussion was probably not to his liking. Despite the political animosity which built up towards the end of the nineteenth century, no lasting antagonism was directed at Webb. Two terms as mayor of Crewe were the highlight of his political career although he also served as an alderman on the Cheshire County Council. Other civic duties included a period as county magistrate, but these activities were more expected due to his position rather than actively sought. Webb certainly had no political aspirations, but seemed to enjoy the authority he had at the works, his domain which he ruled as benevolent dictator.

In November 1902, Webb informed the Board of his intention to retire. The terms of his appointment stated that 12 months notice had to be given, with which he complied.[50] No successor was appointed until the following April, so the Board evidently was in no hurry for him to leave. For many years Webb had suffered from abdominal illness, and his death certificate records show that he died of a malignant disease of the peritoneum, what we would now refer to as peritonitis. That must have given him considerable pain, so it is little wonder that he became short-tempered and irritable. How the disease came about is not known, but it could have resulted from stomach ulcers which in turn might have been brought on by the stress of his job. To some extent that was self-inflicted because he would not trust anybody else and would never delegate. I.K. Brunel had a similar weakness in his character.

A Board Meeting in April appointed George Whale as Webb's successor[51], and both men then attended meetings which required the presence of the CME. Illness prevented Webb from attending a number of them as it had in previous years, so Whale went by himself. This has been taken by some as an indication that Webb was being forced out, and his presence at later meetings as a sign of his unwillingness to leave. Logic defies such argument — the man was simply ill and could not attend. In June the Board announced that Whale would take over as CME on 1 July 1903, Webb officially retiring on that date.[52] In fact, the changeover took place some weeks earlier as Webb became ill and had to be assisted from the works.

Mental illness certainly cast a shadow over those final months, even years, but the nature of that illness cannot now be defined. Stomach pain and the stress of work, aggravated by the actions of Harrison and his team, obviously made Webb's life difficult and it is highly likely that he suffered a nervous breakdown. In those days mental illness of whatever sort was all classed together, and little in the way of effective treatment was available. In

1930 W.H. Chaloner was able to interview Webb's Assistant Chief Clerk, William Horabin, and he indicated that during those final months Webb was obsessed with the fear of poverty.[53] There was no reason for that as he left over £200,000 in his will, but the mind can play strange tricks. Work was Webb's life, he had no real outside interests, and it is likely that retirement with no active work to do worried him, and lack of money was an excuse for continuing to work.

Webb knew that he had adequate funds to last the rest of his life, and before he actually retired he donated £5,000 to the Crewe Memorial Cottage Hospital.[54] His will must have been drawn up at about the same time, and contained many large bequests. His two brothers and assorted relatives were taken care of, whilst charities and educational institutions were not forgotten. Donations of £2,000 each to University College, Liverpool, and Owens College, Manchester, provided funds for scholarships whilst the Institution of Civil Engineers received £1,000 in order to provide prizes for engineering papers. After all bequests, the residue, amounting to some £70,000, went towards founding the Webb Orphanage. Kindness in death mirrored similar sentiments in life, but Webb never appeared to like outward demonstrations of that sort.

There is a story, again from the recollections of W. Davies, which recounts Webb's final day at Crewe. The CME returned to his office in the late afternoon following a morning visit to Manchester, and Horabin noticed that his usual abrupt manner had become rather peculiar, although what is meant by 'peculiar' is not

Above left *F. W. Webb in the regalia as mayor of Crewe.*

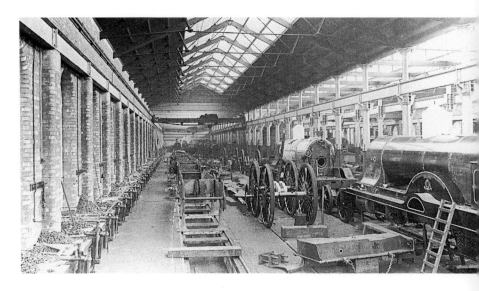

Right *The erecting shop at Crewe works.* (G. Charles collection)

recorded. Webb asked Horabin if he would like his, Webb's, overcoat which the latter accepted, but as the clerk was much smaller than the CME, it struck Horabin as a very odd offer. If Webb had become mentally unbalanced during his trip to Manchester it was an unbalance which apparently resulted in kindness and consideration rather than aggression or offensiveness. Some writers have intimated that the latter characterized Webb's life, but if that had really been the dominant part of his nature his actions at the end might have tended that way.

Webb's brother, Canon A.H. Webb, was called and escorted the sick CME away from Crewe for the last time. According to the local newspaper, which simply reported that he had been taken seriously ill, Webb was moved to Colwyn Bay for treatment.[55] A relapse saw him moved to a mental hospital in Staffordshire, but within a few weeks he had recovered sufficiently to leave. Webb purchased a house in Bournemouth and it was there that he died on 6 June 1906. Crewe Works was represented at the funeral by A.R. Trevithick, the Works Manager, but neither the LNWR Chairman nor the new CME attended. Webb had gone, but many distortions of his life and works lived after him.

George Whale

In nature and character, Whale was almost the opposite of Webb and he seems to have held a certain amount of resentment for his predecessor. The fact that he neither attended the funeral nor named a locomotive after Webb gives some indication of animosity. Whale was not a works man but spent most of his life in the running department and would, therefore, have had to deal with operational problems and take responsibility for locomotive failures. Improved service timings must have caused him many headaches and it is likely that his resentment resulted from the CME's insistence on using compounds which Whale considered were not up to the job.

Whale was an LNWR man, having spent his entire working life on that railway. His devotion and effort are beyond question, but the animosity he fostered certainly does him no credit. It would appear that he went out of his way to expunge the memory of Webb from Crewe and the entire railway. The charge has been made that he would not allow anything good to be written about Webb or his works, and the evidence seems to confirm that. Many of the exaggerated stories about Webb and his compounds appeared during the Whale era and no attempt seems to have been made by Crewe or Euston to contradict them. Whale's bit-

terness must have been considerable.

George Whale was born at Bocking, Essex, on 7 December 1842 and he received his education at a private school in Lewisham. At the age of 16 years he became a pupil of J.E. McConnell at Wolverton and he remained there as a pupil of Ramsbottom even after McConnell resigned. The latter part of his time at Wolverton was spent in the drawing office, but in 1865 he moved to the drawing office at Crewe. A two-year spell there was the last actual contact Whale had with mechanical engineering design work until he became CME nearly 40 years later. In 1867 he became assistant to John Rigg who was then Superintendent of the locomotive running department.[56]

It was during this period that Whale encountered J.A.F. Aspinall and Henry Ivatt, who were then pupils at Crewe, and the group formed a close friendship.[57] Whale took enthusiastically to the running department and was obviously more at home there than at the works. When Rigg retired in 1877, Whale was appointed to superintend the running department of the Northern Division, Rigg having had control of the entire department for the previous ten years. In 1899, when J. Mumford, Running Superintendent of the Southern Division, retired, Whale had control

Below left *George Whale.*

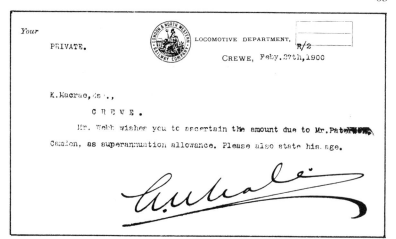

Right *A memo from George Whale, written in 1900 when he was working under F. W. Webb.*

over running matters throughout the LNWR system.

As an official of the Northern Division, Whale was based at Crewe and became active in the political life of the town. He was elected to the council in 1880 but was defeated in the election two years later. However, the elections of 1885 returned the Independents to power and Whale was appointed mayor that year. Political matters were, however, something of a distraction, and Whale resigned from the council in September 1890, a month after Webb resigned his aldermanic seat.[58] Whale also served as a town magistrate, practically an obligatory role for major railway officials in all railway towns.

Whale never became involved in matters educational, nor did he have much interest in learned societies, never presenting a paper to any of them nor even taking part in a discussion. He joined the Institution of Civil Engineers as an Associate Member in 1886 and transferred to the class of Member at the end of 1903, after he became CME.[59] His connection with the 'Mechanicals' was even shorter, joining as a Member in 1900 and serving on the council from 1907 until 1909.[60] It is difficult to understand why any engineer holding such responsible positions would not take a more active interest in the learned societies of his profession. There was always much knowledge to be gained from the discussion of papers.

Whale did, however, get a mention in certain papers, one of these being that by Dr Brislee concerning the combustion of coal in locomotive fireboxes. Whale had granted permission for this academic from the University of Liverpool to carry out tests on two of the LNWR's newer loco-

motive classes, but he was not present at the 'Mechanicals' when the paper was discussed. It was left to C.J.B. Cooke to apologize for his chief's absence. At least Whale had allowed experimental work to take place, but the trials did not produce any results which were of immediate use for design purposes. The locomotive classes involved, 'Precursor' and 'Experiment', were ideally suited to such trials, as one had a deep firebox and the other a shallow one, thus allowing for comparisons to be made. From a locomotive design and operating point of view, the tests allowed comparisons of fire depths to be made and they proved, as far as Cooke was concerned, that a shallow firebox with a large grate area, as on the 'Experiment' Class, produced better results. Cooke added that expert firing was essential with a shallow fire.[61]

This was certainly so, and it also required greater effort on the part of the fireman. It is difficult to understand why Whale, with his running experience and presumed concern for footplate crew, allowed such a feature to be employed. A number of 'Precursor' cab controls were also new to LNWR footplate crew, and their use presented problems which careful observance and consideration should have avoided. The regulator handle, left-hand injector steam valve and tender water-scoop hand-wheel were either difficult to operate or to reach. Such details were normally worked out by the drawing office, but Whale must have been aware of the changes if he actually had any dealings with the design work; alternatively, he may simply have authorized the drawing office to produce a locomotive for a particular power and left everything to be decided by the Chief Draughtsman. Whale was by no means a design

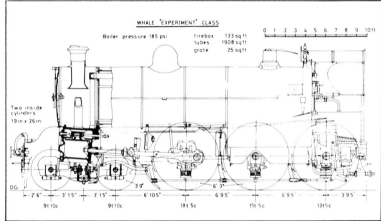

WHALE 'EXPERIMENT' CLASS

Boiler pressure 185 psi   firebox   133 sq ft
                         tubes   1908 sq ft
                         grate   25 sq ft

Two inside
cylinders
19in x 26in

Above *Whale 'Precursor' Class No 1102* Thunderbolt *at Crewe.* (D. K. Jones collection)

Left *Whale's 'Experiment' class.*

Below right *'Benbow' No 1944* Victoria and Albert *at Northampton in 1920.* (G. Charles collection)

engineer and will certainly have relied heavily on the drawing office staff; however, allowing such footplate inconveniences to be fitted and perpetuated does seem a little inept.

Allowing those tests to be conducted was, in effect, Whale's only contribution to the development of locomotive design knowledge. This could be taken as a lack of interest, or it may be that he was preoccupied with other matters. Whatever the reason, the Crewe 'School of Science' which was to the fore during the time of Ramsbottom and Webb lost its lead and sense of direction.

When Whale replaced Webb he was faced with problems regarding the performance of compounds and their difficulty in maintaining services. As a running man he had seen at first hand the difficulties of making up lost time over certain sections. Locomotives will be considered in more detail later, but it is worth mentioning here that compounds were not thoroughly bad — they just had little in reserve and were not able to run fast over the easier sections to make up time lost at

other points. Webb had designed them that way because he considered that working to the limit was more efficient. There were other problems with individual classes, but with experience modifications were made to solve them. The major problem was that lack of reserve power which presented difficulties whenever services were accelerated. Whale's solution was to produce locomotives which could be thrashed should circumstances dictate. There was a price to pay for that philosophy, but the economic days of Webb were gone forever.

Two new classes were produced very quickly, the 4-4-0 'Precursor' in 1904 and the 4-6-0 'Experiment' a year later. It is fairly obvious that Whale had no practical involvement in the design work; his drawing office experience had finished some 40 years earlier, but he will have indicated to the Crewe design office his requirement with respect to power, speed and performance. The speed with which the first 'Precursor' was designed and built is really a compliment to Webb

— his foresight set up the design team and planned the workshops. Although the design was considered to be new, it was really a development of earlier Webb 'simple' locomotives using a number of their features. To have not used already standardized items would have been the height of folly; a completely new design could never have been produced in the short time demanded by Whale.

Very quickly the workshops were in full production and new 4-4-0 and 4-6-0 locomotives rolled out. These had the reserve of power not available in the Webb compounds, but they were not the panacea that contemporary publicity had the railway world believe. Double heading was still required north of Preston on many trains due to increased train loads and the desired higher service speeds. Whale was being faced with the same problem as Webb, and his locomotives were not entirely up to the job. Double-heading in itself was not difficult to deal with provided sufficient locomotives were available. As a good engineer Webb always had enough locomotives to meet demand, but Whale fell short. Due to a blind desire to eliminate compounds, or an inability to control the scrapping mania of his Works Manager, A.R. Trevithick, compounds were cut up with undue haste at Crewe. If Trevithick was acting on his own, Whale would have been totally incompetent as a manager, so the CME must have been instrumental in allowing mass destruction of the compounds. That in itself may not have been a bad thing provided that sufficient locomotives were being constructed to replace them and so maintain services, but such was not the case.

By the end of 1909 there had been a reduction in LNWR locomotive stock of 5 per cent compared with 1903.[62] This was not compensated for by the higher power of the newer designs, as these were only just keeping up with the demands of increased train weights and speeds. The result was a shortage in power to meet normal services. If complaints were made about the inability to provide sufficient locomotives during Webb's time, they were more pertinent during the Whale era. Scrapping good serviceable locomotives for reasons of dogma was stupidity and extremely poor management.

So serious became the locomotive shortage in 1908 that Whale was forced to issue a directive insisting that locomotives be returned to their home depot rather than be employed for onward traffic. That made matters worse rather than better as trains could be kept at a location because there was no engine available to work it onwards although there might be several available to haul it in the opposite direction. A number of shed foremen used their own judgement and employed 'foreign' engines for onward traffic in order to keep it moving, only to receive a reprimand for their resourcefulness.[63]

An early engine modification during the Whale administration was the provision of additional sets of valve gear for the outside high-pressure cylinders on the four-cylinder compounds of the 'Alfred the Great' Class. Webb had provided his four-cylinder compounds with two sets of Joy valve gear between the frames to directly operate the valves of the inside low-pressure cylinders, the outside HP cylinders had their valves driven by the corresponding inside gear acting through rocking levers. This meant that all four cylinders were notched up simultaneously, and independent control of the HP and LP cylinders, which had been successful with the three-cylinder compounds, was not available. Whale has been credited with fitting separate valve gear to the HP cylinders, thus providing independent control, but that may not be the case.

Locomotive No 1952 *Benbow* was fitted with the additional sets of outside Joy gear during August/September 1903, barely three months after Webb retired. Design of the gear, manufacture of parts and fitting in such a short period, if not impossible, would certainly be a difficult task. The possibility exists that Webb was contemplating such a modification before his retirement and had already set the design work in motion. The correct design of valve gear is a very precise science and any error in dimension can result in a totally defective gear. Webb had full-size models of valve gears which were used to determine optimum valve settings; each new gear would first

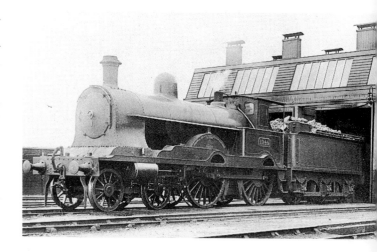

need a wooden model to be made, and that took time.

In contrast to Webb, Whale got on well with the operating department and the General Manager. That certainly improved the atmosphere on the railway and his mild manner was more attractive to the lower ranks. However, it has been claimed that he would not generally support his drivers and fitters in disputes with other departments. W.N. Davies considered him to be like a genial 'John Bull', neither easily ruffled nor upset. Failing health at the beginning of 1908 changed that, as his doctor banned him from smoking cigars, to which he seemed addicted, and from taking other delights such as certain foods and alcoholic beverages.[64] An internal complaint was the reason, and an operation failed to resolve the situation. By the end of that year his health had deteriorated so much that he decided to retire and accordingly informed the Board. In January 1909 it was announced that Whale would retire on 30 June of that year[65] but for long periods he was absent from work and during the final few weeks his successor, C.J.B Cooke, was essentially in charge.

During Whale's period in office, no real changes in operating practice or machinery took place at Crewe — he relied very much on the legacy of Webb. The only changes which came about whilst he was CME were the new large locomotive designs and the rapid scrapping of the still useful compounds. Considering his years in the running department, little else could really be expected, for he had little experience of the works and any interference would likely have been deleterious. After Webb, however, Crewe and the LNWR in general probably needed a pause for breath. The twentieth-century world was going to be different from that of the Victorian age. The problem seems to have been that the railway did not appreciate what it had been given by Webb, and set out to destroy without asking why.

Whale's salary as CME was £3,000 per year, less than half that paid to Webb, but in addition he was allowed to keep half of the £150 per year fees paid by up to six pupils. When he died his total estate amounted to only £15,600. Following retirement, Whale underwent a second operation but did not fully recover and he died at Hove on 7 March 1909, leaving a widow and two grown-up sons. Throughout his life, Whale worked hard but achieved little of lasting note apart from the satisfaction of doing his job to the best of his ability. It is a measure of that achievement that journals such as *The Engineer* and *Engineering* devoted little

space to his obituary. Had there not been such disenchantment with the Webb compounds, it is unlikely that the achievement for which he is remembered, the 'Precursor' and 'Experiment' Class locomotives, would have been built.

Charles John Bowen Cooke

Like his predecessor, Cooke was essentially a running man and apart from his training had little experience in design and manufacture. Locomotive designs which were produced during his stewardship essentially followed those of the Whale period with improvements in the form of superheating, piston valves and Belpaire fireboxes. This would indicate that the same drawing office regime remained in charge of locomotive design and that the CME simply indicated the requirements for meeting traffic demand. In this respect Cooke was no different from Whale, but he did take a more active interest in learned societies and in the works. The latter interest was really forced upon him as a result of the First World War, when the demands of the conflict required that all railway establishments made a contribution to war production.

Cooke became a member of the War

Charles John Bowen Cooke.

Manufacturers Sub-committee and the Locomotive Superintendents' Sub-committee of the Railway Executive Committee, so was at the hub of the railway input to the war effort. Crewe Works played its part in manufacturing armaments and other items for use by the military, but much credit for that should really go to Webb for it was he who ensured that the works had the capacity and tools. Cooke did introduce a large drop-stamping hammer which played a very useful part in producing trunnion brackets for howitzers, drop-stamping having been considered up to that time as an impossible manufacturing process for such large items. A novel introduction was the Crewe tractor, a Ford car converted into a self-propelled rail vehicle, and 138 were supplied for use abroad. For these works Cooke received letters of praise from the Ministry of Munitions; he was also awarded a CBE in 1918.[66]

C.J.B. Cooke was born 11 January 1859 at Orton Longueville, near Peterborough, where his father was rector. Initial education was obtained at the Preparatory School, Cheltenham, and then at King's College, London. A year of technical education was obtained at the Technical High School, Neuwied, Germany, before Cooke obtained a premium apprenticeship at Crewe in 1875. In 1878 he became one of Webb's private pupils. Upon completion of that training he was appointed Assistant to the Running Superintendent of the Southern Division with headquarters at Rugby. When Mumford retired, Cooke was given responsibility for the southern lines, Whale being Running Superintendent for the entire railway, but when Whale became CME Cooke was made Superintendent of the Southern Division.[67]

At a Board Meeting on 19 February 1909, Cooke was selected to succeed Whale on his retirement, but the poor health of the latter meant that Cooke was in effective control some weeks before the official date of 30 June. Whilst based at Rugby, Cooke took a considerable interest in the Mechanics' Institute, was a member of the County Council Technical Education Committee and also took an interest in the activities of the local fire brigade.[68] Following his appointment as CME, Crewe became the centre of Cooke's world and he played his part in the life of the local community. Railway involvement in the town's political affairs was less obvious than during Webb's time, but there was still a considerable role to be played and Cooke seems to have taken to it enthusiastically. He served as mayor of Crewe in 1918-9, was a member of the Cheshire County Council, a magistrate and also a major in the Engineering and Railway Staff Corps, a body Webb had been instrumental in founding. In addition to these, Cooke was a member of both the 'Civils' and 'Mechanicals', although full membership of the latter was not obtained until 1912.[69]

Unlike Whale, Cooke played a very active part in the discussion of papers at these institutions and also presented one himself. Writing was something of a passion, and a number of his articles appeared in print, as did two books. These came before he attained high office, but the technical paper appeared whilst he was CME.

Earliest amongst his literary output was an article about Crewe Works for the *English Illustrated Magazine*.[70] This illustrated article was in the form of a guided tour of that establishment and it also described some of the notable locomotive products. For such a non-technical journal, the account was very detailed and must have been useful to the general reader; even today it gives a valuable first-hand account of that place. Webb obviously must have sanctioned the article and may even have given the job to Cooke, although at this distance it is not possible to determine when the latter's interest in writing commenced. As a piece of Crewe publicity, few advertising agencies could have done better, and the illustrations came from official sources including one of the famous teams which erected a locomotive in 25.5 hours.

A major work followed in 1893 with publication of his book *British Locomotives: Their History, Construction and Modern Development*. This work became very popular and ran to three editions, the final one being published in 1899. Although the book concentrated on LNWR locomotives, there was general coverage given to engines operated by most of the railways of Britain, with special mention of unusual fixtures or fittings. What comes across is Cooke's enthusiasm for the steam locomotive, both in construction and operation, but his preference for Crewe products is obvious. Comments concerning Webb's compounds are favourable, and are backed up with data relating to operation which can be taken to indicate that these machines produced some favourable runs. However, it is natural that Cooke would be unlikely to include details of any poor performances, and it has been stated that Cooke's favourable comments regarding compounds were only used in order to placate his boss, F.W. Webb.

No individual would wish to upset his superior if that person had control over promotion prospects but to make inaccurate statements in a published work for such reasons would put a

question mark against the writer's integrity. If that was the case, all of Cooke's subsequent works must be read with caution. In his preface, Cooke states that, 'The endeavour has been made to avoid all controversial matters in these pages', but he does consider the compounds in some detail and, at that time, they were somewhat controversial. Details of LNWR compound runs are given in a number of instances and, though these are favourable, Cooke does not make any direct comparison with other compounds — that is left to the reader.

Two subsequent works also deal with locomotives and make more specific, and more favourable, reference to the Webb compounds. Again it might be considered that Cooke was looking after his own interests, but that again raises the question of integrity. In 1901 Webb was asked by the Commandant of Military Engineering at Chatham to present two lectures on locomotive practice to the Royal Engineers' Institute, but he was unable to spare the time and delegated the task to Cooke. These lectures, 'Recent Developments in Locomotive Practice', were delivered and published by the Institute in its papers but they were also published for general consumption the following year.[71] An abbreviated form with slight changes appeared as an article in *Cassiers Magazine* during 1901.[72]

In both publications more definite statements were made concerning compounds, particularly the Webb variety, and they were by no means unfavourable. Each publication dealt with general British locomotive practice but the emphasis was on Crewe products. Statements were made indicating that Cooke was part of the compounding fraternity, for he uses the term 'we' at certain

times. 'If we can show that a compound engine, the boiler of which only has to feed a pair of 15 inch cylinders, can successfully work the heaviest and fastest trains in the country, it ought, I think, to be a very strong argument in favour of the application of the compound principle to locomotive engines. This conclusion also seems to point to the fact that any further development required to meet the ever increasing demands for additional power will have to be on the same lines.'[73] In both publications he then went on to show that Webb compounds were working the heaviest and fastest trains. 'It is an undoubted fact that the Webb four-cylinder compounds are working the heaviest and fastest passenger trains in Great Britain.'[74]

Statements in the book, and especially the article, give Cooke's unequivocal views with respect to the compounds, and they are backed up with statements of fact about running. With respect to the three-cylinder 'Teutonic' and 'Greater Britain' Classes, Cooke stated that they had done and were still doing excellent work (1901). He added that they worked Scotch express trains most successfully and with absolute punctuality, often making up for lost time. Writing about the 'Jubilee' Class four-cylinder compounds, he stated that each was 'in steam six days of every week and has a minimum of 316 miles cut out for its daily work'. In additional they were drawing loads of 333 tons, 414 tons including engine and tender, but maintained average speeds of 52 miles per hour.[75] The book also gives details of average coal consumption for seven different classes over many years running, and these compare more than favourably with other locomotives then in service or later produced.

The 1902 information was given as:

No of engines	Class	Total miles run	Coal consumption (lbs/mile)
10	'Teutonic,' 7 ft, 3-cyl	6,180,648	38.0
29	'Jubilee,' 7 ft, 4-cyl	2,897,916	42.8

It was stated that figures for consumption included 1.2 lbs/mile for lighting up, standing, waiting for trains, delays, experimental runs and all other purposes.

Figures quoted in 1910 were more selective and dealt with a six months period only on the Euston to Crewe line:

Class	Total train miles	Coal consumption (lbs/mile)
'Teutonic'	180,229	48.9
'Jubilee'	264,238	43.6
'Precursor'	379,957	47.2

For any real conclusion to be drawn, train loads must be considered, as must state of repair, but no comparison was made per ton mile. The reader must make up his own mind as to performance; these figures are given only to show how selective such data can be if there is a desire to make a specific case.

Having made such definite statements in print on a number of occasions, Cooke seems to have had second thoughts when a new chief with different ideas came into power. When discussing Hughes' paper on compounding and superheating, Cooke presented figures which put the compounds in a poor light compared with the Whale 'Precursor' Class.[76] Figures must be related to an operating situation and so real comparisons are not possible, but that it is not the point. What is surprising is the dramatic change of heart on compounding. Cooke seems to have agreed completely with Whale's wholesale scrapping of the compounds and paid little regard to their usefulness. During the discussion, Cooke based much of his argument against compounds on the basis of repair costs, and questioned Hughes' information that Lancashire & Yorkshire compounds were no heavier on repairs than simple engines. In view of his 'updated' coal cost figures for compounds, which differed markedly from values given in earlier publications, there can be reason for querying the complete accuracy of his figures relating to shopping mileages which showed simples to be much superior. It is not suggested that Cooke provided inaccurate data, but it must have been highly selective.

The impression may be formed that Cooke was able to move with prevailing conditions and satisfy whoever was in control at the time. This can be useful, but may leave integrity open to question. On the whole, however, C.J.B. Cooke was looked upon with respect and was well liked by the workforce at Crewe and throughout the railway. Few who actually knew him put pen to paper, but a number of people have provided some information, though its objectivity may be coloured by their personal experiences.

T. Lovatt Williams considered it to be no bad thing to be a pupil at Crewe during Cooke's period of office. As far as he was concerned, the CME was a loved and respected gentleman who never threatened his pupils with anything more dreadful than a posting to Rugby.[77] A different view was held by W.N. Davies who considered Cooke to be somewhat vindictive and harsh in the way he treated his subordinates. Davies was witness to some incidents involving Cooke and junior ranks, so his opinions may be given credence, although they are also based on other events which he heard from fellow LNWR employees. In that category is an incident involving a driver whom Cooke, when an assistant at Rugby, failed to support at a Locomotive and Traffic Department joint enquiry.[78]

R.A. Riddles, who became a premium apprentice at Crewe shortly after Cooke became CME, also did not think too highly of his boss. Although there was little contact between them, Riddles formed the opinion that Cooke was pompous and he doubted his ability as an engineer. He also believed that the CME was something of a showman who liked people to recognize him and his position. Locomotive design under Cooke was strictly a matter for the drawing office — at least

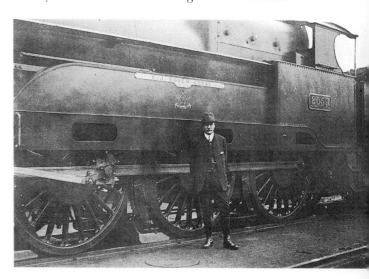

that was the view of Riddles, who was to become the final British steam designer.[79]

For an independent view it is necessary to read C.S. Lake. He met Cooke a number of times and found him to be pleasant and charming with a deep interest in locomotives. The first meeting was difficult due to Cooke's reserved nature, but as soon as that was broken both men got on well together and Lake considered him to be one of his best friends in the locomotive world. That might have prevented Lake from viewing Cooke in a completely objective manner, but his opinions are still valid and they add to the knowledge of Cooke. Cooke would frequently use the term 'we' rather than 'I' concerning matters which transpired at Crewe[80], so it is right to consider that he believed himself to be part of a team rather than an isolated individual.

That was certainly true in locomotive design matters, for he certainly leaned heavily on the experiences of J.N. Jackson, the Chief Draughtsman, and T.E. Sackville, Assistant Chief Draughtsman. Jackson occupied the post from 1888 until he retired in 1919, and Sackville from 1893 until 1924. T. Lovatt Williams held the opinion that no man during his time at Crewe had a greater influence on locomotive design than Sackville.[81] Whilst Cooke, and Whale, may have indicated the basic requirements for a locomotive, it seems fairly obvious that all designs were formulated in the drawing office by Jackson and Sackville, and the continuity in many aspects of design under these CMEs leads to the conclusion that other hands than theirs rocked the locomotive cradle. They were not locomotive, or even mechanical, engineers in the sense of Ramsbottom and Webb, but were locomotive operators; that is in no way meant to be a derogatory remark, but is simply a statement of fact. Both men seemed to recognize that, and let their well-qualified drawing office staff get on with the job of producing designs to fit their basic specifications.

Apart from his change of mind regarding compounding, Cooke also had thoughts on locomotive design, paramount amongst these being that any locomotive should be as simple as possible with the minimum of gadgets. During discussion of Henry Fowler's paper on superheating, he made known his dislike of features such as steam-controlled dampers, pyrometers, tailrods and cylinder bypass valves. These devices were sometimes known to cause problems and a running man did not like anything which could go wrong even if it made engineering sense. With superheated steam, piston rod packing did cause some difficulties and Cooke was sceptical that Fowler had found a solution. Raising the matter, he made the remark that 'the Author appeared to have found a way out of the difficulties'.[82]

This may have been an attempt at a polite put-down, but Fowler was well informed in metallurgical matters and Cooke certainly was not. The remainder of his contribution dealt with LNWR applications of superheating, and gave information about trials which had been carried out. In fact, it was something of an LNWR publicity statement rather along the lines of those produced by Webb in some of his discussion contributions. By this time, Cooke was a convert to the advantages of superheating, but it had taken some time in coming, other railways already having a number

Left *'Prince of Wales' No 951* Bulwer Lytton, *a Cooke superheated version of a Whale 'Experiment'.* (D. K. Jones collection)

Above right *The erecting shop at Crewe: a 'Claughton' Class locomotive on the crane hooks.* (G. Charles collection)

of years experience before Crewe saw the light. Even then, Cooke was cautious. Following tests with a superheated variant of the 'Precursor', *George the Fifth*, and its unsuperheated consort *Queen Mary,* he arranged for construction of another nine engines of each type in order to carry out further tests. Crewe favoured the Schmidt-type superheater, and used Dr Schmidt as a consultant. Whilst Horwich and Swindon carried out trials with different types to determine the best form for their locomotives, Cooke seems to have decided early on that a superheater was a superheater and there was little to be gained by such an exercise. In any event, the results were certainly favourable.

Webb would never have adopted such an approach to an engineering matter, but Cooke was not a mechanical engineer in that sense and was more concerned with obtaining locomotives which performed the duties intended; economy of performance and the engineering niceties of a solution were not the priority. His interest remained on the operating side, and his only major paper before a learned society, 'Mechanical Handling of Coal', concerned that aspect of his job.[83] In order to improve the coaling of locomotives, an automatic plant was installed at Crewe and Cooke's paper detailed its construction and operation. Churchward opened the discussion of what was a very detailed and informative paper by stating that he considered the audience to be indebted to the author, not only for presenting the information but also for having the courage to erect such a plant. He went on to say that he had considered constructing an automatic coaling plant at Old Oak Common but had sufficient reliance upon Crewe to believe that they would take the initiative in the matter. From other comments it appears that Churchward had a high regard for his fellow CME from Crewe.

The paper itself was complete in all aspects, for it not only included technical matters relating to construction but also gave details regarding operating costs and the savings expected by faster coaling and earlier release of wagons. Cooke knew what he wanted in terms of locomotive operations.

Another literary effort directed at locomotive operation rather than engineering was offered in the first volume of *The Railway Magazine*. This detailed description of an engine driver's duties was very informative, and must have been appreciated by the majority of readers of that new magazine which was aimed at the railway enthusiast rather than the technically interested.[84] Such writings can have done Cooke's standing with the

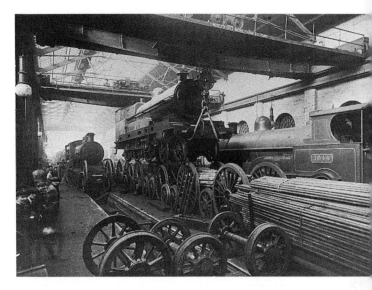

railway authorities no harm at all, for they helped to promote the LNWR and gave valuable free publicity. Whether or not they assisted him in obtaining the position of CME is unknown, but many people expected A.R. Trevithick, Works Manager at Crewe, to be appointed upon Whale's retirement — Cooke's appointment came as a surprise.

Cooke made a number of trips to France during the First World War in connection with the working of the military railways and he also visited America in 1917 in order to purchase materials. This hectic life cannot have been good for his health, nor were the troubled times after the armistice when he had to supervize a return to normal railway working. Periods of illness preceded his death on 18 October 1920 at his daughter's home in Falmouth. The legacy he left was not great, but much that might have been done was prevented by the war. Superheating had been introduced, but credit for locomotive design really belongs to the drawing office. Some steps forward such as the automatic coaling stage, had been made, but Crewe Works was in decline. When Hughes inspected the works after the amalgamation of the L&YR and LNWR in 1922, he was horrified at the production methods and standards of accuracy. He also saw many machines on which he had worked during his apprenticeship days in the 1880s.[85] It was sad how the gains of Webb had been squandered.

Hewitt Pearson Montague Beames
Poor Hewitt Beames, seemingly always the bridesmaid and never the bride. If any engineer can be

considered unfortunate in terms of promotion, it must be him. Just over a year after being appointed CME to replace Cooke, he was ousted by George Hughes following the amalgamation with the L&YR. Three more times others received the prize rather than him, but Beames appeared to be philosophical to the end and when Stanier was brought from the GWR to take the position he so earnestly wanted, it is reported that he wrote a most friendly letter to his new boss in which he expressed his own disappointment but added that there was nobody else under whom he would rather serve. That was typical of the man who in later years twice wrote to R.A. Riddles congratulating him on appointment to high office.[86]

The youngest son of Major Pearson T. Beames, H.P.M. Beames was born near Dublin on 9 May 1875 and was educated at Corrig School, Kingstown, and at Dover College before entering Crawley's Military Academy, Dublin. It would appear that engineering rather than military life proved the greater attraction, however, for he entered Crewe Works as a premium apprentice in 1895 and later became one of Webb's private pupils. Junior positions at Carlisle running shed and Crewe Works followed, but with the outbreak of the South African war Beames enlisted, with the railway's permission. At the end of the conflict he resumed his LNWR service and occupied several positions in the works and in the running department.

In January 1910 Beames became personal assistant to Cooke and remained in that post until the outbreak of the war in 1914. Again with permission of the Board he enlisted and was given command of the 110th Railway Company, Royal Engineers. Rising to the rank of Captain he remained in military service until the LNWR requested his release so that he could take over as Works Manager at Crewe on 1 April 1916.[87]

In 1919 Beames became deputy CME whilst retaining his position as works manager. Cooke's death then pushed him into the post of CME, although he had been carrying out those duties during Cooke's periods of absence. During his period in command from 1 December 1920 until Hughes took over on 1 January 1922 there was little he could do to impose his character. Much of the time was spent trying to put the Crewe house in order after the war and dealing with the locomotive needs of the running department. New locomotive designs had to wait, but modifications to existing stock was planned.

Beames became in effect a Divisional Manager at Crewe, with Hughes in overall control, but he did make plans to deal with the LNWR locomotive stock. A scheme for fitting outside Walschaerts valve gear to the 'Prince of Wales' Class was drawn up and conversions made. Some of Cooke's 'Claughton' Class engines were selected for conversion in order to try out the Caprotti rotary valve gear. There was even a proposal to develop a variant of the 'Prince of Wales' Class with inside Caprotti valve gear. The high running plate and simple stove pipe chimney gave it very much the austerity look which was to come into fashion much later.[88]

Beames never had any real control and he did play his part in the development of the London Midland & Scottish Railway when that came into existence. He was responsible for modernizing Crewe Works and read a very interesting paper before the 'Mechanicals' on the subject.[89] Authority lay elsewhere, but he did his job effectively and it is an interesting exercise to imagine what might have come about had he become Chief Mechanical Engineer of the LMS following Fowler's departure. It was, after all, his turn.

Beames died at his home in Chester Place, Crewe, on 5 March 1948 at the age of 72 years. He had served the LNWR and LMS to the best of his ability and without complaint. He served the town of Crewe and the County of Cheshire, being Chairman of the County Council at the time of his death.[90] Other charitable organizations had the benefit of his experience; he became a Vice President of the Institution of Locomotive Engineers and the nation honoured him with a CBE. But he only held the post of Chief Mechanical Engineer for 13 months, and with all of his heart he wanted to have the same position on the LMS.

Left *Hewitt Pearson Montague Beames.*

Right *Beames' outside Walschaerts valve gear arrangement.*

Below *'Prince of Wales' No 964* Bret Harte, *with Beames' arrangement of valve gear.* (G. Charles collection)

Bottom *An impression of Beames' proposed locomotive with inside Caprotti valve gear.*

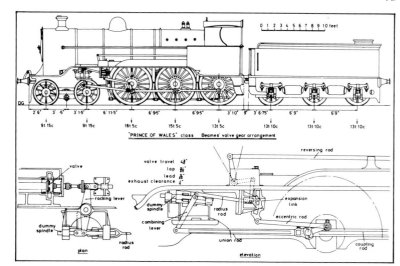

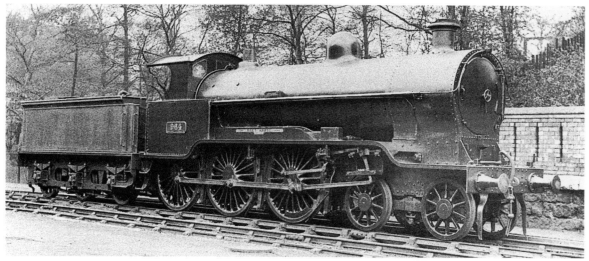

4. Midland Railway Locomotive Engineers

Matthew Kirtley

Frequently the lives of people go unrecorded and only their works seem to survive in the memory. In many respects that is the case with Matthew Kirtley, for whilst locomotive designs produced during his period in command of the Midland Railway's locomotive department are recorded, little detail of his life has been chronicled. One reason for that is probably the fact that Kirtley was something of a private individual who did not court publicity — his works spoke for him. Another is that his working life came at a time when few general publications took much notice of railways, let alone their employees. It was the likes of Brunel and the Stephensons who attracted attention because of the railways they constructed, and not because of the locomotives they built.

Technical journals did take notice but again usually of the inventions and not the inventors. Matthew Kirtley was not idle, but he did not indulge in the passion for invention which

gripped many of his contemporary Locomotive Superintendents. He did, however, take some part in the inventing mania and in 1848 patented an improved process for manufacturing railway wheels.[1] Compared with John Ramsbottom he was very much in the minor league, but he did encourage members of his staff to experiment and develop ideas. One of the most notable and successful was the arrangement for burning coal in locomotive fireboxes.

Charles Markham, one of Kirtley's assistants, carried out trials over a considerable period of time with firebox arrangements until he hit on the right combination of brick arch and air deflector. Only with Kirtley's approval and encouragement could such trials have been carried out and they were certainly justified by the results. One of the main commodities shipped by the Midland Railway was coal, and it could be obtained directly from the pits for a fraction of the cost of coke — Kirtley was as much constrained by operating costs as anybody else. Markham published details of his experiment and the results in a paper read before the Institution of Mechanical Engineers in 1861[2], and it was not long before other locomotive engineers were making use of the system.

Matthew Kirtley was born at Tanfield, County Durham, on 6 February 1813, his father owning a colliery in that county. At the age of 13 years he obtained an engineering apprenticeship with the Stephensons on the Stockton & Darlington Railway, and over the next five years he learned about steam locomotive construction and operation. However, at the time there was little locomotive construction going on compared with later days, and after completing his training Kirtley obtained locomotive work as a fireman and subsequently a driver. Initial employment must have been through the Stephensons as their railway works expanded, firing experience being gained on the Liverpool & Manchester Railway as well as the Warrington & Newton Railway. After this, driving experience was gained on the Hull & Selby Railway and then the London & Birmingham Railway.[3] It has been claimed that, in 1839, Kirtley drove the first locomotive to enter London, but such an honour does not appear to have been well recorded. It is interesting to speculate how British locomotive design might have developed had that sort of initial training situation remained. In Britain, drivers came up from the ranks of cleaners, whilst in many continental

Below left *Matthew Kirtley.*

Right *A view of Derby Works near the turn of the century. The old roundhouse sheds may be seen in the distance.* (G. Charles collection)

countries engineering apprentices upon completing their training could opt to stay in the works or become footplate crew. Drivers in those countries were, therefore better informed on technical matters and able to cope with technically more complex machines. That compounding proved to be more successful in France that in Britain could be due to the fact that drivers were better able to handle the complexities of such locomotives.

The Stephensons were not only responsible for constructing the Birmingham & Derby Junction Railway but were also expected to find staff for the more senior posts. Under these circumstances it was reasonable for them to select people with whom they had dealings and who had proved themselves to be capable. Kirtley fell into the category and was appointed Locomotive Foreman. He must have demonstrated his capabilities, for when the Midland Railway was formed in 1844 it was the relatively young Matthew Kirtley who was chosen to head its locomotive department in preference to the older and more experienced incumbents on the other two constituent lines. Thus at the age of 31 years he became Locomotive and Carriage Superintendent of one of the largest railway companies in Britain.[4]

Kirtley received a starting salary of £250 per year, this being an increase of £50 on that paid by the Birmingham & Derby Junction Railway.[5] This may not appear much by modern standards, but it was an appreciable amount at that time; however, Kirtley earned his money for the Midland's locomotive stock was rather varied in type and quality. Nothing could be done immediately to improve the situation and Kirtley did not try; a period of consolidation was required in which the complete picture could be assessed. It is unlikely that the new board would have sanctioned rash

spending, but the new Locomotive Superintendent was in not hurry to stamp his authority as far as locomotive design was concerned, age being definitely on his side. In the matter of repairs he was more definite — major expansion at Derby would be needed if all such work was to be centralized. Requests for more covered accommodation were granted and construction of a new roundhouse at Derby commenced almost immediately. Kirtley had his priorities and his employers had the benefit of his judgement.

At the end of 1846 Kirtley reported the locomotive position to the Board and received permission to extend the workshops with a view to locomotive construction.This commenced in 1851 when more modern facilities were available and the departments of three constituent companies had been properly reorganized. Over the years since the formation of the Midland, some locomotives had been built by outside contractors, but Kirtley had tried to exercise some influence over design in order to reach a degree of standardization. With respect to the existing stock, which was in a very much run-down state, little could be done apart from keeping those which were fit for service running, and disposing of those which were not. As an interim measure the Board allowed him to make a contract with Henry Wright of Saltley Works, Birmingham, for the supply of 10 or 12 engines, complete with drivers, firemen and cleaners, in order to work trains between Derby and Birmingham[6]. This may have irritated many Locomotive Superindendents and it probably annoyed Kirtley, but he knew what was needed and was willing to take distasteful measures in order to achieve proper working of the railway.

Gradually Kirtley got on top of matters and was

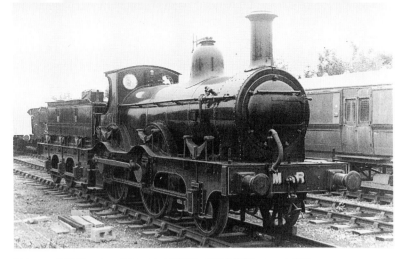

Left *Preserved Kirtley 2-4-0 No 158A, originally built in 1866.* (Patrick Griffiths)

Left *A typical Kirtley 0-6-0 goods engine—No 724, built by Neilsen.*

Below right *Samuel Waite Johnson.*

in a position not only to repair the locomotives but also to construct new ones to his own designs. Ideas on locomotive design are very much a personal matter especially in terms of styling, and during those Victorian days visual impact was considered to be a main ingredient of design. Kirtley seems to have had a preference for six-wheeled locomotives generally, but not exclusively of the 0–6–0 form. Locomotives were constructed to suit loads carried, but they had to be within the restrictions of loading gauge and of weight imposed by the Civil Engineer. Sandwich frames for passenger engines and outside frames for goods engines found favour with him during the early years, but in later passenger designs double frames were employed. Many designs were built at Derby but a number still came from contractors; however, Kirtley exercised control of the designs and they had to fit in with his standardization policy.

In terms of styling, the Kirtley locomotives were very attractive but they could also do the work and were long lasting, or at least adaptable. Following rebuilds, a number of Kirtley-designed locomotives lasted until after nationalization, and

that was possible because of the well-thought-out standardization policy.

The works at Derby expanded dramatically over the years with many new processes being introduced, but the requirements of standardization had to be satisfied. It was not simply a case of deciding upon the use of standard parts — they had to be made and their manufacture had to be within strictly controlled tolerances. John Fernie, the Works Manager, or General Foreman as he was then called, introduced a system of gauges and templates to Derby from 1858 onwards which allowed for greater accuracy in manufacture.Interchangeability of parts became a practical proposition and that increased efficiency in terms of the provision of spares and the construction of new locomotives. This was not the first such arrangement to be instituted in a railway manufactory, but it was one of the first and shows how Derby was developing under Kirtley's guidance. In the foundry, templates were used to ensure that mould sections and cores were correctly aligned, and Derby took the lead in the application of such techniques to the casting of locomotive cylinders. Fernie described the system in an 1863 'Civils' paper, and acknowledged that Kirtley had sanctioned the introduction of the machinery.[7]

Although Matthew Kirtley did not produce any papers for learned societies, he appears to have been a very keen member of the 'Civils' and 'Mechanicals', actually being a founder member of the latter. He died, still in Midland service, on 24 May 1873 at the age of 60 years. Most of his working life had been devoted to that railway and to him credit must go for developing Derby into one of the major railway centres in Britain. His works tend to be overshadowed by those of his better-known successors, but without that pioneering work their tasks would have been more difficult. When he commenced Midland service in the 1840s, few other major railway centres then existed and private manufacturers produced most of the rolling-stock. It took courage by the Board to back its Locomotive Superintendent, but only his engineering wisdom ensured success. Lack of formal technical education never stood in his way, and he could be classed as a natural engineer.

Williams, in his book covering the rise and progress of the Midland Railway, quotes an obituary, and the words admirably sum up Kirtley's life: 'He was a man of clear sagacity and well balanced judgement, and possessed a power of organization and arrangement which enabled him to exercise an effective control over the whole of the extensive concern for which he was responsible. In nothing was he more distinguished than in his command of men. Simple in his manners, easily approachable, able to sympathize with the workmen's position and difficulties, and strictly candid, he was singularly happy in dealing with complaints. Whilst sympathizing and conciliating, he was also firm and decisive, and, like all strong men, employed few words to convey his resolves'[8]. There can be few people who would not wish to be thought of in such terms.

Samuel Waite Johnson

Experience was a valuable commodity for locomotive engineers during the Victorian era, and it was considered important to move about in order to gain that experience; not many engineers reached high office with the railway on which they had served their apprenticeship. When it came to gathering experience, few Locomotive Superintendents could compare with S. W. Johnson, who served a number of railways in senior posts before arriving at the Midland.

Samuel Johnson was born at Bramley, near Leeds, on 14 October 1831. His father, James, was an engineer who was subsequently connected with the Great Northern Railway. With the completion of his education at Leeds Grammar School, Johnson became a pupil of James Fenton at the works of E. B. Wilson in Leeds. Whilst there he assisted in the design of the 'Jenny Lind' Class of locomotive, for which that concern was well known, and also with construction of the L&NWR 'Bloomers'. On completion of his training, Johnson obtained a post as manager of the Great Northern Railway's locomotive repair shops at Peterborough, possibly through family influence. In 1859 he moved to Gorton, Manchester, where he became manager of the locomotive, carriage and wagon works of the Manchester, Sheffield & Lincolnshire Railway. For a time at Gorton he was also Acting Locomotive Superintendent, and that position obviously suited him, for in 1864 he sought and obtained the post of Locomotive Superintendent to the Endinburgh & Glasgow Railway based at Cowlairs, Glasgow.

Johnson never let things drag and always seems to have been seeking his ideal in the way of employment. There is no indication that he was ever dissatisfied with any of his employers nor they with him — it just seems that he had could not settle down. Events sometimes prevailed against him, for a year after taking up his new post in Glasgow that line amalgamated with others to become the North British Railway and Johnson had to be content with the position of Locomotive Superintendent for the Western Division only of the NBR. In 1866 he was off again as the opportunity arose for sole charge of a railway's locomotive stock, and of a return to England. As successor to Robert Sinclair he was selected by the Directors of the Great Eastern Railway, and took up his post at Stratford, London, during 1866.[9]

Such moving about never allowed Johnson to show what he was like as an engineer, but it is probable that he realized that he was still learning and did not intend to settle into any of the posts. That on the GER certainly offered more scope for the development of engineering ideas than the others, and it also allowed him to both produce locomotive designs and actually see the engines in service. He designed a 2-4-0 passenger class which proved to be very successful and then introduced an 0-4-4 tank locomotive for general duties. Johnson was, however, still not satisfied, and when the position at Derby became vacant he decided that it was for him. On Kirtley's death the Directors decided to separate locomotive matters from carriage and wagons, thus Johnson was appointed as Locomotive Superintendent only.

Although Johnson was very different in character and background from Kirtley, they had one thing in common, and that was longevity of service to the Midland Railway. It is obvious that Johnson had found his niche at Derby — he stayed there for 31 years.

The locomotive works developed further during his stewardship but he did not immediately set out to change locomotive design to suit his own ideas. Many of Kirtley's machines were still performing useful service and Johnson simply decided upon rebuilding; this was not only cheaper than completely new construction, but it also allowed facilities at the works to be used more effectively. Johnson does not appear to have been dominated by his own ego for he was happy to let matters change gradually rather thn force the issue, indicating a caution and unwillingness to spend money without real cause.

Changes were none the less made in design and inside frames soon became the norm for all new construction; but Kirtley's outside frames remained on rebuilt locomotives. His predecessor's parts standardization policy was eventually extended to locomotive classes, Johnson considering that six classes was sufficient for working any railway in Britain.[10]

Johnson's locomotives will be considered later, but it is worth mentioning that they were generally considered to be amongst the most attractive ever built in Britain. They were also efficient and well constructed with a long life expectancy. Johnson returned to the single driving wheel design for fast passenger locomotives when steam sanding gear was introduced, for that allowed such machines to haul heavier loads without slipping. His beautifully proportioned 4-2-2 locomotives were constructed between 1887 and 1893, some lasting service until 1927. This was more due to a policy of small engine operation than to the fact that the design was thoroughly modern, but it does illustrate the effectiveness of many Johnson designs. The single-wheelers were something of a retrograde step in locomotive design terms, but Johnson did think things out and took care to reach what he considered to be the correct decision. Nothing was hurried and he preferred to find things out for himself rather than rely on other people. His introduction of compounding illustrates this well.

As late as April 1898 he was still not convinced that compounding offered any advantages:

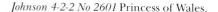

Johnson 4-2-2 No 2601 Princess of Wales.

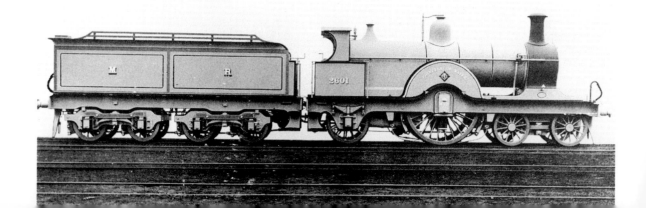

'. . . The results of the working of compound locomotives, which I have studied somewhat closely, have not been such as in my opinion would up to the present time have warranted my adopting the compound system.'[11] To make such a statement in a Presidential Address before the Institution of Mechanical Engineers, Johnson must have been definite in his views. However the appearance of two compound locomotives from Derby in January 1902 indicates a major change in opinion. Because Johnson retired the following year it has been suggested that his successor, R. M. Deeley, then doyen of the testing department and Locomotive Works Manager from 1902, was actually responsible. However, in 1897 Deeley himself publicly stated similar views on the matter. 'Compounding and other devices have been tried with a view to increased economy in the use of steam, but it is doubtful whether results have yet been obtained which justify the additional complication and expense'.[12]

At the end of his period in office Deeley put the record straight. 'When Mr Johnson discussed the question with me, and stated that he contemplated building such an engine, I strongly advised him to do so more especially as the late Mr W. M. Smith had designed a three-cylinder arrangement which promised to start away well with a heavy train under all conditions of load and gradient.' Thus it would appear that Johnson had decided to try compounding but Deeley pointed him towards the Smith system. Deeley, and so probably Johnson as well, considered there to be good reasons for testing the merits of compounding at that stage. Amongst these was the introduction of heavier trains due to corridor, dining and sleeping coaches, and these frequently required more than one locomotive, thus increasing labour costs in terms of firemen and drivers. Enlarging a simple engine was not considered to be suitable on mechanical grounds whilst it was thought that compounding would greatly ease demand on the boiler.[13]

Responsibility for locomotive design and construction was only part of Johnson's duties, but he does appear to have enjoyed producing attractive locomotives. To what extent he actually involved himself in design is not known, but he must have had close links with the drawing office for in his Presidential Address to the 'Mechanicals' he uses phrases such as 'I have designed', my single driving wheel locomotive' and 'my engines' when describing the products of Derby works. Thus he seems to have taken an active interest in the design process rather than just indicating the basic requirements for his drawing office to fol-

low. Beauty is always in the eye of the beholder, but Derby locomotives of the Johnson era were, for the most part, very attractive to the eye. As one journalist put it, 'they are remarkable for their symmetrical lines which give one the idea of a careful avoidance of all unnecessary complication'.[14]

Prizes at international exhibitions came Johnson's way, but the criteria upon which the judging was based in such cases were never explained. Certainly if style and grace were deciding factors, the award of a Gold Medal at the 1887 Royal Jubilee Exhibition, Saltaire, for his 4–4–0 express locomotive No 1757, *Beatrice,* was certainly justified. The 7 ft 6 in 4–2–2 engine No 1853 was awarded a Grand Prix at the Paris exhibition of 1889, whilst *Prince of Wales*, a larger 4–2–2, took a similar prize at the 1900 exhibition held in the same city. Although these engines were from normal production classes, they were specially finished in order to attract attention, and Johnson probably considered the additional expense to be justified. It was, after all, publicity for the railway.

This contrasts with the style of F. W. Webb, never one to shun the chance of publicity, who also exhibited a locomotive at the 1900 Paris exhibtion. According to C. J. B. Cooke, the 'Jubilee' Class 4–4–0 four-cylinder compound, *La France,* was just a normal production machine without any embellishments or additional polish. All bright parts such as the connecting rods were exactly as turned out by the machine tools without any additional filing. Cooke did, however, recognize beauty, and considered *Prince of Wales* to be 'a splendid speciment of British design and first class workmanship'.[15]

Away from work, Johnson took an interest in both major engineering institutions, becoming a member of the 'Civils' in 1867 and the 'Mechanicals' in 1861. He was not active in terms of presenting papers or even taking part in discussions, but he did involve himself actively in other ways, especially with the latter institution. Elected to the council of the Institution of Mechanical Engineers, in 1884, he became a Vice President in 1895 and was elected President in 1898. An important role accompanying that honour was the delivery of a Presidential Address and Johnson chose the subject of 'Railway Progress'. Compared with many such addresses it was very detailed and contained much useful information relating to railways and locomotives, with particular emphasis on the Midland. In order to produce such a document he must have called upon assistance from branches of the Midland Railway which were not his direct concern, but the sec-

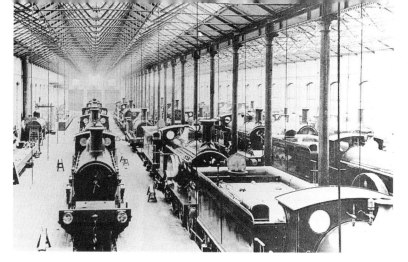

The paint shop at Derby Works circa 1890. (G. Charles collection)

tions dealing with locomotives gives a good insight into his knowledge and thinking. His attitude to compounding has already been mentioned, but Johnson also took trouble to indicate his views of railway gauge.

Despite the fact that the Stephenson 4 ft 8.5 in gauge was firmly established for all British main lines, Johnson felt justified in expressing his opinion. 'My ideal gauge for a railway is 5 ft 3 in'. He considered that the additional space between the frames would avoid the difficulties associated with the machinery which had to be crowded there, and that larger boilers would be possible even with large driving wheels. Fireboxes, crankshaft bearings and crank webs could all be made wider if more space was available, he correctly reasoned, but such points had been raised before and 1898 was too late to change matters.[16] Why then did Johnson raise the matter of gauge when there was no possibility of doing anything about it? Maybe he considered it appropriate to mention that he, together with his fellow Locomotive Superintendents, were saddled with a restriction without which greater advances might have been possible. The astute person will always pre-empt criticism of himself or his profession by making excuses first. Johnson seems to have been telling his fellow engineers, most of whom where not concerned with the railways, what difficulties the locomotive designer faced. Maybe this gives an indication of his character.

During that Presidential year, Johnson took a more active part in the discussion of papers than he normally did; however, this was to be expected, as the President would generally take the chair at such meetings. Invited by its President, the Institution held its summer meeting in Derby with several visits to places of interest arranged to supplement the papers which were presented. Naturally, the Midland Railway workshops were high on the list of locations worth visiting. Deeley was put in charge of organizing the events and seems to have done so admirably.

Several papers were read during that summer meeting and a number had a Midland flavour. One of these was by Leonard Archbutt and concerned the water softening process devised by himself and R. M. Deeley. This process had been introduced by Johnson in 1892 and had proved very effective in reducing boiler scale. Johnson himself considered the question of whether it was better to clean a boiler mechanically or soften the water, and he mentioned that John Ramsbottom held firmly to the former view, being of the opinion it was better to let a boiler get dirty and then take tubes out to allow cleaning when necessary. Johnson, however, preferred water softening except in districts with high quality water.[17]

In a paper during the same session dealing with aluminium, a relatively new material as far as railway engineering was concerned, Johnson showed that he was open minded on innovative ideas and mentioned that by adding a small amount of aluminium to steel it was possible to make good cast-steel wheels. He added that three years earlier he would not have dared using steel castings for wheels, but at that time he had the utmost confidence and all new engines were then being fitted with that type of wheel.[18]

Later that year, W. G. Peet, head of the locomotive testing department at Derby, presented a paper on materials testing, Johnson having requested him to do so because of the interest raised by the visit of the 'Mechanicals' to Derby Works. The paper itself illustrated how thoroughly the Midland's locomotive department tested its materials before any use was made of them.[19] Locomotive manufacture was not simply a case of producing fine-looking machines — a great deal of scientific thought went into their construction. Johnson's engines were stylish, but they also worked, and worked well, and that was due to sound engineering under the direction of a leader who knew about engineering as well as artistry.

During the Institution of Civil Engineers' engineering conference of 1897, Johnson presented a short paper on piston valves which was detailed in content but only reported on briefly in the Institution's published papers. Johnson was an early advocate of piston valves for locomotives, having being convinced of their usefulness by considering the frictional losses involved with slide valves. His main concern with their use was during periods of drifting with steam shut off, as he correctly considered that their pumping action would draw in ash and grit from the smokebox. In order to avoid this problem, an anti-vacuum valve was designed to accompany the piston valve; this operated automatically when the regulator was closed, allowing a mixture of air and steam into the steam chest. Johnson's piston valve was sealed by means of a gun-metal ring made in three segments which was forced against the valve chest liner by means of steam pressure, but would fall away when the steam was shut off. This minimized wear and reduced power losses because there was less friction when coasting.[20]

In replying to questions, Johnson stated that he had slide- and piston-valved engines of the same type in operation doing similar work, and the results indicated that the piston type was preferable. In six-month period, eight piston-valved engines ran 36,559 miles with an average coal consumption of 29 lbs per mile, whilst 13 slide-valved engines of the same type running the same sort of mileage burned coal at the rate of 30.04 lbs per mile. He added that drivers preferred piston-valved engines and emphasized his opinion that frictional losses, and hence loadings on eccentrics and linkages, were considerably reduced with piston valves.[21]

During the Johnson era many innovative ideas came from Derby and he must have been responsible for some of these. Unlike some other chiefs, Johnson took out very few patents although the output from Midland workshops show that he was keen on development. Staff were encouraged to develop ideas and the testing department thrived under him. People working there were, obviously, responsible, but Johnson had to select those individuals in the first place. Design for a new pattern of firebox door which allowed easier replacement was attributed to him by *The Engineer*[22] and that same journal also gave him credit for introducing the combined steam and vacuum brake.[23] As Locomotive Superintendent, S. W. Johnson was in overall control and so received much of the credit for the work of other people but, as in all positions of responsibility, he also took the blame for mistakes. Whilst the ideas may not always have been his, he could certainly see which were good and worth pursuing and which would simply be a waste of time. He only adopted compounding after much thought, and that proved to be a successful venture; the good engineer knows when to proceed and when to wait.

The expansion in services and increased train loadings of the late 1890s, which subse-

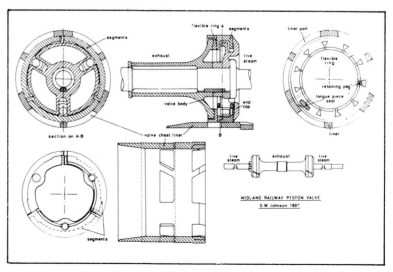

Johnson's piston valve arrangement.

quently resulted in the design of the compounds, produced an immediate locomotive shortage. Although Johnson had greatly extended locomotive construction and repair facilities at Derby since he took over from Kirtley, it was evidently still insufficient to meet demand. The Midland tended to favour smaller and more frequent trains in those days, and a large number of relatively low-powered engines was considered to be suitable for all purposes. Johnson simply provided the locomotives and kept them running — he did not make policy over traffic. When the traffic demands increased, the works could not build new, more powerful, locomotives quickly enough, and still had to repair a large number of the small machines. With strikes preventing British private builders from supplying locomotives in the desired time, America provided the only alternative. The Baldwin Locomotive Works of Philadelphia and the Schenectady Locomotive Works, New York, were awarded contracts for locomotives, 30 from the former and 10 from the latter. These were standard 2–6–0 designs of the companies concerned, but Johnson ordered that a number of Midland features should be fitted. He stipulated that fireboxes, firebox stays and tubes should be of copper whilst wheel centres had to be of steel. Injectors, steam sanding and brake gear also had to comply with Midland practice[24]. What he thought about having to order these locomotives from overseas is unknown, but there was no other choice — they were desperately needed and Derby could not build them.

The Midland was not alone in this for the Great Central and Great Northern Railways had to adopt similar tactics. Webb on the L&NWR did not have to suffer this indignity for Crewe Works was able to meet any demand despite the new traffic regulations and allegations that his compounds could not perform. It is certain that he would have fought vigorously to prevent locomotive orders going away from Crewe. Johnson was trapped by the Midland Railway Board, but Webb never allowed himself to be dictated to — he always took the initiative. However, there was not the reserve capacity at Derby which so characterized Crewe during the Webb era.

Johnson was well respected in the engineering world and would act as consultant to other railways when asked. For the assistance he gave to the Egyptian government on railway matters, the Khedive of Egypt made hime a commander of the Imperial Order of Mehjidieh and also an officer of the Order of Osmanieh. He was appointed a magistrate for the city of Nottingham in 1895 and also served as an Income Tax Commissioner[25].

With the formation of the Association of Railway Locomotive Engineers in 1890, Johnson became its first Chairman and he continued to serve that organization with enthusiasm until he retired, becoming its President in 1895. His standing in the railway engineering world was very high and he was considered as something of an elder statesman by most members of that organization. He had, after all, been in charge of the locomotive department of a major railway for some 16 years when the Association was formed.

As we have seen Johnson was rather a reserved man in engineering matters and did not actively seek publicity. Because he did not present many papers it is easy to overlook his achievements in the experimental field. Credit for much of the work has rightly gone to Deeley, but it was the Locomotive Superintendent who directed matters and had to justify the expenditure; no work would be carried out unless it was necessary and he authorized it. During the discussion of Webb's paper on firebox stays, Johnson waded in with details of a large number of experiments he had ordered into copper alloy for stays. Figures were presented which indicated how extensive the testing had been and Johnson then went on to give details of the problems he had faced, especially with higher steam pressures employed in the newer, more powerful locomotives[26].

He also spoke when Webb's paper, 'Permanent Way', was discussed at the Institution of Civil Engineers' engineering conference in 1897, but was rather disparaging about the merits of the joint chair which was described. Johnson recalled a similar arrangement being tried by the Great Northern Railway and described the problems of keeping the chairs firmly attached to the sleepers.[27]

Despite the fact that the Midland's main traffic was the haulage of coal, and that there was an abundant and inexpensive supply of that fuel close at hand, Johnson fitted one of his engines with an oil-burning apparatus. According to J. A. F. Aspinall, the system worked remarkably well, but because of the plentiful coal supply it became Midland policy not to encourage oil burning[28]. Johnson obviously had an eye on the futre and was prepared to consider how steam locomotive operation might be improved.

Johnson retired at the end of December 1903 after serving the Midland for 30 years. During the ensuing years he remained clear of any involvement in railway or public matters; in fact, he took little part in public life at any time. Johnson died on 14 January 1912, at the age of 80 years, following a short illness. He was survived by five daughters and a son, his wife having been killed the year previously in a carriage accident. The single son, John, had been Locomotive Superintendent of the Great North of Scotland railway in the years 1890-4.

Richard Mountford Deeley

When Johnson decided to retire, the Directors were faced with choosing a successor; however, they were not exactly experienced in the matter, for in the company's 60 year history to that date only two people had occupied the post of Locomotive Superintendent. There had been an heir apparent for some time, R. M. Deeley, but rumours spread during the spring of 1903 that Deeley's deputy, Cecil W. Paget, would take the honour. Paget had strong family connections with the Midland Railway, his father, Sir

Richard Mountford Deeley.

Ernest Paget, being Chairman, but it would be grossly unfair to consider the nepotism was responsible for C. W. Paget's advancement. As it turned out, the rumours were just remours and Deeley was appointed Locomotive Superintendent; C. W. Paget was a very well qualified engineer in his own right, but as he never became Locomotive Superintendent or CME his career forms no part of this book.

R. M. Deeley was born in Chester on 24 October 1855 and, following completion of his formal education at Chester Cathedral Grammar School, he decided that the engineering profession was for him. In 1873 he became a pupil of Edward B. Ellington, Managing Director of the Chester firm, Johnson and Ellington, later to become the Hydraulic Engineering Company. A year later Deeley went to Messrs Brotherhood and Hardingham, Patentees of the Brotherhood three-cylinder hydraulic engine, the manufacturing rights to which had been secured by Johnson and Ellington. Railway work then seemed to offer the most attraction, and Deeley became a pupil of S. W. Johnson at Derby in 1875.

At Derby all work proved most interesting, and he obtained experience in most of the shops, but developed a special liking for work involving experiment. Because of his aptitude for this, in 1880, when only 25 years old, he was appointed to head the experimental section[29].

Experimental work came under the drawing office, but Deeley was in charge of experimentation and carried out investigations into the power development of existing locomotives. These were part of a plan aimed at increasing the power and speed of newer designs within the weight restrictions imposed by the Civil Engineer. The small engine policy which afflicted the Midland throughout its entire existence and caused chaos for the LMS in its early years was not dreamed up by a series of obsessed Locomotive Superintendents — these men simply worked within the limits imposed upon them. Midland lines had a low axle loading limit, by comparison with other British railways, which imposed weight restrictions. Other factors such as turntables and track curvature restricted the overall length of locomotives. The Directors had it within their control to change matters, but for their own reasons decided not to do anything even when it became obvious that there were problems. The locomotive engineers had to work within those restrictions, and in many cases provided very good quality machines under the circumstances.

It was during his time in the testing section that Deeley would have encountered Leonard Archbutt, subsequently the Chief Chemist, and the pair must have become close friends as well as working colleagues. They collaborated on a number of ventures over the years, many of which were highly successful. An early one was the system for chemically softening and purifying water used for locomotives. A patent on the process was taken out, and in 1892 a plant was installed at Derby for treating water taken from the River Derwent for locomotive purposes. In addition to that, several other plants were installed on the Midland system as well as at industrial sites in Britain and abroad. Archbutt's Institution of Mechanical Engineers paper of 1898 explained the chemical reactions involved in the process and gave details of the effects of scale on a boiler.[30]

During 1890, Deeley and Archbutt published a two-part article in *The Engineer* entitled 'The Thermodynamics of the Automatic Vacuum Brake'. This followed a series of detailed experiments, and argued that a vacuum brake was a dry brake and that any water, or ice, found in the system did not emanate from outside but was due to leakage from the steam ejector. At the time there was considerable discussion on the subject because a number of vacuum brake systems had failed due to ice. Tests had proved the theory that

any water leaking into a vacuum would be immediately vapourized and removed by means of the ejector or pump — no free water could exist. Despite the detailed case presented in the two articles, a number of people were not convinced and would only believe that water from outside would leak into the vacuum pipe and form ice during frosty weather.

This is no place to repeat the arguments, as any interested individual may read the correspondence in that journal which was carried on in a very heated manner over many weeks.[31] Notable amongst the opposition was Clement E. Stretton, whilst many others sprang to the defence of the Midland pair. There was no final capitulation by either party and the matter just died a natural death as such correspondence is apt to do. Deeley and Archbutt had their facts correct and could prove matters by careful experiment, while their opponents based their case on the fact that water, or ice, found in vacuum brake systems must have leaked in from outside because there was no other explanation. They could not, however, see the scientific analysis that at reduced pressure any water would vapourize and be extracted by the ejector. It was a case of a little knowledge not being sufficient to understand the whole case.

Oils and lubrication were of special interest to Deeley and again he collaborated with Archbutt on a number of occasions. Most notable of these was with respect to the book *Lubrication and Lubricants*, first published in 1900 and subse-

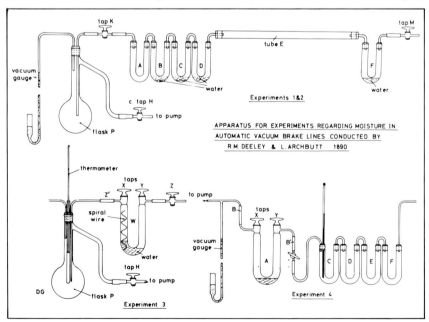

The Deeley-Archbutt apparatus for conducting experiments on moisture in vacuum brake lines.

quently running to four editions.[32] Deeley had long been interested in lubrication from a scientific as well as a practical point of view, and his work in this field continued long after he left Midland employ. It may be difficult for the modern railway enthusiast to appreciate, but it was necessary for engineers of this period to understand the problems, and hopefully the solutions, before they could even start asking others to produce drawings of locomotives.

Over a number of years Deeley provided several articles on lubrication for publication in *The Engineer*. These were very mathematical and show a scientific understanding of the subject rather than just an engineering appreciation. In 1896, in conjunction with C. E. Wolff, he described the theory of lubrication between plain paralleled surfaces,[33] and the following year other aspects concerned with oils including viscous flow in capillary tubes[34] and surface tension of lubricants.[35] These items may not appear important to the railway enthusiast, but they are vital to the engineer. However, as far as the steam locomotive is concerned lubrication is more hit and miss than pure theory.

In 1921 Deeley devised a machine for testing the lubricating qualities of different oils and used this to carry out many experiments. This machine, the experiments and the problems of friction were also described in *The Engineer*.[36] The following year an article appeared concerning static friction and the associated problem of lubrication.[37] Over the years Deeley had produced papers on friction and lubrication for presentating to many societies and these gave him a well-deserved reputation in the subject. There were however, more strings to his bow than that of lubricants, for in 1914 he produced an article for *The Engineer*, on the theory of the radiator. Again this may not seem important in locomotive terms but the article illustrates Deeley's thorough understanding of engineering in general, for it dealt not only with heat transfer but also fluid flows and ventilation.[38]

Deeley did, in fact, have many interests and it seems certain that his talents were wasted by the Midland Railway. Had they been used more effectively by higher management, the railway would have been better equipped as far as locomotives and other engineering plant were concerned. After retirement from the railway, his active mind would not allow him to settle, but at the age of 54 years he was still a relatively young man. He was a Fellow of the Geological Society and had an interest in meteorology, actually writing a book on the subject in 1935. His final publication, entitled *A*

Geneological History of Montfortsur-Risle and Deeley of Halesowen, was published in 1941 and was a history of part of his family. Unfortunately it contained nothing about his life — an autobiography would have been more interesting!

Following his spell in the testing department, Deeley was appointed Inspector of Locomotives, which included responsibility for the inspection of all materials supplied to Derby Works. Additional responsibilities were added over the years including inspection of boilers and all electrical plant on the Midland system. Throughout his time in the testing department, which lasted from 1893 to 1902, Deeley retained his interest in experimental matters as is witnessed by the articles he produced during that period.[39]

When John Lane resigned his position as Works Manager in January 1902, Deeley was appointed to take charge of that establishment which employed some 4,000 men at that time. Within months, further responsibilities came his way when he was charged with supervision of the electrical engineering section as well as the electric lighting and power departments. When Johnson gave notice of his wish to retire, the Directors looked around for a replacement and must have quickly decided that Deeley was their man. He was appointed Assistant Locomotive Superintendent in July 1903 and took over from Johnson completely the following January.[40]

Deeley had been involved with the Johnson compounds from the start and held strong views on their use and development. Although he had been sceptical about the benefits of compound locomotives, he evidently changed his mind when faced with the reality that the Midland Directors were demanding far more powerful locomotives but were not prepared to sanction track improvements to allow for increased axle loading. Deeley did much to improve the basic Johnson compound machine following the introduction of the initial five locomotives. A great many experiments were conducted in order to find any defects in the basic design of the first batch, and the results of these tests were used in order to make improvements. The extent of the testing may be judged from the account published in *Engineering* during February and March 1903 which details the trials conducted on locomotive No 2631, subsequently renumbered 1000, on the line between Leeds and Carlisle during October 1902.[41]

Although Johnson was still Locomotive Superintendent, it is fairly certain that Deeley played a major part in those tests. Many indicator diagrams were taken and these allowed engine power to be calculated at particular speeds. By

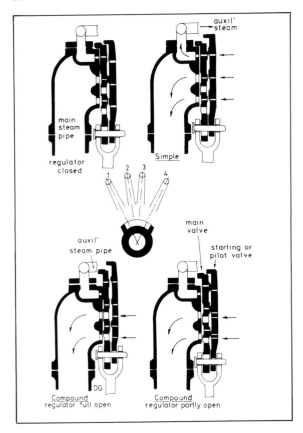

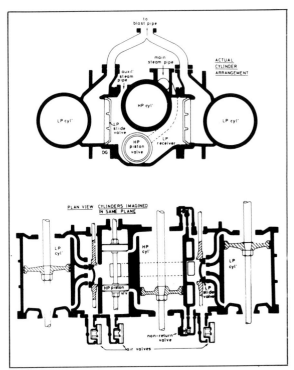

Above *Cylinder arrangements for the Johnson-Deeley compound.*

Left *The Deeley compound regulator.*

averaging a large number of such diagrams, a graph was produced relating power to speed. This showed that the maximum power of 1,000 horsepower (746 kw) could be developed at 42 mph (67 km/h).

Deeley was, in general, happy with the compounds, but considered that they could be made less complicated in order to allow for easier operation. A major innovation was his patented regulator which allowed high-pressure steam to be sent directly to the low-pressure cylinders for starting rather than travelling by way of an automatic regulating valve positioned on the right-hand side of the smokebox. This certainly made for easier control by the driver, for all he had to do was to move the regulator handle to certain positions for operating the locomotive as a simple or as a compound. When operating as a simple, for starting or on heavy gradients, full boiler pressure would be sent to the low-pressure cylinders and an equal pressure allowed at each side of the high-pressure piston in order to avoid any breaking effect. That device certainly made for easier driving of the 40 compounds Deeley built.

With the original five Johnson compounds, Deeley had found that starting under certain circumstances could be difficult unless there were equalizing valves provided which allowed for a pressure balance on either side of the HP piston.[42] These were fitted to the Johnson compounds and Deeley must have carried out these tests in order to see what would happen if they were not present; he made certain that they were retained for his compounds. Extensive trials were carried out in order to compare the compound with the '700' Class simple engines. These were not fair tests as the classes were not really equivalent due to differences in boiler pressure, grate area and, naturally, cylinder dimensions. They did, however, allow Deeley to obtain favourable results for the compounds, which was probably the intention. Over a long period, fuel consumption, distances and loads were measured allowing reasonable average figures to be obtained. The total ton mileage for the compounds was nearly 5,000,000, and that for the simples almost 3,000,000, so nobody could accuse Deeley of speculation. Compound coal consumption amounted to 37.5 lbs per mile and 0.129 lbs per ton mile, whilst, simples produced figures of 39.2 lbs per mile and 0.139 lbs per ton mile.

This information was actually given by Deeley in December 1909, the year he retired, and the figures indicate a coal consumption in favour of the compound amounting to 7.75 per cent. At the same time, Deeley said that tests with two engines in good condition showed the compound to be more economical by about 14 per cent. The difference he attributed to leakage losses from the compounds during long-term tests. The compounds operated at a boiler pressure of 220 psi as opposed to the simples' 180 psi, so increased leakage might be expected when the compounds were in a slightly run-down condition. Long-term consumption had included lighting up and shunting, but the short-term tests were only carried out on runs.

At the end of the article Deeley stated that he had no hesitation in saying that compounds did better work than the simples and that their fuel economy more than paid for their higher initial cost. It was his final sentence which was, perhaps, more revealing, for he had added, 'By increasing the heating surface of the boiler, and therefore the weight of the engine, greater economy of fuel could have been obtained, but such a plan was not admissible'.[43] Evidently Deeley hd intentions of building larger and more powerful loco-motives, but other authorities would not allow the increased weight or axle loading; that must have

been the Civil Engineer's department, and the Board was not prepared to sanction expenditure on track improvements. It must have been rather frustrating to work under such restrictions which were imposed for economic rather than safety or practical reasons, and even more annoying when one believed, as Deeley did, that by means of larg-er locomotives even greater economies might be obtained.

During his time as Locomotive Superintendent, Deeley did try to work within those restrictions whilst still attempting to produce more powerful engines. Drawing offices were regularly asked to produce designs for new loco-motives and most never got further than the basic outline stage for various reasons, not least being that of cost; how-ever, they were not necessarily rejected by higher authority, as the Locomotive Superintendent himself might have halted a project because it no longer fitted his ideas.

A locomotive diagram of 1906 illustrates Deeley's novel approach to higher power but low axle loading. Obviously the drawing office would have been responsible for production of the dia-gram, but the ingenuity of the solution suggests that the fertile mind of Deeley was behind it. Compounds had an axle loading in excess of 19 tons, but that of the proposed locomotive was below this figure. The four-cylinder compound arrangement would certainly have had power and steam, for its boiler had the same heating and grate area as the Deeley compounds. Adhesion

Deeley's proposed 2-4-4-2 compound.

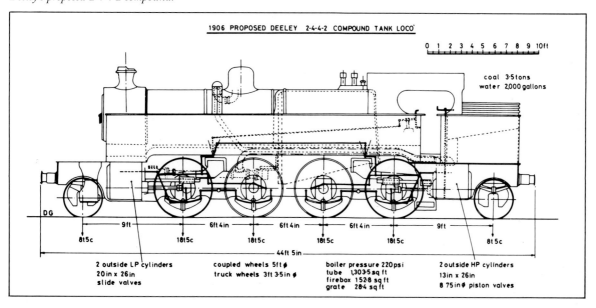

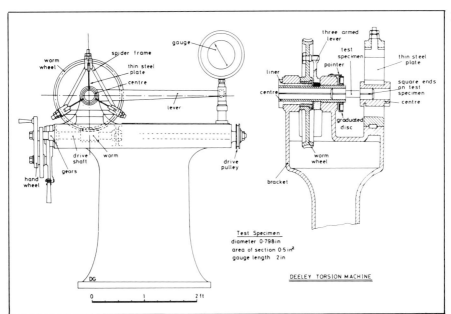

Left *Deeley's design for a torsion testing machine.*

Left *Deeley's design for a torsion testing machine.*

Below right *Proposed Deeley compound 4-6-0.*

would have been good because the locomotive was of a tank arrangement, and tractive effort would have been high due to the 5 ft diameter driving wheels. Compensating levers connected the springing on each pair of coupled driving wheels and that should have allowed for imperfections in the Midland track. As a goods engine for the coal traffic it would have been ideal and economical. However, it was just one of the schemes which failed to get beyond the starting post due to outside interference.[44]

As an inventor Deeley would turn his hand to any matter which required attention. Some examples of his expertise have already been mentioned, but his interest in testing and experimentation resulted in a number of items being devised for use in the testing room. One such piece of equipment to attract widespread interest was his torsion testing machine. Standard tensile, compressive and shear tests were carried out on any materials used in the works, but at the turn of the century there was no machine readily available for satisfactorily testing the torsional strength of metals. Deeley's piece of equipment used test speciments with square ends which were held in hollow centres. One of these was kept still and free from frictional effects by means of a spider frame, but the other end was twisted by its centre. The value of torque applied could be read from a gauge which employed rollers for operating the pointer in order to eliminate friction. This piece of manually operated equipment was sim-

ple, effective and, most important, accurate.[45] Whilst few railway enthusiasts would give such a piece of equipment a second glance compared with a locomotive, it was of great importance in obtaining knowledge so that locomotives sould be properly designed and built.

Like other locomotive engineers, Deeley carried out experiments in order to determine train resistance and some of these tests took place whilst Johnson was still Locomotive Superintendent. Results seem to have been for internal use only and were not published directly, but Deeley did comment on them in an 1898 letter to the editor of *The Engineer*, in which he alludes to 'many hundreds of experiments I have made', but gives no indication as to when, where, or with what locomotives. Results were given of some experiments with passenger trains with figures indicating train weight, speed, tractive effort and mean cylinder pressure. Unfortunately no mention was made as to how train resistance was determined, as the Midland did not have its own dynamometer car. Results were very detailed and it is possible that Deeley derived values from indicated power making allowance for losses in the cylinders, valve gears and linkages. Gradients were also measured and forces due to these determined.[46]

The formula for train resistance derived by Deeley was very close to that determined by Aspinall from his very extensive tests a few years later:

$$R = 3 + \frac{V^2}{290}$$

where R is resistance in lbs per ton
V is speed in miles per hour

Deeley was very much a progressive engineer and was always looking for ways in which to improve performance. He quickly took to the idea of superheating but was thwarted by a penny-pinching management which was reluctant to part with money for the payment of royalties. The Locomotive Superintendent wanted to fit superheaters to the compounds he had built after the Johnson machines had proved their worth, but the Board would only sanction discussions with representatives of the Schmidt company. A royalty request of £30 for each of the 40 compounds was considered to be too high, and Deeley had to have them built as saturated engines. For the sake of £1,200 the Midland Railway Directors cost their shareholders much more over the succeeding years due to additional coal consumption[47] — the stupidity of not listening to the man paid to know what was best in engineering terms was quite amazing, and the situation still exists to a great extent when accountants who can only see the next balance sheet are allowed to rule companies.

Deeley was an exceptional engineer who seemed to know instinctively the best engineering line to follow, but nobody listened to engineering sense — it was management ideas and financial control which dominated. Superheating was raised again during 1909, but again fell on deaf ears. By the time Deeley had actually resigned, no longer able to stand the impositions of higher management. Rather than allow its Locomotive Superintendent to run his own department, the Midland Board sought to divide and rule. Small-minded individuals seemed to be wedded to a small locomotive policy and were unwilling to sanction any diversion from that, no matter what the logic. Deeley had to accept that the Board had control, but he still did his best to ensure that an effective fleet of locomotives existed. He encouraged design of larger and more powerful locomotives but these got no further than the diagram stage, the Board not allowing them to proceed because it considered that development costs were too high. One 1907 proposal was for a 4–6–0 compound which would certainly have removed many of the Midland's traction problems, but it was not to be.

Matters worsened in 1908 when Deeley was told to take over development work on the Paget sleeve-valve locomotive upon which construction had been started at Paget's own expense. When he ran out of funds the Midland took over the project, but it is unlikely that anybody else would have been treated so well unless they also had family in high places. Certainly double standards were applied, for although the Paget locomotive was innovative it was much too complex for the Midland and also too heavy for general use.

Guy Granet became General Manager in 1906 and began immediately to impose his style on the railway. This is not the place to go into the details of his style or his policies, which were aimed at increasing the railway's profits and so could be considered as justified, but brief mention has to be made regarding his influence on the engineering side. Cecil Paget suggested that there should be a General Superintendent who would be responsible for all aspects of traffic operations. This was agreed and Paget was given the job. Such a post was not a bad thing but the way in which the decisions effected locomotive use was. Paget devised a scheme for locomotive classification, and rules were drawn up regarding the use of particular classes on trains of given size. These load restrictions caused problems, as they had with similar rules on the LNWR, because no account was taken of a locomotive's condition. Double-heading became the norm for many trains even through a single locomotive in good condition could have handled the load.

Deeley had no alternative but to comply with these restrictions, but working under such circumstances for this brilliant and imaginative engineer must have been very frustrating. The fact that his former subordinate, Paget, was instrumental in bringing about these changes must have made life particularly irritating. Despite

DEELEY 4-6-0 COMPOUND

these conditions, Deeley strove hard to raise Midland locomotive standards, but the policies of Granet and Paget were aimed at mediocrity not superiority. His problems serve to illustrate only too well that the Locomotive Superintendent was a servant of the company and had to do as he was told. Though some may have exercised influence over higher management, they were few and far between; most CMEs had to fight for money in order to keep their departments functioning. That fight was a losing one with a short-sighted management.

In the end Deeley admitted defeat and resigned. He left the Midland at the end of 1909 and had nothing else to do with locomotives, work as a consultant and on topics of his own choosing occupying the years following retirement. That life must have suited him for he lived to a ripe old age, his death occurring on 19 June 1944 during his 90th year. As an engineer he has been overlooked and even blamed for the poor state of Midland locomotive affairs — but for that he was not responsible.

Henry Fowler

Deeley's resignation did not cause any major

problems regarding a successor, even though it had been unexpected. There appeared to be a concerted effort by management to take charge of all matters, leaving the departmental heads with less responsibility than they had previously enjoyed. Deeley had been unwilling to work under such conditions, but his successor would have to and it has been suggested that Henry Fowler was something of a subservient individual who would do as he was told. There is no real evidence to support that premise apart from that fact that Fowler did take the job when Deeley resigned and the Midland's small locomotive policy continued during his period in office. In effect, Fowler did try to break free of that policy and introduce larger machines, but financial constraints and the lack of suitable track imposed restrictions over which he also had no control.

The other major accusation aimed at Fowler was that he did not design locomotives. If the word 'design' is used to imply sitting at a drawing board and producing drawings of new locomotives, then the claim is certainly true — he was much too busy for that, as were all CMEs. In fact, management policy actually stifled design for it did not encourage the production of new locomotives by making money available, and track restrictions meant that the basic 0–6–0 wheel arrangement for goods engines were generally sufficient. The experienced drawing office team under the control of James Edward Anderson, the Chief Draughtsman, was well able to deal with any minor changes in design which were required with Fowler simply having to indicate what was wanted.

From the time he took control of the locomotive department on 1 January 1910 until the Midland ceased to exist with the 1923 grouping, Fowler did not need to introduce many new designs for Midland lines. He may have wanted to do so; indeed, the number of schemes worked out suggest that many plans were afoot, but circumstances did not allow for any major introductions. However, when the restrictions imposed on him were eased, some very good designs were produced. The 2–8–0 freight locomotives designed and built for operation on the Somerset & Dorset Railway are a major change from traditional Derby practice although certain standard parts, like the boiler, were incorporated. The strange thing is that despite the success of these locomotives from their introduction in 1914, no attempt was made to make use of similar designs on Midland lines. This was certainly no fault of Fowler and the locomotive department — the running department was simply quite content to

Below left *Henry Fowler.*

Right *A typical long-lived Midland 0–6–0 design. Introduced by Johnson in 1885, it was rebuilt by Fowler from 1916 onwards with a Belpaire firebox, and became '3F' No 43751 in BR days.* (D. K. Jones collection)

stick with the basic 0–6–0 type.

It is the opinion of Roland C. Bond, who was an apprentice and pupil under Fowler, that Anderson was the guiding hand behind locomotive design and the CME obviously trusted his Chief Draughtsman.[48] Nonetheless, Fowler thoroughly understood locomotives and was also concerned about improvements in operation such as superheating, in materials for construction and in the organization for manufacture and repair. As a complete engineer Fowler was certainly in a class apart from most other heads of railway locomotive departments who let their departments decay whilst introducing new locomotives. His major problem lay not in lack of talent but in a misguided higher management.

Locomotive design was but a small part of the Chief Mechanical Engineer's work, however, and Fowler indulged himself in all aspects of his job. By nature he appears to have been what is now called a 'workaholic', and once said to C. S. Lake that he was not aware of having any enemy but the clock.[49] There is a story that he would arrange meetings with junior staff whilst walking from his Derby office to catch a train to London, and whilst on that journey would dictate letters to his clerk.[50] These tales may be apocryphal but serve to indicate the sort of man he was.

Henry Fowler was born at Evesham on 29 July 1870 and spent six years at Evesham Grammar School before progressing to the Mason Science College, Birmingham, in 1885. Two years later he obtained an apprenticeship at Horwich under J. A. F. Aspinall and upon completion of that training in 1891 he was appointed assistant to George Hughes in the testing department. Natural interest allowed him to progress rapidly, for he never appeared content with knowledge of only one aspect of engineering — everything interested him. Education also continued at the Horwich Mechanics' Institute where, in 1891, he gained the first Whitworth Exhibition to be awarded to any member of the Institute. It can be difficult to appreciate today, with an education system geared to full-time degree courses, that people studying then did so in the evening after a full day at work. To obtain such high award was no mean achievement. Fowler not only gained from the Institute but he put something back, for he later taught classes there.[51]

Fowler always took a keen interest in ensuring that pupils and apprentices received the correct training and studied seriously. Roland Bond tells of his experiences at Derby, where Fowler would gather all pupils and apprentices together once each year in order to deliver a pep talk on how privileged they were in being allowed to work in his department. He also received regular reports from various workshops and technical colleges on the progress of individuals and would each year sent a report to their parents.[52] This may not appear unusual, but it was — few Locomotive Superintendents took any real interest in apprentices or pupils, although they did take the premiums.

When Hughes moved on, Fowler took over as chief of the testing department and was also appointed Gas Engineer. At the time considerable use was made of gas for the illumination of carriages, workshops and stations, so the post was one of some responsibility. Fowler certainly took it seriously and made a thorough study of gas generation, detailed enough to enable him to present a paper connected with the subject to the Institution of Civil Engineers in 1898.[53] Entitled 'Calcium Carbide and Acetylene', the paper covered the subject in considerable detail, showing the author's knowledge and understanding of what was essentially a chemical topic. The paper was considered to be so good that Fowler was awarded a Telford Premium. This was not the first award Fowler had been given for a technical paper, for a few years earlier he had obtained a Miller prize as a student for a paper on 'The Testing and Inspection of Plates'.[54]

In 1900 Fowler was appointed as Gas Engineer on the Midland Railway, a post similar to that he had held at Horwich. Why he decided to leave the L&YR is not known, but he must have felt that the chances of promotion to high office were slim, Hoy having only just been appointed CME and George Hughes being a relatively young second-in-command. After five years with the Midland, Fowler became Assistant Works Manager at Derby and two years later was promoted to the position of Works Manager. From this it is clear that his potential had been recognized by those in authority. Although there was no distinct promotional system on the Midland, nor any railway for that matter, the post of Works Manager at Derby was as close as could be considered to 'CME-in-waiting'. It is however, unlikely that anybody envisaged that Deeley would resign so quickly, leaving Fowler as the logical successor. Thus in January 1910 Henry Fowler became Chief Mechanical Engineer of the Midland Railway.[55]

During his time in the works, Fowler had demonstrated his considerable abilities as a 'works man', ensuring that repairs were carried out effectively and efficiently. He made a trip to America in 1907 and gained much valuable knowledge from visits to several railways there.[56] He was thus able to ensure that, within the restrictions imposed by the Board, the best locomotives were available for the services envisaged. Being available was not just a case of constructing locomotives — it was also keeping them at work, and as far as Fowler was concerned that had priority. There was little opportunity for new construction anyway, due to the Board's restrictions. In a paper read before the Institute of Transport in 1929, his opening remarks made those views crystal clear. 'Probably the most important work done on the mechanical engineering side of a railway is the maintenance of locomotive stock in an efficient condition'.[57] He went on to say that one of the

essentials for rapid and economic repair was the standardization of renewable parts, including the boiler. He also considered that standardization resulted in reduced stocks of spares being kept, but parts were always available and there were benefits to be gained from mass production.

Boilers came in for particular attention; these Fowler considered to be the most important part of any locomotive and the provision of spare boilers was the best means of avoiding many repair bottlenecks. During the final 15 years of the Midland Railway, 13 of which were under Fowler, the number of boiler types had been reduced to seven standard units, and these were fitted to 2,841 of the 3,019 locomotives owned by the railway. Fowler loved boilers and, according to C. S. Lake, would almost habitually dive inside any which had been stripped down for inspection or repair! He quotes an incident which occurred when he was on a visit to Kentish Town locomotive depot. The District Superintendent told Lake that Fowler was due that morning, and when he arrived he would quickly don a boiler suit and dive into the firebox of the boiler under inspection. True to prediction, Fowler did just that, but insisted that Lake join him. Within the confined space Fowler proceeded to instruct the journalist on boiler construction and had him assist in hammer-testing stays. When he had finished, the portly CME extricated himself with the ease of an experienced boilermaker, whilst Lake struggled out of the firebox door. The comment of a shed mechanic confirmed Lake's view that Fowler was great on boilers.[58]

The views Fowler expressed to the Institute of Transport were based upon years of experience during peacetime and wartime manufacturing and they were extremely valid as far as railway production and repair was concerned. He believed that the key to satisfactory locomotive repair was to have what you want, where you want it and when you want it, but everything had to be carefully organized with floor space being kept clear — 'the floor is not a store'. A concluding remark following discussion of the paper illustrates well his views: 'Some people could not see an empty engine pit without wanting to place an engine on it, but the idea should be if one saw an engine on a pit to endeavour to take it off.'

Fowler's enthusiasm for effective maintenance and repair of locomotive stock was again the subject of his Presidential address to the Institution of Locomotive Engineers in 1913. In it he emphasized the importance of an efficient system for organizing repairs, but once more paid particular attention to the boiler. '. . . the boiler is the main factor in everything pertaining to the subject of this paper.'[59]

The diversity of Fowler's interest has often been used to denigrate him as a locomotive engineer, but the opposite is really true. His wide interest in engineering production and metallurgy helped the cause of locomotive engineering on the Midland and LMS railways. Throughout engineering in general, Henry Fowler was a well-respected figure whose opinions were much valued. In 1920 the Institution of Automobile Engineers elected him President and in proposing a vote of thanks for Fowler's Presidential address, Colonel R. E. Compton said of him: 'This is a man of character. Asked for a definition of character, I should say a man of character is a man who holds strong clear views and is not afraid of telling other people what those views are, and that is our President.'[60]

In the address Fowler expressed his opinions on engineering manufacture in general, and that wider view of the world seems to have irritated some railway enthusiasts and writers who believed, and perhaps still believe, that railway engineering existed in isolation. It is true that in the railway workshop conditions differed from other branches of engineering, but similar production, supply and labour problems existed. Management of any engineering organization has to be effective in order that the establishment be efficient, and in the complex railway works during the days of steam that was certainly true. Fowler was a good manager, and ensured that he had a good team around him thus freeing himself to deal with those tasks which particularly took his interest; that does not make him any less accomplished as an engineer. Fowler did, however, regret that as CME so much time was spent with committees and that prevented him from being closely involved in more practical matters on a regular basis: '. . . the saying that we are ceasing to be engineers and becoming labour administrators seems to be justified if some instances'. He believed that a stable workforce could be achieved if families were able to see where and how the breadwinner spent his working day, and to that end he encouraged family visits to workshops during holiday periods.[61]

Fowler involved himself with many engineering societies and organizations which aimed at promoting education. Although a very busy man, time could always be made available for these bodies in the form of papers, as well as membership of committees and councils. Apart from those organizations already mentioned, he became President of the Institution of Locomotive Inspectors and Foreman (1921), the Institute of Metals (1932), and the Institution of Mechanical Engineers (1927). Undoubtedly it was Presidency of the 'Mechanicals' which was the major honour, but the subject chosen for his address, metallurgy, again seems to antagonize many railway enthusiasts who feel that all such addresses by railway engineers must be about locomotives. At its basic level a locomotive is simply a collection of metal parts, and the correct choice of material is as important as the correct design of the parts. Proper choice of material allowed for increased boiler pressure, application of superheating and better design of bearings amongst many other matters connected with locomotive design.

Fowler enjoyed metallurgy, which was one of the subjects he had studied at Mason College, and

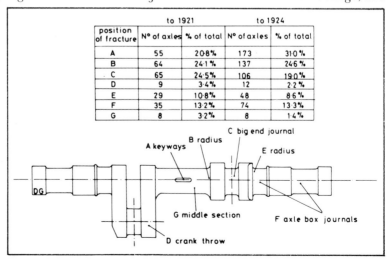

position of fracture	to 1921		to 1924	
	N° of axles	% of total	N° of axles	% of total
A	55	20·8%	173	31·0%
B	64	24·1%	137	24·6%
C	65	24·5%	106	19·0%
D	9	3·4%	12	2·2%
E	29	10·8%	48	8·6%
F	35	13·2%	74	13·3%
G	8	3·2%	8	1·4%

A keyways B radius C big end journal E radius
DG
G middle section F axle box journals
D crank throw

Fowler's analysis of cranked axle failures.

the classes he attended '. . . had instilled into me an appreciation and devotion to this side of our work which I am thankful to say I have never lost'.[62] Two papers read before the Institution of Locomotive Engineers indicate both Fowler's enthusiasm for the subject and the detail of the research he carried out. At the opening of his paper 'Steels for Locomotive Purposes' (1921), he expressed his regrets that greater emphasis was not placed upon the teaching of metallurgy: '. . . in the technical training which those entering upon locomotives work have to receive there is usually no room for this subject of steels, or if it has been touched upon it has only been done in a cursory manner'.[63] In that paper Fowler gave those present a concise but detailed look at steels as used for locomotives. He gave some information regarding steel locomotive axles, and followed with a paper on that subject before the same organization three years later. Nobody could ever say that Fowler did not give value.

That paper, 'Solid Crank Axles', concerned a subject which was not to the fore with most railways, for built-up cranked axles were usually the norm. However, it was more a paper concerning fatigue cracking than one advocating the use of solid crankshafts. Considerable information was presented regarding construction and materials together with analyses of failures, but Fowler did not claim credit for the experiments and investigation. 'I thank you very much for your vote of thanks, but you will appreciate that although I am the Author the work has been done by my colleagues'.[64] As CME, Fowler had authorized the investigations and the results would be used in reducing future failures by better design — but no CME had time to do everything himself. But a lesser man without his reputation as an engineer might not have been so willing to give the credit to the underlings who actually carried out the work.

Apart from metallurgy, another practical locomotive engineering area of interest to Fowler was superheating. He actually inherited Deeley's proposal to try superheating, but first he needed to obtain Board approval. This was given, and one of the '990' Class 4-4-0s was fitted with a Schmidt superheater for trials between London and Leeds. Details of the 1910 tests carried out with No 998 were provided by Fowler in his 1914 paper for the 'Civils'[65] and these indicated a coal saving of 23 per cent and a water saving of 22 per cent compared with a similar saturated engine. Such improvements had also been obtained from superheating elsewhere, but the Board was still reluctant to give support or money for widespread conversion to superheating, mainly because of the royalty payment to the Schmidt company. After protracted negotiations, agreement was reached on a package deal for the conversion of older engines, with the payment being made for the equipment also to include the royalty. In effect, the rebuilds were nothing less than new engines, but that accounting ruse saved a considerable sum of money.[66]

Fowler's paper on superheating not only gave details with respect to Midland application but included a history of the subject as far as British locomotive practice was concerned. That allowed other locomotive engineers their say, for reference was made to the two early protagonists, J. A. F. Aspinall and G. J. Churchward. Aspinall corrected Fowler on the point of the number of locomotives fitted with his type of superheater in 1898, and then went on to say how happy those on the L&YR were with the superheaters then being used. Churchward seems rather put out that Fowler referred to Swindon as employing a low degree of superheat, but he refused to give any actual superheat temperatures, simply mentioning temperature in the steam chest. Vincent Raven also took part in the discussion and related his experiences, but Fowler does not appear to have been intimidated by the gathering of such notable engineers. He presented his ideas on many matters connected with superheating including the use of dampers and the matter of materials and lubrication.

Although at that time superheating had become established practice amongst the more enlightened locomotive engineers, there was still a wide difference of opinion as to the detail. Fowler concerned himself with discussing this detail as well as the general principle, and the paper gives some indication as to his attitude to design. To a number of people, including C. J. B. Cooke, Fowler indulged too much in the provision of devices which, although assisting in the overall operation, required maintenance. As far as Fowler was concerned constructional complication seems to have been secondary to effectiveness and efficiency of performance.

During those early days of superheating, it was generally considered that when the regulator was closed the flow of combustion gases over the superheater elements had to be stopped, especially when the blower was operating, in order to prevent the elements from burning out. A damper box arrangement surrounding the flue tubes was frequently fitted and Fowler adopted the same idea. To operate the damper, steam from the superheater header would act on a piston

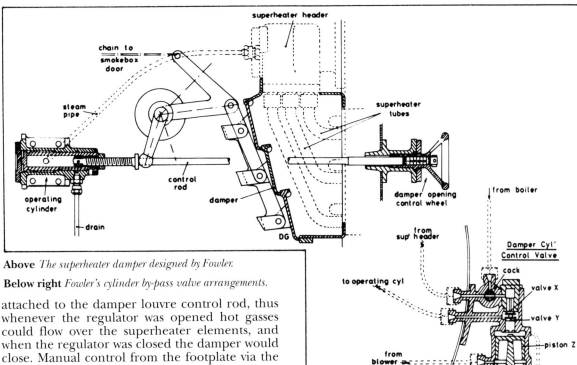

Above *The superheater damper designed by Fowler.*

Below right *Fowler's cylinder by-pass valve arrangements.*

attached to the damper louvre control rod, thus whenever the regulator was opened hot gasses could flow over the superheater elements, and when the regulator was closed the damper would close. Manual control from the footplate via the rod was also provided. Such arrangements prevented superheater elements from overheating, but these elements did cool down considerably when the damper was closed causing operational difficulties with goods and stopping trains.

Fowler devised an elegant solution to the problem which involved a neat control value arrangement which directed steam to the damper operating cylinder under particular circumstances. A three-way cock allowed the boiler or superheater header to be placed in communication with the control valve, and under normal circumstances for long-distance work the superheater header would have direct connection. With the regulator open, steam would pass through valve 'X' to the operating cylinder and keep the damper open; with the regulator closed, steam supply would be interrupted and the damper would close. For stopping trains, the three-way cock allowed direct boiler connection with the operating cylinder and the damper remained open at all times except when the blower was operated. In this case steam from the blower would lift piston 'Z' which in turn would lift valves 'Y' and 'X'. With 'Y' open, the operating cylinder would drain and the damper would close, thus preventing the draught induced by the blower from producing too high a temperature in the superheater elements.[67]

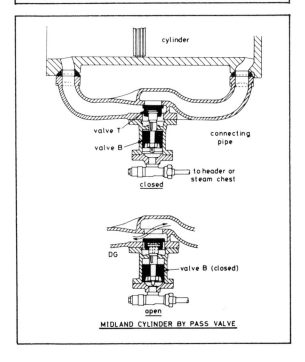

It may not have been to the liking of the simplistic Cooke, but the device allowed superheated steam to be effectively employed with goods and stopping passenger trains. Fowler's imaginative and agile mind must certainly have been involved in devising the system. He also made reference to metals and the problem of lubrication caused by the use of superheated steam, and then described several other devices which had to be fitted. Considerable use was made of cast iron, as Fowler had found this an ideal material for high temperatures and where rubbing was taking place, such as at a tail rod bushing, due to its self-lubricating properties. Because of lubrication problems caused by the use of superheated steam, it was usual to employ piston valves rather than slide valves. The latter, however, did have an advantage in that they lifted from the seat and so prevented pressure build-up on one side of the piston when running with steam shut off. If piston valves were used compression could occur, causing mechanical problems, and to avoid this Fowler provided a cylinder by-pass valve. With the engine operating normally, steam from the header forced valve 'T' on to its seat thus closing the connection between the ends of the cylinder. With steam shut off, valve 'T' opened allowing such connection and enabling the locomotive to coast easily.

Presentation of that paper marked the end of Fowler's initial period as CME of the Midland Railway, for the First World War broke out soon afterwards and his talents were required to assist in the war effort. The posts he held during that conflict illustrate the respect those in authority had for his abilities in the field of manufacture and organization. The railway still had to function, but it was to assist in the war effort rather than in commercial business, so Fowler could be released to concentrate on the demands of his country, not his employers. Although his war work does not contribute directly to consideration of him as a locomotive engineer, it does throw light on his abilities in the general manufacturing and engineering field, so a brief mention is necessary.

Initially he was secretary to the Railway Companies Munitions Sub-Committee, but when the Ministry of Munitions came into existence in 1915 he was appointed Director of Production. This essentially administrative post does not appear to have been to his liking, so he moved on to become Superintendent of the Royal Aircraft Factory at Farnborough in 1916. The following year he became Assistant Director General of Aircraft Production and during 1918 and 1919 held various posts at the Ministry of Munitions.

Several visits were made to the USA and Canada to liaise with allied members of the various committees of which he was member; these included the committees involved with aeronautics, light alloys and motor transport, and they illustrate the breadth of Fowler's engineering knowledge. For his war efforts he was awarded an OBE in 1917, and this was advanced to a KBE the following year[68]

Back on the railway after hostilities ceased, Fowler soon had to contend with a demotion of sorts due to the grouping. It was reasonable that the senior engineer of the grouped companies, George Hughes, should be appointed CME of the entire London Midland & Scottish Railway because he had greater experience, and few would really doubt that he was the best man available. Fowler became head of a division based at Derby, but he did not seem to object and continued to pursue his interests and undertook all work requested of him. In many respects matters continued as they had before, except that Hughes had overall control of mechanical engineering.

The fact that Fowler and Hughes had worked together previously and both were essentially amiable characters certainly will have eased what might have been a difficult situation for more egocentric individuals. From comments made by each when the other was presenting a paper, there was obviously mutual respect for engineering talents. A few years after he had left the L&YR, Fowler presented a paper to the 'Mechanicals' on the lighting of railway premises. This continued part of the theme of his earlier paper on acetylene and dealt with a topic of considerable interest to Hughes, who had only recently became CME of the L&YR. Opening the discussion Hughes commented, 'The paper was an admirable one, and he had not the slightest doubt it would form a valuable record for reference.'[69]

Praise from CMEs or others in high office was to be expected following a Fowler paper, for he devoted considerable time to ensuring accuracy especially when others had been delegated to carry out experimental work. Few were more glowing in their tributes than J. A. F. Aspinall, under whom Fowler had trained. In proposing the vote of thanks following Fowler's Institution of Mechanical Engineers Presidential Address, Aspinall mentioned how proud he was to see one of his young engineers reach such a position. He commented on the choice of metallurgy as the subject for the address, saying that it came as no surprise to him as Fowler had developed a keen interest in metallurgy from his early days at Horwich. Aspinall also stated that Fowler had provided each of the main works of the LMS with a chemical laboratory and mechanical testing appliances so that research facilities were readily available.[70]

That thirst for knowledge had been with Fowler from his early days and he encouraged all connected with the railway to take an interest in education. At the second annual dinner of the Institution of Locomotive Engineers, he told the members of his delight to be associated with that body because he had always been a locomotive man interested in the question of education. It is interesting that he referred to himself as a locomotive man, for subsequent popular belief has it that he took no interest in such matters. He took an active interest in the Locomotive Society at Horwich and also belonged to the Great Western Junior Engineering Society at Swindon.[71]

Most of his papers were individual affairs although he did rely upon others for the gather-

ing of data, as he freely acknowledged. For the presentation of one paper, however, he collaborated with Nigel Gresley. This concerned trials of vacuum brakes on long freight trains which has been conducted jointly by the Midland and Great Northern railways and which resulted from their both being members of an Inter-Allied Commission on brakes.[72] Gresley was very interested in the braking of freight trains and asked Fowler to provide assitance. Naturally most of the experimental work was done by assistants, and this was acknowledged, but both CMEs were responsible for organizing the experiments and dictating their progress.

This example and the support Fowler received from other CMEs during discussion of his papers illustrates the respect they had for him. Sir Henry Fowler was a popular individual who was held in high esteem as an engineer by his peers. Many would envy such a reputation. Whenever he

Right Class '2P' No 685, a Fowler development of the Johnson 4-4-0 design, at Leeds in 1947. (D. K. Jones collection)

Below Preserved 0-6-0 tank, Class '1F' No 41708, a Fowler rebuild of a Johnson design introduced in 1878.

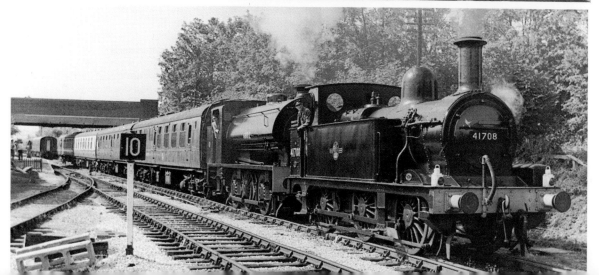

The proposed Fowler design for a three-cylinder compound 4-6-0.

spoke, engineers listened. He was an intellectual engineer with a thorough understanding of all aspects of his profession. The study of metals and their properties occupied much of his time and he was always willing to share his knowledge with his fellows. Although some of his papers on this subject appear to have been purely scientific, most had a practical bias towards the steam locomotive. A 1921 paper for the Faraday Society concerned the fracture of locomotive boiler tubes[73] whilst a year later he delivered a lecture to the Institute of Metals concerning the effect of superheated steam on metals used for locomotives.[74]

Fowler was a regular contributor of papers to the International Railway Congress and in 1922 his offering concerned the use of oil fuel for locomotives. After summarizing the systems available, he concluded that the internal combustion engine was a better option for fuel oil than the steam locomotive.[75] He obviously had an eye on the future.

When George Hughes retired, Sir Henry Fowler became CME of the London Midland & Scottish Railway but because former Midland men occupied many of the high managerial posts, particularly with respect to traffic, the locomotive department was still under severe restrictions as to locomotive size. The Midland small engine policy remained and neither Fowler nor anybody in the locomotive department could do anything to alter it. Designs for larger and more powerful compounds were produced, but internal politics and narrow-minded individuals conspired against any advance. A 4–6–0 three-cylinder compound was schemed at Derby in 1924 before Fowler actually became CME, but Hughes was working on his own 'Pacific' design and the extended 'Midland Compound' went no further. Shortly afterwards, designs for four-cylinder compound 4-6-2 and 2-8-2 locomotives were produced[76], but these failed to go into production because the Superintendent of Motive Power, J. E. Anderson, did

not like the idea and wanted a 4-6-0. Anderson was able to convince the traffic department and the Board against Fowler's views and this resulted in the loan of *Launceston Castle* from the GWR and the subsequent construction of the 'Royal Scot' Class.[77]

Where others might have felt slighted, Fowler simply got on with the job for which he was paid. He was a first class engineer and locomotive design was but part of his duties — if others cared to deal with that problem he did not appear to mind. A major task had been to reorganize the main works at Derby, Crewe and Horwich. Fowler dealt with Derby himself and laid down the main direction for Beames to follow at Crewe, and Shawcross at Horwich.[78] These were different sites with different problems and solutions, so Fowler did not insist on a standard works layout, allowing his engineers at these sites to modernize within a broadly-based plan.

With a new management team in charge of the LMS, long overdue changes came about, including reorganization of mechanical engineering matters. Sir Henry Fowler, then 60 years old, was moved to research, a demotion as far as many people were concerned but a move which probably delighted Fowler himself, always having been an inquisitive engineer. As assistant to the Vice President (Sir Harold Hartley) for research, Fowler could indulge in what he enjoyed best, engineering investigation. He continued working even after his wife died in 1934, and never actually retired from active research duties.

He was always an active man and probably wore himself out. He died at his home in Derby on 16 October 1938 following an illness which resulted from overwork. In its obituary *The Engineer* considered that his restless energy impelled him to undertake too much[79] whilst *Engineering* stated that he would be remembered for his good fellowship and kindly manner with a geniality which kept him young among young folk.[80]

5. LMS Locomotive Engineers

Before actually considering those Locomotive Engineers who were appointed after the formation of the LMS, it is worth looking at the managerial structure of that concern. At the grouping, six Directors were appointed from each of the three major companies, L&YR, LNWR and Midland Railway, and one from each of the smaller constituent companies. It was the intention that higher managerial posts would be spread evenly amongst officers from the constituent companies, but in practice it did not work out that way and many of the posts eventually went to Midland men. In some cases this was not immediately planned, but retirements, as in the case of George Hughes, allowed Derby's influence to dominate. In 1924 Sir Guy Granet, formerly of the Midland Railway, became Chairman and the LMS almost become an enlarged version of the Midland Railway. That in itself was not necessarily a bad thing because one of the larger constituents had to dominate during those early years, such being the nature of amalgamations. The sad thing is that the dominance had to be so complete, with little credit being given to things not of Midland origin. The other regrettable feature of the takeover as far as locomotive matters were concerned lay in the restrictions which applied on Midland routes being extended throughout the system without any need.

As has been pointed out before, Locomotive Engineers did not dictate policy — they were simply required to implement it. The situation gradually deteriorated as far as locomotive matters were concerned, not in terms of maintenance but in terms of the ability of locomotives to haul the heavier loads on accelerated services. It is amazing that lessons from similar incidents with railways during former years had not been heeded. Certain aspects of Midland locomotive design policy did not lend itself to extension throughout the LMS, and this was particularly so with regards to the rather narrow bearings fitted to Midland locomotives. Deeley explained the reason for fitting narrow as opposed to wide bearings in his article on compound locomotives, stating that Midland engines were given a fair degree of flexibility in their frames and wheels in order to allow them to run around the system's tight curves, and with such flexibility wide bearings were apt to run hot.[1] What was a useful idea on locomotives for Midland lines was not applicable to the higher-powered machines for the West Coast Main Line or under subsequent circumstances.

Standardizing on Midland locomotives for the widely varying situations found throughout the LMS was definitely not the ideal solution, and was standardizing to suit the lowest common denominator, the condition of Midland track, when a more suitable situation would have been to improve the track to conform with higher standards found elsewhere. Over these matters the CME had no control and time after time both Hughes and Fowler were hindered in their attempts to improve matters. Higher management seemed to be unaware of the deteriorating situation until disaster was almost upon the railway, and no immediate effect could be expected from action taken. Steady decline could not be rectified overnight.

Granet reorganized higher management and formed an Executive, comprising of a President and four Vice-Presidents, which was given the brief of running the railway. As President of the Executive, Granet secured the services of Sir Josiah Stamp who took up office on 1 January 1926. Stamp had a first class business brain, was a former civil servant and held a degree in economics. During 1927, Granet resigned and Stamp also became Company Chairman. It took some time for matters to settle down, but the need for larger locomotives was evident and matters were put in hand to secure a fleet of powerful machines. Fowler was still in control of locomotive matters and is likely to have been delighted at the chance of building larger and more powerful locomotives, but there were still old prejudices of Midland origin in the LMS system. Fowler was unable to obtain permission to build compound 4-6-2 and 2-8-2 engines, and had to be content with what became 'Royal Scot' 4-6-0s as insisted upon by the operating department.

Fowler was getting on in years and probably discussed with Stamp the need for a 'new broom' to get the locomotive department back on its feet. In 1930 he was 60 years old, and that was a good age to retire from his role as CME, if not from all duties — he was much too active ever to retire completely. The problem was that the obvious successor, Hewitt Beames, held old allegiances to the LNWR and that did not suit Stamp's ideas — the 'new broom' had to sweep completely clean and must come from outside. In the meantime there was the problem of how to fill the post left vacant by Fowler's elevation to research.

E. J. H. Lemon, Superintendent of the Carriage & Wagon department, was appointed CME in

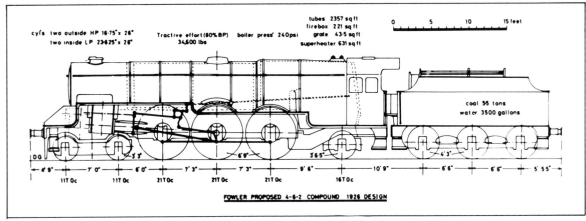

Fowler's design for a 4-6-2 compound, 1926.

1931 and it is certain that this was looked upon by all parties as purely a temporary affair whilst Stamp searched for a more permanent replacement for Fowler. To act in this way may seem to be rather ungainly, but it did have advantages. Fowler could retire at the age of 60 — he may even have expressed a wish to do so — and take up a post in keeping with his talents, whilst the new man would not have to follow on directly from a CME of long standing. Stamp probably through that he had a greater chance of getting the right man if the spectre of Fowler was not immediately evident.

Ernest John Hutchings Lemon

There can be little doubt that Stamp and Lemon both considered the appointment of the latter as CME to be a temporary measure. Lemon's subsequent history indicates that Stamp had probably already singled him out for higher things in the LMS management structure. To the locomotive enthusiast, the post of CME may be considered to be the zenith of any career but in railway terms it was just another position as head of a department. For Lemon the prospect of promotion to a high management post must have been dangled like a carrot in order to encourage him to follow Stamp's line. As events turned out, it was a very good move both for him and for the LMS.

Lemon was born in 1884 and received his early engineering education at the Heriot Watt College in Edinburgh. Leaving college he obtained an apprenticeship with the North British Locomotive Company, serving his time at the company's Hyde Park works, and then went to the heavy engineering company of Brown Brothers in Edinburgh, that concern specializing in marine steering gear. Initial railway employment came

through service with the Highland Railway at Inverness where he gained running shed experience. A short spell with the general engineering concern of Hurst, Nelson & Co of Motherwell preceded an appointment with the Midland Railway, where he was appointed Chief Wagon Inspector at Derby in August 1911.

Lemon remained in that post for six years and was then, at the age of 32, appointed manager of the Derby Carriage & Wagon Works of the Midland Railway. Like many in similar posts, Lemon simply became a Divisional Superintendent at the 1923 grouping, and in 1925 was given control over the Newton Heath and Earlestown sites. In 1927 he was appointed to superintend the entire Carriage & Wagon department of the LMS. For his efforts at the Midland's works during the war, Lemon was awarded an OBE.[2]

With Fowler's movement to research, Lemon became Chief Mechanical Engineer of the LMS, but he did not attempt to do anything other than keep things ticking over, obviously aware that his position was purely temporary. Up to that time the Carriage & Wagon department had been separate from that dealing with locomotives, and Lemon's promotion gave him the opportunity to combine them under a single head, the new man, when he was appointed, then being able to take control over all mechanical engineering matters. R. C. Bond, who came to know Lemon well, the CME being instrumental in Bond's return to LMS service, considered Lemon to be a brilliant organizer and an outstandingly good production engineer who belived in setting higher standards than current practice was achieving. Lemon did not have time to indulge in locomotive design, but he was able to improve matters related to repair. He practically doubled the mileage being achieved between general repairs to 100,000 miles by insisting that general repairs only be carried out when firebox condition, tyre wear or axlebox dictated that it should. This avoided general repairs being undertaken simply on the basis of hours in steam or mileage run.[3] This was sound engineering practice and essential to economic working of the railway in general.

J. H. Follows, one of the LMS Vice Presidents, was due to retire at the end of 1931 and Stamp was in something of a hurry to ensure that a new CME was in place by that time so that Lemon could fill the vacancy. However, nothing regarding the temporary nature of Lemon's appointment leaked out and most of the engineering staff considered it to be permanent. This caused R. A. Riddles and his colleagues some dismay, for they considered that a locomotive, not a Carriage & Wagon, man was required. In the later years Riddles discovered that Lemon was instrumental in finding his own replacement. Lemon had been discussing the problem with a business friend who suggested that William Stanier from the Great Western would make an ideal CME, and the matter was taken from there. Lemon made the initial

contact with Stanier during a lunch at the Athenaeum club, of which the latter was a member, and that set in motion the course of events which changed LMS locomotive practice completely.[4]

In January 1932, Lemon succeeded J. H. Follows as a Vice President and during his early years in that post he played an active role in bring about modernization of motive power depots and goods terminals. Lemon also encouraged Stanier in the introduction of continuous production methods for locomotives, carriages and wagons. Under his direction, the School of Transport at Derby was started and many training schemes were introduced. The Air Ministry obtained his services on secondment in 1938 and he became Director of general aircraft production with a seat on the Air Council. For this work he received a knighthood.

Returning to the LMS in 1940, Lemon resumed his administrative duties but also became involved with several govermental committees, one of which was concerned with the planning of the post-war railway system. Sir Ernest Lemon died on 15 December 1954 at the age of 70.[5] He is the least well known CME of the LMS or its constituents, basically due to the shortness of his period in office. In that post he was able to achieve little, but in some ways he did leave his mark. Improved production methods were introduced to the LMS but, perhaps more importantly, so was William Stanier.

William Arthur Stanier

To say that the arrival of William Stanier on the LMS improved that railway's locomotive affairs would be an understatement — he revolutionized them. However, Stanier would be the first to admit that he did not do things alone, for he had a very strong team behind him. The amazing thing is that the rest of the team was comprised of existing LMS men, and Stanier simply became the catalyst which fused that undoubted talent into an effective working unit. There never had been any shortage of skilled and dedicated engineers on the LMS — it just seems that their talents had not been utilized properly. Stanier moved people around, but he did not need to draft in new engineers, although Stamp would have certainly allowed him to do so. The new CME recognized the worth of men such as S. J. Symes, H. G. Ivatt, R. A. Riddles, R. C. Bond and many others already holding posts of responsibility, and he made use of them. That ability to recognize talent and make use of it is probably more valuable to an engineer than mathematical or design skills.

Earnest John Hutchings Lemon.

William Arthur Stanier.

rather to consider his influence on the LMS in engineering terms. His life and works have been covered in great detail by O. S. Nock's biography[6], that author having had personal contact with Stanier and first-hand experience of riding on and behind his locomotives. Another work, *Gresley and Stanier* by Bellwood and Jenkinson[7], is also worth consulting for details of locomotive construction and performance.

William Stanier was Great Western through and through. Born at Swindon on 27 May 1876, his father W. H. Stanier, then being William Dean's confidential clerk. The young Stanier was destined for service with the Great Western, and following education at Wycliffe College he commenced his apprenticeship at Swindon in 1892. Upon its completion he moved to the drawing office in 1897 and became engaged in locomotive design work. Positions as Inspector of Materials (1900) and Division Technical Inspector of Locomotives, Carriages and Wagons at Swindon (1902) soon followed. Running shed experience was gained during a temporary posting to Westbourne Park where he had charge of the London locomotive sheds whilst the Divisional Superintendent was in America. The way in which he acquitted himself during this time attracted attention and he was made assistant to John Armstrong who was Divisional Locomotive Superintendent for London.

Returning to Swindon in 1906, Stanier became assistant to the Locomotive Works Manager and other promotions followed until he became Manager himself in 1920. When Collett replaced Churchward as CME of the Great Western in 1922, Stanier was appointed Principal Assistant and there he stayed until moving to the LMS.[8] Considerable experience was gained in that post, and as Collett took little interest in matters away from engineering it was Stanier who had to undertake most social duties expected of a CME.[9] Stanier had no desire to leave the GWR and would have dearly loved to be CME at Swindon, but that was not to be. Despite his move to the LMS, he retained his affection for his mentor G. J. Churchward and all things Swindon. Some idea of the intensity of his desire to have been CME on the Great Western can be gauged from the fact that he named his house 'Newburn', the name of the CME's official residence at Swindon.

Stanier became Chief Mechanical Engineer of the LMS on 1 January 1932, his transfer from the GWR being with the approval of its Chairman, Viscount Churchill, and with the best of wishes from the workforce at Swindon who held him in high esteem. Stamp more or less gave him a free

In changing very little and emphasizing that full use would be made of capable engineers already occupying posts, Stanier gained the confidence of his team very quickly. He had no axe to grind as far as pre-grouping loyalties were concerned, and as an outsider he could gain the confidence of the engineering staff. Respect would come only with time, but Stanier's attitude and actions ensured that he very quickly earned that respect. Stamp's support obviously helped, as did the fact that J. E. Anderson, Superintendent of Motive Power and very much a thorn in the side of Henry Fowler, actually got on well with him. However, Anderson retired at the end of 1932 to be replaced by D. C. Urie, formerly of the Highland Railway and Division Mechanical Engineer for Scotland since the grouping. Urie was not known for favouring things Great Western, and Stanier was cast in that mould; a certain antagonism between mechanical engineering and operating departments could, therefore, be expected and did occur at times.

In this section it is not intended to go into great detail regarding the life of William Stanier but hand to improve the locomotive stock, but Stanier was too shrewd a person and too good an engineer to convert Crewe, Derby and Horwich to images of Swindon. The GWR had much to offer and certain practices were transferred, but Stanier soon discovered that everything Swindon fashion did not suit railways in general. However, the young engineering staff he quickly assessed as being very capable for the work he had in mind.

Those staff members also found Stanier much to their liking. E. S. Cox states that they soon found him to be a man of few words who would come quickly to the point and make a decision rapidly when presented with facts. He did not procrastinate, nor was he doctrinaire, but when mistakes were made they were freely admitted and rectifying action ordered. Despite the high office he held, Cox considered him to be very approachable and an individual who would just as freely converse with a fitter, fireman or draughtsman on the same terms as with the Chairman.[10] Few would wish for their boss to be any different.

Riddles held similar views to his new chief, and found Stanier easy to talk to and extremely willing to discuss any and all of the problems which were encountered in designing new locomotives. A close relationship developed between the two men and this was based upon mutual respect. The CME would willingly explain anything Riddles did not understand when they discussed locomotive matters, but would also listen to suggestions and just as willingly accept them provided that they were logical. The close relationship continued long after both men had ceased railway service and Riddles often referred to his former chief as 'the great man'. He was in the habit of visiting the Stanier home during later years but would telephone first and did so the morning that 'the great man' died. Riddles immediately visited the Stanier home and was considerably moved to see his former chief for the last time.[11] The close bond of affection between the two great engineers says much for the friendly and good natured character of both men.

R. C. Bond, who also served under Stanier, gives similar views of the Stanier character in his own autobiography, whilst another contemporary LMS engineer who rose to high office in British Railways, E. J. Larkin, speaks equally highly of the man from Swindon. When Stanier retired, Larkin, then Staff Assistant to the CME, was called into his office and told to choose any volumes from his bookcase as a memento.[12] It is likely that similar gestures were afforded to others on Stanier's staff, and although quite minor in nature were magnificent in terms of sentiment.

They illustrate a deep bond which must have developed between Stanier and his team, a bond which allowed the LMS locomotive department to forge ahead of any other in Britain. With this spirit it is, perhaps, understandable that former LMS engineers dominated the locomotive side of a nationalized British Railways.

Many words have been written about William Stanier and his locomotive products and it is pointless to repeat them again. The man was at the forefront of his profession during his years with the LMS and was well respected for his knowledge by all mechanical engineers, and not only those from railway circles. He must have known his worth even during the days at Swindon, when he remained in the shadow of Collett, but he never made any attempts to move elsewhere. Personal ambition certainly did not drive him, but he was a professional railway engineer who sought perfection and was only satisfied with the best results. This does not mean that all of his ideas were first class — they weren't — but he was prepared to quickly make changes when initial plans did not bear fruit.

A lifetime on the Great Western — he was 55 years old when he moved to the LMS — left him somewhat indoctrinated by matters Swindon, especially whose developed by Churchward for whom he had the greatest respect. Following his appointment as CME, Stanier would visit his former chief at Swindon as frequently as he could and the two would discuss many things including locomotive matters. Those visits came to an end with Churchward's tragic death in December 1933. It was thus understandable that Swindon's ideas would find their way into LMS locomotive designs; many were already proven to be good practice, although Stanier did make some mistakes.

The taper boiler, long-travel piston valves, the jumper-top blast pipe and many other features of Swindon origin found their way into the first Stanier design, the 2-6-0 mixed traffic class. Whether as a joke, a symbol of respect or a sign of pique by some that matters had gone too far Great Western, the first of the class, No 13245, was fitted with a GWR-style safety valve cover. Stanier had the offending appendage removed when he heard about it, and little publicity was given to the unauthorized version. Who was responsible was never determined, but Herbert Chambers, the LMS Chief Draughtman and a former Midland man, was known not to like many of Stanier's innovative ideas.[13]

The fact that such an obvious embellishment could be fitted without Stanier knowing illustrates

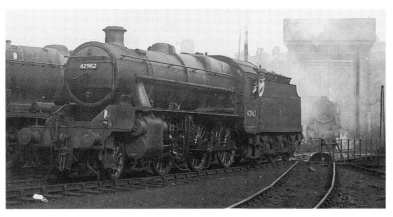

Left *Stanier's first LMS class: 2-6-0 No 42962 in BR days.* (D. K. Jones collection)

Below right *Streamlined Stanier 'Pacific' No 6244,* King George VI. (LMS official)

how separated the CME was from day-to-day affairs at the works. Detail drawings of the class were produced at Horwich, the safety valves being housed in a dome-like casing combined with the clack valves. After the first ten were constructed modification called for the use of shorter 'pop'-type safety valves placed above the firebox. Whether Horwich or Crewe, where the locomotive were built, was responsible for the GWR trade mark is unknown.

E. S. Cox makes the point that Stanier would produce rough sketches of details he wished to introduce but never, as far as Cox was aware, sketched out a scheme for a whole locomotive. The drawing office produced diagrams of locomotives which were considered to fit in with Stanier's ideas and these were submitted for approval. (Several such diagrams would have included the Swindon 'coffee pot' safety valve cover and it was when he was shown the drawing of the 2-6-0 that he made clear his feelings that LMS engines were to be no carbon copies of Swindon products.[14])

Although the LMS had become less Midland-dominated, there were still some who hankered for the old days. Stanier had no experience in dealing with such people, the Great Western having been very much a settled society. His lack of political acumen was noticed by Riddles and the latter tried to help his chief to deal with the intrigues which still afflicted the railway. Riddles had, after all, been weaned on infighting and admits that he developed something of a suspicious mind.[15]

In engineering matters Stanier was as shrewd as anybody, and would not let simple civil engineering restrictions get in the way of a good idea. All CMEs had problems in getting locomotive schemes passed by their respective Civil Engineers' departments, most of which appear to have been very conservative and reluctant to change trackwork and structures just because the locomotive side wanted to use heavier engines. The 2-6-0 was schemed with horizontal cylinders and the Civil Engineer produced lists of lines over which it would not be allowed to run because of clearance problems. Past LMS and Midland CMEs had bowed to such restrictions, but not Stanier, who set out to prove his fellow senior officer wrong. Three Hughes 2-6-0 locomotives were fitted with projecting fingers of lead at platform level in order to give the basic outline of the intended design, then they moved around the system wherever problems of fouling were considered to be serious. Only in a few cases was minor adjustment to platform edging subsequently required and the 2-6-0s were able to run throughout the entire system within their axle loading restrictions.[16] By this relatively simple arrangement an imagined restriction was overcome, a restriction which had probably hampered other CMEs who had not bothered to ask 'Why?' and then shown 'Why not?'.

Stanier took an active interest in design and production and held very definite ideas on locomotive design, many of which were conditioned by experience — and that came from Swindon. He was, however, prepared to admit that his experience upon joining the LMS was limited and also that at first he had believed that GWR practice was right and everybody else was wrong. This acknowledgement of past errors was made during the discussion of R. C. Bond's paper about the LMS turbine locomotive when the matter of superheat temperature was considered. Stanier's early opinion was that the GWR-type two-row superheater was all that was necessary for any locomotive, but he soon had cause to change his mind. Problems with the first 'Pacifics' soon gave cause for reconsideration, and the larger three-

or four-row superheater became standard. During the same discussion, Stanier confessed that he had learned a great deal from the superheating of LMS locomotives.[17]

To introduce such an unproven form of propulsion as the turbine for the third of his 'Pacifics' took considerable courage, the more so because it also introduced other features such as roller bearings on all wheels. The idea for constructing the engine came following a trip Stanier made to Sweden in order to observe a turbine locomotive that Ljungstrom had in operation. Stanier, with the approval of Sir Harold Hartley, went to Sweden with Dr Guy of Metropolitan-Vickers and the outcome was that the LMS and Metropolitan-Vickers collaborated on constructing the 'Turbomotive'. Stanier considered the move to be a wise one and in 1946, when the paper was discussed, felt that the locomotive had been a success.

One step he does not appear to have considered wise, although he never directly said so, was that of streamlining. His 1936 Institution of Locomotive Engineers Presidential Address dealt with the subject of developments in locomotive design, in Britain and abroad. The paper covered a wide range of topics including that of streamlining, and details were given of a number of different streamlining arrangements then in service. At no point did he come out definitely for or against streamlining, but he did state that tests had shown savings were to be obtained with a properly streamlined locomotive and coaches when running against a headwind at speeds above 60 miles per hour. This was known from wind tunnel tests, but Stanier appears to have had his doubts. He stated: 'Streamlining may be something like that blessed word "Mesopotamia" to the old lady. At any rate it has good publicity value'.[18] In his bio-graphy of R. A. Riddles, Rogers states that the LMS engineers disliked streamlining and that Stanier loathed it.[19] Such views must have come from Riddles himself.

Stanier locomotives have been discussed in detail over the years whilst many books have been devoted to them, so it is not the intention to cover that same material again. As far as design is concerned, Stanier was very progressive and would make use of new ideas if he could see an advantage; as already mentioned, several old ideas were also employed until proven wrong. If necessary, tests were carried out in order to ensure that the best possible approach was used and the ideal arrangement devised. Although streamlining of locomotives on the outside might have been unpopular, the same could not be true about streamlining the steam passages between cylinders and valves. The French locomotive engineer André Chapelon had shown the importance of streamlined passages for economic working, and Stanier was following along well-established lines. However, experimental work had to be carried out in order to determine the optimum form and no matter how innovative was his team, something new could always be learned.

One-third-full-size models of streamlined and standard valve arrangements were tested in order to determine the frictional loss during steam passage to and from a cylinder at different port openings. Such tests were carried out for pressure differences across the ports of 10 psi, 20 psi and 30 psi using the apparatus as shown in the accompanying diagram. The orifice between the drums, in conjunction with the manometer, was used to determine steam flow rate at each of the pressure differences and valve openings for standard and streamlined ports. The results showed that there was reduced flow resistance with streamlined ports varying from zero to 18 per cent for admission and 18 to 37 per cent for exhaust. Streamlined valves and modified ports thus became the order of the day.[20]

Stanier encouraged such tests with components, and road tests with locomotives and dynamometer car, but by 1938 he was a firm believer in stationary testing plants. Only by such

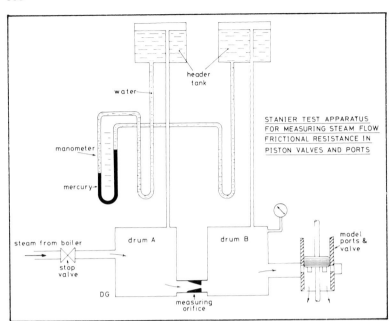

STANIER TEST APPARATUS
FOR MEASURING STEAM FLOW
FRICTIONAL RESISTANCE IN
PISTON VALVES AND PORTS

header tank

water

manometer

mercury

steam from boiler

stop valve

drum A

drum B

model ports & valve

DG

measuring orifice

Below right *Streamlined port arrangements.*

means, he considered, was it possible to isolate the large number of variables which were present when operating a steam locomotive.[21] The enthusiastic way in which he collaborated with Gresley in setting up a national testing plant at Rugby indicates his feelings on the importance of such matters. That, however, was not his opinion in 1931. When discussing a Gresley paper, 'Locomotive Experimental Stations', he doubted the benefits of such a testing plant, evidently believing that electric traction would soon take over from steam power.[22] His experience of testing plants was greater than that of other engineers present at the meeting, but that was of the Swindon plant which was of limited power-absorbing capacity and had given trouble with shaft bearings.

As an engineer, Stanier was held in high regard, not only by his colleagues on the LMS but throughout the railway community in general. In 1936 he and Sir Ralph Wedgwood, Chief General Manager of the LNER, were invited to conduct an enquiry into the operations of Indian Railways. Stanier left for India in November 1936 and did not return until the following March. During his absence most of the initial design work was undertaken for the 'Coronation' Class 'Pacifics', but Stanier obviously felt happy in leaving that work to his design team.

Whilst Stanier was in India, S. J. Symes, Chief Stores Superintendent, was acting CME, but he appears to have left Riddles to oversee the design

work. The locomotives were enlarged versions of the 'Princess' 'Pacifics' and several members of the team had contributed ideas for improvement. T. F. Coleman, the Chief Draughtsman who was in overall charge of the design project, devised the streamlined casing after wind tunnel tests on models had been carried out by the research department at Derby.[23]

Stanier returned from India early in March 1937 and the report was issued in July. Although the inquiry was concerned with all aspects of Indian Railways it is likely that Stanier concerned himself mainly with engineering affairs. He found that there was an abnormally high percentage of locomotives stopped awaiting repairs whilst repair work was being undertaken on more locomotives than were actually required. Such problems had been faced in Britain, and Fowler had directed that the major workshops streamline their repair facilities; thus Stanier was able to compare Indian practice with those of differently-sized workshops on the LMS, especially Crewe and Derby.

No sooner had the report been published than a major express train crash took place. The night express from Punjab to Calcutta became detrailed near Bihita with the loss of 100 lives. Political considerations had to be taken into account, India then being under British control, and it was felt that an inquiry into the accident was required. Sir John Thom published his report in April 1938 and suggested that excessive speed was a likely cause. With acceptance of the report by the Indian Government, a further inquiry was announced to investigate the 'Pacific'-type locomotives working in India, an 'XB' 'Pacific' having been involved in the Bihita derailment. Once again Stanier found himself heading for the subcontinent to join other committee members drawn from European and Indian railways, illustrating once again his standing in the railway engineering community.

William Stanier had few interests outside engineering and Riddles contends that he found his main entertainment at meetings of the 'Mechanicals', to which he was devoted.[24] He was elected President in 1941, his Presidential Address dealing with the steam locomotive in mechanical engineering terms. Such addresses were not intended to be controversial and Stanier maintained that practice, but he did produce a very readable account of the recent (to that time) development of the steam locomotive. The emphasis was on LMS locomotives and he also dealt with the matter of locomotive testing, mentioning the joint LMS/LNER testing station, construction of which had been suspended due to the war. He also again emphasized the point he had raised in earlier addresses before the Institution of Locomotive Engineers, that the greatest operational efficiency resulted from maximum availability and minimum maintenance costs. The address finished with praise for his staff, Stanier acknowledging that anything he had achieved was due to their loyalty, co-operation and help.[25]

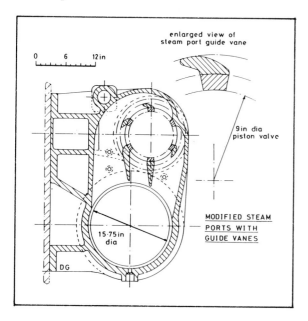

enlarged view of steam port guide vane

0   6   12in

9 in dia piston valve

15·75 in dia

MODIFIED STEAM PORTS WITH GUIDE VANES

DG

In 1936 and again in 1938 Stanier was elected President of the Institution of Locomotive Engineers, his 1936 address being entitled 'Recent Developments in Locomotive Design', whilst that of 1938 covered the problems of locomotive design. The first address covered a wide range of design matters and dealt with the topic of streamlining in some detail. Whilst discussing boilers he regretted the restriction on boiler size and weight imposed by British loading gauge and axle weight limits compared with American and Continental practice. The boiler section was thorough, and Stanier considered that unless hardness could be reduced to zero, the advantage of water softening was lost due to corrosion and priming. He advocated the use of continuous blowdown in order to reduce the level of dissolved solids in the boiler water, high levels being the cause of priming. Such high levels of dissolved solids resulted from treating hard water with soda, and he mentioned that all LMS engines were to be provided with continuous blowdown.[26]

The 1938 address dealt with more specific design matters, but he did emphasize that in his opinion safety, reliability, availability and efficiency were the main requirements of any locomotive design. Concluding the address, he took care to warn his audience that each succeeding improvement was subject to the law of diminishing returns and that gains were becoming harder to win. That allowed him to finish by emphasizing the importance of a stationary testing plant.[27]

Apart from these addresses Stanier read few papers himself, although he took a very active part in the discussion of many. The breadth of his knowledge and understanding can be gauged from his 1939 'Mechanicals' paper, 'Lightweight Passenger Rolling Stock'. This was actually intended for presentation at a meeting of the 'Mechanicals' in New York but the outbreak of war prevented that from taking place.[28] The paper was printed by the IME and gave a very thorough account of LMS carriage construction at that time together with design considerations from a strength point of view. As a mechanical engineer, Stanier was concerned about structural design for safety and ease of production. He also covered in some detail structural and bogie design for the new stock to be employed on the electrified Liverpool and Southport line. Body framing was based on the Vierendeel truss which allowed the roof and underframe to contribute to the bending strength of the body unit, indicating the progress in carriage design made under Stanier.[29]

Above *A classic design of the Stanier regime: 'Black Five' No 44777 at Crewe in 1965.* (D. K. Jones collection)

Left *The standard Stanier LMS freight design: No 48151 as preserved.* (Patrick Griffiths)

Right *Charles Edward Fairburn.*

The other paper worthy of mention, and one of which Stanier must have taken great delight in presenting, concerned G. J. Churchward. This biographical sketch of Churchward's engineering life was presented to the Newcomen Society at the Science Museum during October 1955 and attracted many of Stanier's old associates, including R. A. Riddles and R. C. Bond. At the age of 79 Stanier was still prepared to stand up and publicly praise his old mentor.[30]

The war took Stanier away from the LMS and involved him more and more in national work. This first centred on the Railway Executive, which operated the railways of Britain on behalf of the Goverment, but posts in the Ministry of Production and the Aeronautical Research Council as well as a directorship of Power Jets Ltd moved him away from railways altogether. In 1944 he resigned his position of Chief Mechanical Engineer of the LMS, although he had not been directly involved in matters at Euston for some time.

Many honours came Stanier's way. The Institution of Locomotive Engineers awarded him its Gold Medal in 1957, whilst the 'Mechanicals' awarded him the James Watt International Medal in 1963. He was knighted in 1943 and became a Fellow of the Royal Society the following year. In America he was awarded an honorary Doctorate of Science and was also granted honorary membership of the American Society of Mechanical Engineers.[31] Few would deny that Stanier deserved these honours for he had served his employers, his profession and his country to the utmost of his exceptional ability. He died peacefully at his home in Rickmansworth on 27 September 1965 aged 89 years.

Charles Edward Fairburn

Of all Chief Mechanical Engineers employed by the post-grouping companies, apart from E. J. H. Lemon, Fairburn has attracted the least attention, primarily because he held office for such a short period and was therefore able to achieve very little. Although he took over from Stanier officially in 1944, he had for some time been acting as CME whilst Stanier was engaged in war work. His death, at the age of 58 years, on 12 October 1945 could have plunged the LMS into a mechanical engineering crisis had the CME's department not been so well organized and disciplined. Higher management had not nominated a successor, but the wealth of talent which had come to the fore during the reign of Stanier ensured that one would be readily found from within the existing ranks, and such proved to be the case.

C. E. Fairburn was born in Bradford on 5 September 1887, being the only son of Mr Robert Fairburn. His early education at Bradford Grammar School showed him to be particularly gifted in Mathematics and in 1905 he gain an open scholarship to read that subject at Brasenose College, Oxford. In 1908 he was awarded a first class honours degree in Mathematical Moderations and Final Schools, the college awarding him a senior Hulme Exhibition for his high attainment. That allowed him to continue his studies and in 1910 he obtained a first class honours degree in the Engineering Science Final Honours School; indeed, he was the first person to take the Engineering School at Oxford

University. The BA degree was converted to an MA in 1912.

During his final vacation, Fairburn spent three months with the Bradford firm of Boldy & Son where he gained experience of machine shop and millwright work. Upon leaving University in 1910 he obtained a two year pupilage under Henry Fowler at Derby, at the same time continuing his studies, metallurgy at Sheffield University and technical drawing at Derby Technical College.[32]

Upon completion of his time under Fowler he obtained a position as an engineering assistant in the railway department of Seimens Dynamo Works Ltd at Stafford. The following year he became assistant to the resident engineer for the electrification of the North Eastern Railway line between Newport and Shildon. During that period, which lasted until 1916, he was responsible for the design and erection of that 1500-volt system as well as testing during its first year of operation.

Determined to do his duty in the conflict then raging, Fairburn joined the Royal Flying Corps, subsequently the Royal Air Force, as an experimental officer, eventually achieving the rank of major in command of an experimental squadron. During that time he conducted experiments into bomb and gun sights as well as testing different types of aircraft. Special attention was given to the problems of flying at night and through clouds.

Returning to civilian life in 1919, Fairburn joined the English Electric Company where he became head of the railway section, then rather a small unit. He built up the railway business both in Britain and overseas before moving to Preston in 1926 as manager of the former Dick Kerr works, that concern then being part of English Electric. In 1928 he also took over as manager of the Stafford plant and so increased his contacts with railway affairs.[33]

Fairburn's talents were readily recognized by those in authority and in 1929 he became a member of the Executive Committee of the English Electric Company, two years later being appointed Chief Engineer and Manager of the company's traction department. Foreign governments consulted him on electrification matters and in 1933 he became Chairman of the contractors' committee for the electrification of the Polish State Railways. Fairburn was, then, essentially an electrical engineer who specialized in railway matters, but he was also a very good engineer with high academic attainment and an appreciation of mechanical engineering including the steam locomotive. As a pupil of Fowler he would have gained steam experience and, whilst studying metallurgy and technical drawing, an understanding of practical problems will have been obtained.

In 1934 the LMS invited him to take up the position of Chief Electrical Engineer, a post which was responsible for all electrical plant throughout the system, including traction and stationary equipment. In 1938 he was appointed deputy Chief Mechanical Engineer whilst still retaining responsibility for electrical matters.[34] This move singled Fairburn out as Stanier's successor and rather put the brakes on R. A. Riddles' progress, Riddles having already been Principal Assistant to the CME for a number of years. Sir Harold Hartley, the Vice President for engineering matters, would appear to have favoured Fairburn and been instrumental in his advancement up the LMS tree. Despite the undoubted claims of Riddles, and other equally able mechanical engineers in the LMS team, Fairburn was well qualified for the position he held and which he subsequently achieved.

By 1938 it was obvious that Stanier was well on the way to achieving the result for which he had been appointed, namely to give the LMS a stock of locomotives which could deal with all envisaged services both efficiently and economically. It was also plain to see that a first class engineering team had been formed and that as far as mechanical matters were concerned the LMS was well set for the future. Hartley had his eyes set on that future, although the prospects of another war were already evident, and it is probable that he considered an academic engineer could better plan for years to come. Electric traction was already applied to a number of branch lines and its extension could well produce benefits. Diesel traction also had to be considered, and Fairburn had an open mind on such matters. Others were equally open-minded, but not being brought up in the steam mould must have been considered an advantage.

Fairburn did produce two papers for the Institution of Locomotive Engineers, both concerned with diesel shunting locomotives. Diesel shunters had been introduced to the LMS in 1932, before Fairburn arrived, when a small steam locomotive had been converted, the drive being by hydraulic means. Others from outside contractors followed, and in 1934 a number of electrical-drive as well as mechanical-drive machines arrived from different manufacturers, including English Electric. In his first paper, entitled 'Diesel Shunting Locomotives' and presented in 1941, Fairburn described the types of locomotives which had been put into service and

gave details of their operational performance, usefulness in service and financial results. As a record of diesel locomotive development on the LMS it was a first class paper, and Fairburn firmly came down on the side of electric rather than mechanical drive.

Stanier opened the discussion and remarked that events had shown diesels to be at an economic advantage compared with steam shunters, provided that two shifts were worked rather than one. Discussing the fitting of double brake blocks rather than less expensive single blocks, Fairburn simply stated that double blocks were used because they were more effective and had proved themselves to be economically justified. He added that as far as he was concerned the purpose of an engineer was to save money, and mentioned the American adage that the engineer was a man who did for a dollar what any damned fool could do for two.[35]

The second paper was delivered in March 1944 and was concerned with the maintenance of diesel electric shunting locomotives. Fairburn outlined the design requirements for diesel shunters and then discussed the problems involved in their operation and maintenance as far as the LMS was concerned. As no other railway in Britain had as much diesel engine experience, the paper provided plenty of useful information and was a valuable lesson for any organization contemplating the adoption of diesels. Although his specialisation may have been in the field of electricity, it is evident from the paper that Fairburn had a considerable understanding of diesel engines.

By 1944 the LMS had had considerably more experience with the operation of diesel shunters compared with 1941 when the earlier paper had been presented, and Fairburn was able to present updated information regarding availability. Better maintenance schedules allowed for a theoretical availability of 98 per cent, although the actual figure was between 75 and 85 per cent. Such figures compared more than favourably with steam shunters, but Fairburn considered that they could be improved even further if a spare engine unit was available. The small number of shunters then in service did not make such provision an economic proposition, but Fairburn considered that one spare engine unit for every 50 similar locomotives would allow heavy repairs to be carried out in the same time as that needed for light repairs.[36] This was to become a major advantage of the diesel locomotive over its steam counterpart, and Fairburn had a thorough appreciation of the fact.

The LMS diesel shunter design of 1944.

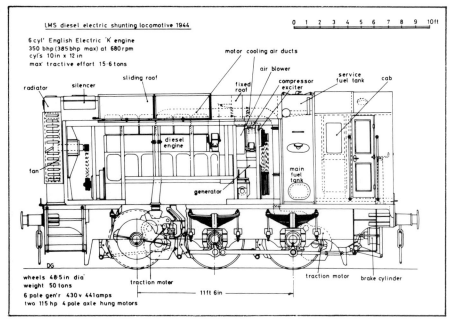

LMS diesel electric shunting locomotive 1944

0 1 2 3 4 5 6 7 8 9 10ft

6 cyl' English Electric 'K' engine
350 bhp (385 bhp max) at 680 rpm
cyl's 10 in x 12 in
max' tractive effort 15·6 tons

motor cooling air ducts
air blower
compressor
exciter
service fuel tank
cab
sliding roof
fixed roof
radiator
silencer
diesel engine
fan
generator
main fuel tank
wheels 48·5 in dia'
weight 50 tons
6 pole gen'r 430 v 441 amps
two 115 hp 4 pole axle hung motors
traction motor
11 ft 6 in
traction motor
brake cylinder
DG

Stanier again opened the discussion, having expressed a desire to do so as he considered the paper to be of significance. He indicated his support for this form of locomotive development and castigated other locomotive engineers who were prone to accept the fact that things had always been done in a certain way as a reason for continuing to do them in that way. At this time Stanier was still officially CME but his resignation was drawing near and Fairburn would soon assume the mantle.

Stanier praised the team system which Fairburn had employed for design and the gathering of information, a system which Stanier himself had used to great effect in his own design work. Fairburn was certainly an individual with his own ideas, but Stanier had laid a good foundation for the locomotive department of the LMS, and British Railways.

Although Fairburn appears to have had control of diesel shunter development, the responsibility lay with Stanier and his enthusiasm for this form of traction is frequently overlooked. Certainly his contribution to the discussion gives every indication that he wholeheartedly supported the scheme, and he even suggested that a similar approach to maintenance might improve the steam locomotive. Diesel locomotives, even shunters, were causing engineers to rethink their ideas on railway traction, but many were very reluctant to believe that such machines could present a challenge to the dominance of steam. In

that second paper Fairburn had presented some figures relating to the operation of LMS diesel shunters and had used mileage as the basis for maintenance schedules. This was in the case of diesel shunters because mileage was easily recorded and there was a very close relationship between mileage and operating hours. However, some people, including Mr Graff-Baker, the 1945 President of the Institution of Locomotive Engineers, simply extrapolated Fairburn's figures and rushed to the conclusion that diesels required very frequent maintenance. The editor of *The Engineer* also seemed to arrive at the same conclusion, and Fairburn was forced to write to that journal and explain his case.

He explained the reason for using the mileage basis and emphasized that hours of engine operation was the correct criterion to use; he also pointed out that, unlike a steam locomotive, the diesel engine generally operated only whilst the locomotive was in actual service. Fairburn also had to explain that the diesel engine's speed would not materially differ between a slow-speed shunter and high-speed main-line locomotive; the engine itself would not know whether it was providing power for a shunter at a low average speed or a main-line locomotive at higher speeds. He concluded his letter by stating that he did not set out to champion any particular form of traction but wished to have the basis correct if comparisons were made.[37] It is fairly evident, however, that Fairburn did favour diesel and electric traction but was not intent on wholesale change; in fact, conditions did not favour this, nor was there any money available. Such forms of traction offered considerable potential and Fairburn was a forward-looking engineer.

Early in 1945 Ivatt approached Fairburn about the possibility of constructing a diesel-electric express passenger locomotive, but the proposal was turned down by the CME. Such a refusal may seem a contradiction of Fairburn's open mind on traction matters, but conditions were just not right at that time. Although experience elsewhere had shown that operating costs for diesels were similar to those for steam, the initial cost was four or five times higher. Wartime conditions did not allow for the high expenditure involved in construction, and repair facilities for such a locomotive did not exist; thus, at that time, it was not

a practical proposition. Fortunately Ivatt did not forget the idea and when conditions were suitable it was resurrected.[38]

When Fairburn was promoted to the position of deputy CME in 1938 it is likely that his usefulness with respect to electrical traction played some part. During April that year he presented a paper before the Institution of Electrical Engineers entitled 'The Trend and Design of Electrical Locomotives'[39] and although the production of a single paper will have played little part in his advancement, the knowledge displayed in that paper indicates Fairburn's potential. The paper, for which he was awarded an Institution prize, outlined the basic mechanical and electrical features of design and then went on to consider features of many electrical locomotives throughout the world. Such understanding and

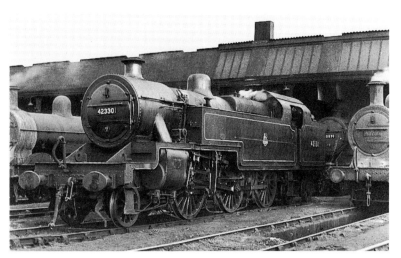

Fowler Class '4' 2-6-4 tank design introduction in 1927. No 42330 is seen at Nuneaton in 1954. (D. K. Jones collection)

Fairburn Class '4' 2-6-4 tank introduced in 1945. This is No 42102 at Watford in 1962. (D. K. Jones collection)

knowledge would certainly have been useful if electrification schemes had progressed further than they did, but the Second World War restricted expansion. Fairburn's death and the retirement of Sir Harold Hartley, together with the implications of that world conflict, certainly slowed the advance towards widespread electrification.

Fairburn had effectively been CME from 1942, some time before Stanier officially resigned, so the transition in 1944 did not produce any changes. H. G. Ivatt became his deputy and, being the steam man, probably had most to do with work on the steam locomotive side, although the war certainly restricted any real developments. The only steam locomotive design to be introduced during Fairburn's term of office was the 2-6-4 tank which was an improved version of the Fowler and Stanier 2-6-4 tank locomotives, and later became the model for the BR standard 2-6-4 tank.

Fairburn had discussed with British Thomson Houston the construction of a 1,500 hp diesel electric locomotive which could perform the same work as those 2-6-4 tanks[40], so his mind was firmly on the future. However, wartime restrictions limited scope for locomotive production, although Fairburn did attempt to improve construction and maintenance procedures. Aware that considerable time and expense was incurred in modifying new designs, he had built a full-size wooden mock-up of a proposed 2-6-2 tank locomotive, the intention being that many snags regarding construction, operation and maintenance could be detected on the mock-up and so save time and expense when the real thing was built. Whether or not it was justified is open to dispute, and although he does not think that it saved much in the way of time or added expense. E. S. Cox considers it to have been a worthwhile practice.[41] Ivatt did not think much of the idea and had it broken up when he became CME.

Cox had a high regard for Fairburn and enjoyed working with him as much as with any CME under whom he served. In his view, Fairburn was able to devote his whole attention to the subject in hand no matter what the other distractions, but he enjoyed intrigue which caused other heads of departments to treat him with caution.[42] R. C. Bond had similar high regard for his chief, and considered that he had a deep sense of duty but little regard for long-standing railway traditions like interdepartmental golf matches. Fairburn was an engineer who worked on the railway — he was not a born and bred railway engineer — and for some of those heads of depart-

ments who regarded him with caution, his dislike of irrelevant tradition was considered to be suspicious. He was something of a perfectionist who liked others to have similar standards and although very quick to praise good work, would not tolerate inefficiency or slackness. In Bond's opinion Fairburn deserved and gained respect, but he did not engender the affection that Stanier or Ivatt did. This could have been due to his nature which was rather ruthless and more commercially oriented than that of his predecessor or successor.[43]

During the war, LMS workshops, like those of other railways, were effectively turned over to military production and Fairburn played his part in ensuring that hardware was manufactured as required by the services. Locomotive and rolling-stock repairs were still required, but strict control over the workshops ensured that the percentage awaiting repair was kept at a very low level. This allowed the railway to function properly and meet wartime operating demands, and also freed workshop space for military manufacture. Tanks, field guns, assault boats and other items were constructed, but Fairburn must have taken most delight in the manufacture and repair of military aircraft because of his earlier associations with the Royal Air Force. Between February 1941 and September 1944 Fairburn was controller of the Hampden Bomber Repair Organisation, and for the latter part of 1943 he was also controller of the 'Barracuda' production group.

It is difficult today to appreciate the stress such wartime production put on managers of engineering workshops. In the case of the railways the primary task of maintaining a service also had to be attended to, but military production imposed strict deadlines. Fairburn was an enthusiastic worker and probably engrossed himself in his job in the same way that Fowler had done many years earlier. The devotion to his work and the stress involved probably killed him, for he died on 12 October 1945 following a heart attack. Fairburn's health had not been good for some time and had given friends cause for concern, but his death was unexpected.[44]

Had he lived longer the future LMS locomotive policy might have been different, but nationalization would still have taken place and Fairburn's efforts swallowed up in the corporate plan.

Henry George Ivatt

In some respects Ivatt continued the diesel policy of his predecessor and certainly appears to have adopted that form of traction with considerable enthusiasm. As a steam engineer born and bred, he was not willing to throw away the gains made with the basic Stephenson machine, but could see the advantages of the newer form of traction. The work Ivatt did in bringing modern ideas to steam locomotive design and production, as well as his development of main-line diesel locomotives, illustrates his open mind and willingness to change when necessary. He was an engineer, a railway mechanical engineer who wanted to provide machines to suit the needs of his employers; whether that was by means of improved steam locomotives or by diesel locomotives, he was willing to meet the challenge.

H. G. Ivatt was the son of H. A. Ivatt, who became Locomotive Engineer of the Great Northern Railway, so steam locomotive tradition was bred into him. George Ivatt never took to formal schooling and in later years when asked what formal examinations he had passed was willing to respond that he had never even sat any.[45] He was born in Dublin on 4 May 1886 whilst his father was still Assistant Locomotive Engineer on the Great Southern & Western Railway; a few months later H. A. Ivatt became Locomotive Engineer at Inchicore when Aspinall moved to the L&YR.

George Ivatt received his main education at Uppingham School, although if that comment about examinations is to be taken as accurate it was not what could be classed as formal. He did, however, have a considerable interest in mechanical engineering, especially from the craft point of view, and desired to follow his father into railway engineering. As the son of a respected locomotive engineer, any railway workshop in the country would have been open to him, but the reputation of Crewe was still high. George Whale had just succeeded Webb when H. G. Ivatt, aged 18 years, commenced his apprenticeship during October 1904. H. A. Ivatt, Aspinall and Whale had been firm friends during their time at Crewe and it is reasonable that the father would wish his son to be trained under the guidance of an old friend.

Ivatt enjoyed his apprenticeship at Crewe and also his lodgings with Mrs Parry; he stayed there until his marriage 11 years later. The apprenticeship followed the usual pattern with periods spent in various shops and in the drawing office, but Ivatt also gained experience away from Crewe when a one-year training period was arranged with the electrical contractors British Thomson Houston. Electrical power was being applied to workshop and electric traction was believed to have considerable potential; thus Ivatt considered that the training away from Crewe was a valuable experience.[46]

Returning to Crewe in 1909, Ivatt was appoint-

Henry George Ivatt.

ed Assistant Foreman at Crewe North Shed and a year later became Assistant Outdoor Machinery Superintendent. He remained in that post until he enlisted in the Mechanical Transport division of the Army Service Corps during 1915. Prior to that, in 1913, he had married Dorothy Harrison, a good friend of one of his sisters. George Ivatt had a good war, if that is the right term to use — he not only survived without injury but served in France, where his wife worked in a hospital, on the staff of the Director of Transport, and was promoted to the rank of captain and then major.[47]

Whilst still engaged on active duties, Ivatt received a message from C. J. B. Cooke indicating that the post of Deputy Locomotive, Carriage & Wagon Superintendent of the North Staffordshire Railway had become vacant and suggesting that he apply. It seems highly likely that the old network of CME discussions had already taken place and that Ivatt's name had been put forward as the most suitable candidate. The young engineer from the LNWR went to see J. A. Hookham, Locomotive Superintendent of the NSR, and a short while later received notification of his appointment. The £350 annual salary, agreed by

Hookham with his Board, was not to Ivatt's liking, and he wrote to Hookham saying as much. This caused some consternation and Cooke was informed, but Ivatt stuck to his views. Within six months of commencing at Stoke two salary increases had been granted, both back-dated to the official starting date of 8 September 1919.[48] It is unlikely that any such improvement would have been forthcoming had that initial letter not been sent. That directness was part of the Ivatt character — if he did not like matters, he said so, but would always be fair and honest.

Consequent upon the grouping and the subsequent closure of the works at Stoke, Ivatt found himself once more in the mainstream of locomotive matters when he was transferred to Derby in 1928. He was appointed Locomotive Works Superintendent and in 1931 added the outdoor machinery and fire sections of the Midland Division to his sphere of influence. 1932 saw Stanier's arrival at Derby, and later that year D. C. Urie, Divisional Mechanical Engineer for Scotland, became Chief Motive Power Superintendent in place of J. E. Anderson. Stanier immediately promoted Ivatt to fill the vacant Scottish post and he moved to Glasgow at the end of 1932. The promotion was welcome, but Ivatt had enjoyed his time at Derby building up close relationships with R. A. Riddles, his assistant, and with Sir Henry Fowler.

Ivatt had a very relaxed way of dealing with things and, whilst Works Superintendent at Derby, had to call on Riddles to ease off his frantic pace of work. Nonetheless the Ivatt/Riddles combination accomplished all that was asked of them and they reduced the average number of engines under or awaiting repair from about 140 to 60. The pair had an agreement that if that number was below 4 per cent of the stock, Ivatt would pay for the Saturday afternoon drink. He usually did.[49] The improved efficiency pleased everybody including Fowler, and was achieved by teamwork and an attitude that a tidy workshop was an efficient workshop. That was a view with which Fowler wholeheartedly agreed.

The relaxed attitude of Ivatt is typified by an incident in 1929 when he and Riddles decided to visit the theatre in London. Whilst heading for the station they encountered Fowler who asked where they were going. Upon being informed, the CME queried what would happen to the works whilst they were away. Characteristically Ivatt replied that they were so well organized that nobody would notice their absence.[50]

E. J. Larkin also noticed that relaxed attitude, commenting that Ivatt never appeared to be in a hurry. Larkin also considered him to be a most friendly man who always gave unstinting support to his staff. On one occasion Larkin had, at Ivatt's request, written an article about the boiler deparment, but the journal have no credit to the author. Ivatt wrote indignantly to the editor and received an apology for Larkin as well as payment.[51]

Ivatt was well liked by most people around him and certainly by his own staff. E. S. Cox has also referred to him in the most kindly of terms as one who achieved without appearing to make real effort. This sometimes made him appear lazy to those who measured work only by hours expended rather than results. Ivatt did not like such shows and would discourage any member of the office staff from working after the normal 5.30 pm finishing time. Verbal communication found more favour with him than written memos, and long-winded reports were frowned upon. To those around him Ivatt achieved maximum results with the minimum of fuss, or even effort, and that is the true sign of a good manager. Cox, no mean engineer himself, considered Ivatt to be an instinctive engineer who avoided much of the usual trappings involved in calculation and design.[52]

This 'seat of the pants' approach to engineering was widely admired by others at Derby and throughout the LMS system, although a few in high office, including Hartley, still favoured the academic approach. But from what has been written by Ivatt's contemporaries and fellow engineers, there can be little doubt that he was a man who had earned great respect and affection. His rather 'laid back' approach obviously endeared him to many, but such an approach must be backed up by effectiveness of work. The two do not usually go together except in individuals of rare talent.

Ivatt moved to Euston in October 1937 as Chief Assistant to the CME, William Stanier. The chief and his assistant got on well together and it would appear that Stanier liked the relaxed way in which Ivatt dealt with problems and his attitude in managing people. When Fairburn became CME, Ivatt remained as Chief Assistant, but most of his effort was spent on war work rather than locomotives. When Ivatt was appointed CME following Fairburn's death, R. C. Bond says that the news was greeted with thorough satisfaction by all associated with the locomotive department.[53]

As CME Ivatt had little time to establish himself before nationalization took his status, and essentially his job, away from him. Nevertheless he carried on, intent upon doing the job for which he was paid. The promotion to CME does not appear to have been simply a formality, as Hartley had not been convinced of Ivatt's suitability. On Fairburn's death, Ivatt had been asked to take over as acting CME and the advice of Stanier was sought by the LMS President, Sir William Wood, as to the succession. Stanier recommended Ivatt and the matter was resolved. Riddles was disappointed but congratulated his friend most warmly.[54] Riddles, however, eventually, came out on top as towards the end of 1946 he became a Vice President when Sir Harold Hartley retired.

Although the war had ended when Ivatt became CME, there was still much to be done in order to return the railway to some form of normality. Workshops had to be returned to a peacetime role, but the old Stanier team remained very much the same so Ivatt knew that there were experienced engineers he could rely on. R. C. Bond was selected as Deputy Chief Mechanical Engineer with specific responsibility for the locomotive works. Actually Ivatt was Chief Mechanical and Electrical Engineer, but was still known by the abbreviated form CME.

Locomotives had been lost due to enemy action and a number had been taken for military duty overseas. In addition there was a considerable backlog of repair work, and some of the older locomotives were simply worn out and beyond further useful service. The same was, of course, true of the other three railways in Britain. No dramatic building programme was instituted and Ivatt did not wish to impose a range of new designs on the LMS as he considered that what already existed were basically sound. New locomotives were required in order to fill gaps, but Ivatt had his own ideas on these and did not wish to perpetuate some rather old designs merely to placate the running department. Traditionally high-powered locomotives were 'cascaded' in order to operate less demanding services, but again Ivatt wanted something better and more appropriate for the post-war railway.

New designs for Class '2' locomotives of 2-6-0 and 2-6-2 tank arrangements were devised instead of the simple 0-6-0 requested by the operating people. In service these locomotives proved that Ivatt was correct, but it took tenacity and a strong will to impose these on what had formerly been a very strong section of the LMS. Design work on the Class '2' locomotives progressed slowly whilst Fairburn was still in command, but his absences due to illness allowed Ivatt a much freer hand than he would otherwise have had. A Class '4' 2-6-0 design was also schemed out at the same time, but this was later revamped into a much

more austere form with a degree of functionality which owed much to the American locomotives imported to assist the war effort. The high running plate and accessibility of as many parts as possible put the Class '4' 'Mogul' (2-6-0) in a league of its own as far as British locomotives were concerned. The double chimney fitted originally proved to be unsatisfactory and steaming was greatly improved when it was replaced by a single chimney.

These designs, and especially the Class '4', were produced with an eye on ease of maintenance as well as operation. Self-cleaning smokeboxes, rocking grates and self-emptying ashpans were standard on all three types. Tenders were provided with cabs and coal bunkers were inset in order to afford protection for the footplate crew and give a clear view when running tender first. Such features now seem obvious, but they were not at that time and it took a clear-thinking design team to produce such innovative locomotives. Ivatt was well aware that the late 1940s and 1950s were going to be dramatically different from the pre-war years and that the railways would need to compete for labour. If that was to be in short supply the only way to combat the situation was to design locomotives which required less maintenance, and to make it as easy as possible by greater accessibility. This was thoughtful design.

Diesel traction offered similar rewards, but existing steam designs could also be modified in order to bring about improvements and Ivatt set about constructing Stanier locomotives, especially 'Black Fives', with new features incorporated. Roller bearings were provided on the axleboxes of 20 such locomotives, experience with the 'Turbomotive' illustrating that his form of bearing required less routine attention. It was something of a gamble, however, as the smooth turbine drive imposed somewhat lower loading than a reciprocating drive and the same results could not be guaranteed. A further 20 of the class had Caprotti valve gear fitted, whilst double chimneys were also provided in some cases. One locomotive, No 4767, was fitted with outside Stephenson valve gear in order that the effectiveness or otherwise of the variable lead from this type of gear might be tested.

Ivatt rebuilt some of the 'Patriot' or 'Baby Scot' Class 4-6-0 locomotives by fitting them with the type 1A boiler as used for the rebuilt 'Royal Scot' Class. Other detail changes were made to the smokebox and saddle, cylinders, cab and spring suspension, whilst the standard Ivatt features of rocking rates, self-emptying ashpan and self-cleaning smokebox were also fitted.[55]

The first non-streamlined 'Coronations' had

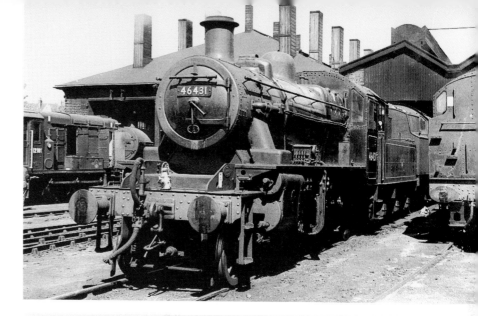

Ivatt Class '2MT' 2-6-0 No 46431 at Watford in 1962. (D. K. Jones collection)

Ivatt 2-6-2 tank No 41212. (D. K. Jones collection)

Ivatt Class '4MT' 2-6-0 No 43098 at Normanton in 1966. (D. K. Jones collection)

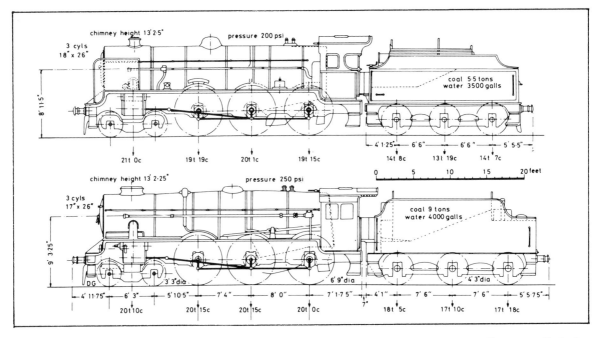

been built in 1938 and wartime conditions had shown how difficult it was to deal effectively with maintenance whilst the streamlined casing was in place. Ivatt commenced removal of these casings in 1946 and only one streamlined 'Coronation' actually remained to receive a British Railways number. Two modified 'Coronation' 'Pacifics' were built by Ivatt in order to determine the influence of newer ideas on what was already a very good design, especially with respect to increased availability. It also allowed a modernized 'Pacific' to be compared with the main-line diesel electric locomotive then on order.

For these 4-6-2s, subsequently named *Sir William A. Stanier, FRS* and *City of Salford*, all axles were fitted with roller bearings, axlebox guides had manganese steel bearing faces, and the pony truck was of a new Ivatt design. Back end framing differed from earlier locomotives of the class and the reversing gear was redesigned. In addition, the usual Ivatt features of ashpan, grate and smokebox were applied.[56]

These new locomotives and their additional features were outlined by Ivatt himself in the only paper he ever contributed to a learned society. During 1947 the Institution of Mechanical Engineers was holding its Centenary Conference, and O.V. S. Bulleid, Ivatt's brother-in-law, was Chairman of the railway power plant section. Bulleid asked the four British CMEs to contribute papers on the current state of their respective railway

stock. Ivatt's paper, essentially compiled by E. S. Cox, outlined the ideas which were being incorporated in modified and newly designed locomotives as well as mentioning the plans for diesel traction.

Ivatt informed the audience that ten locomotive types had been standardized and these would cover all LMS traffic requirements. All newer engines of the chosen types, except for shunters, were to incorporate the basic features of self-cleaning smokeboxes, rocking grates, self-emptying ashpans, manganese steel liners on horns and axlebox faces, outside cylinders (only two whenever possible), and long-lap piston valves. These features and better organization in the workshops were intended to increase availability and the interval between shopping. Complete satisfaction was expressed with regard to the diesel shunters, and Ivatt said that no further steam shunters would be constructed.

Although he stated that advances could still be made with the conventional steam reciprocating locomotive, Ivatt came down firmly on the side of diesel traction for the future. The simple steam locomotive had a part to play, but he did not consider any departure from that basically rugged and relatively inexpensive format was justified in order to obtain improvements in thermal efficiency or availability. It is clear that Ivatt considered his designs and the modified Stanier locomotives were the ultimate in steam traction as far as economics was concerned. Chasing minor gains with fancy ideas was not worth the candle.

The paper gave details of two diesel-electric locomotive types then under construction. A single 800 hp locomotive on two four-wheeled bogies was intended for use on branch and cross country lines. At 67 tons it would have a hauling capacity similar to the Class '2' 2-6-2 tank locomotive. This 827 hp Bo-Bo locomotive was actually turned out by the North British Locomotive Co in 1950 for British Railways as No 10800. The other diesel scheme was much more interesting, for it consisted of two 1,600 hp units which could work independently with capabilities similar to Class '4' 2-6-4 tank locomotives, or be coupled together to work the heaviest Anglo-Scottish main-line trains.

Ivatt was not besotted by diesels — he simply believed in their future. At the conclusion of the paper he stated that trials with the locomotives would enable him to determine whether diesel-electric traction was really worthwhile, and to what extent it was a justified alternative to main-line electrification.[57] It is obvious that Ivatt was considering traction in its broadest sense and was not slavishly tied to one particular form. He may have been a keen and very good steam engineer, but he also had to consider the future of the railway, and for him steam would play a lesser role in years to come.

Although Ivatt's earlier proposal for a main-line diesel had been rather cold-shouldered by Fairburn due to prevailing circumstances, he was determined to resurrect the idea when conditions were right, and as soon as the war ended they were. To be fair it is only right to say that Fairburn himself was interested in main-line diesel traction and shortly before his death had made contact with British Thomson Houston and Paxman, the diesel engine builders, to discuss a 1,500 hp locomotive.[58] Ivatt still had problems regarding finance as the LMS was short of funds and a diesel locomotive would cost considerably more than a steam engine of similar power. One way around the difficulty was by means of a collaborative venture with an outside contractor who could then use the locomotive as a shop window for overseas sales purposes. English Electric proved to be very receptive and agreement was reached, the LMS designing the mechanical part and structure whilst English Electric produced the diesel engines and electrical equipment.[59]

The bolster-type bogies were of a novel design and Ivatt took personal interest in them. He devised an arrangement whereby the weight of the locomotive frame and body was carried by four bearing pads on each bogie, thus leaving the centre bearing free from that load and able to deal with traction force. This idea was later patented in the USA in Ivatt's name by the Commonwealth Steel Corporation. In order to use an existing design of traction motor with this arrangement of bogie, it was necessary to fit three such motors on each bogie, one per axle.

A 16-cylinder V-type turbo-charged engine was provided by English Electric with a continuous rating of 1,600 bhp at 750 rpm. This drove an electrical generator which in turn powered the direct current traction motors. A set of lead-acid batteries supplied power for starting the diesel engine, the main generator acting as a starting motor for this purpose. In order to provide steam

Above left *Comparative drawings of original and rebuilt 'Patriots'.*

Right *The Ivatt version of a Stanier 'Duchess': No 46257* City of Salford *at Carlisle in 1961.* (D. K. Jones collection)

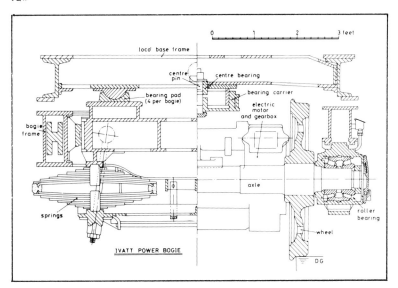

Left *The Ivatt power bogie for main-line diesel locomotives.*

Right *Section drawing of diesel electric No 10000.*

Below right *No 10000 at speed in early BR days.* (D. K. Jones collection)

for carriage heating an automatic oil-fired boiler was provided. The idea of using waste heat from the diesel in order to generate steam had been raised but was abandoned because at low loads insufficient heat would be available.

In keeping with the added comforts provided for footplate crew on his steam locomotives, Ivatt ensured that the crew of his diesels would also be comfortable. E. J. Larkin joined Ivatt on the footplate of No 10000 during its first visit to London and commented to him that the cab was so comfortable it would be a job for the driver to stay awake.[60] As well as comfortable seating there were defrosters, droplights, sun blinds and electric heaters.

Nationalization was drawing nigh but Ivatt was determined that the first of his two main-line diesels would at least always be recognized as LMS. The stainless steel letters 'LMS' fitted to the body side could easily be removed, but not so those cast into the aluminium floorplates of the engine compartment. Ivatt had an eye to the future, but he was just as proud of the past.

On 18 December 1947, No 10000 and Ivatt's modified 'Pacific' No 6256, *Sir William A. Stanier, FRS*, were together at Euston for a brief ceremony which culminated in the naming of the steam locomotive. Stanier was there and must have been pleased not only because of the naming but also at the changes produced by his one-time assistant. Sir George Nelson, Chairman and Managing Director of English Electric, mentioned that the whole main-line diesel locomotive project had come to fruition in a very short period of time following discussions during an informal lunch in

April 1946.[61] The team spirit which produced those results continued during the early years of the nationalized British Railways, but it was primarily the LMS team under the direction of R. A. Riddles which held the reins.

Although Ivatt still got on well with Riddles, he did not take to the new approach and considered the idea of standard locomotive designs to be unnecessary as the regions were already well stocked with useful machines from the former companies. In 1951 he decided to retire from the railway but not from active work, for he became a Director of Brush, Bagnall Traction Ltd, acting as a consultant on diesel traction matters.[62] He later became a Director of Remploy Ltd and remained active as a consultant with the British Electrical Co until 1964.

Henry George Ivatt lead a full life, enjoyed himself and served with assorted employers with distinction. He did not seek fame through the design of his own locomotives but merely sought to improve them and the work they did. His style was certainly easier than many other CMEs, but he did obtain results from those about him. Although Ivatt would be the last person to claim responsibility, some credit must go to him for the team spirit which remained with the LMS locomotive department until the end, and even into British Railways days. He encouraged the team-work which Stanier had started where some would have wished to impose their own will. Ivatt died on 4 October 1972 aged 86 years, and it would be fitting simply to say that 'he let his works speak for him'.

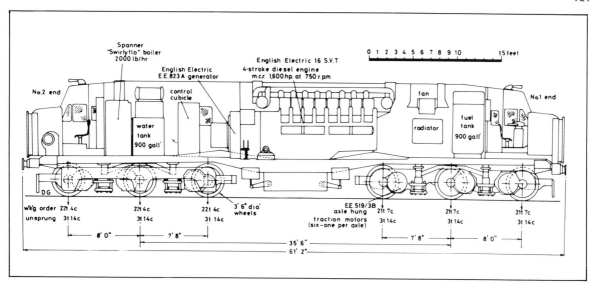

6. Locomotives of the Lancashire & Yorkshire Railway

Aspinall had no time to indulge in immediate locomotive design work when he was appointed CME, as he was busily engaged with the workshops at Horwich. New locomotives had to be provided in order to meet the increasing traffic demands, but Wright designs were able to satisfy the immediate requirement. Orders for 0-6-0 and 4-4-0 locomotives were placed with outside contractors, but Aspinall had intentions to introduce some form of standardization in order to allow interchangeability of parts. The operation of some 4-4-0s fitted with Joy valve gear had shown lower coal consumption compared with similar locomotives fitted with Stephenson link motion, and Aspinall decided to adopt that form of valve gear for future locomotive construction.[1] In later years, when 200 locomotives with Joy gear were in operation, it was claimed that a coal saving of 0.85 lb per mile could be obtained with that form of gear.[2]

A royalty had to be paid for use of the Joy gear, but the amount charged must have been considered worth paying in view of the expected savings. A batch of 4-4-0s ordered from the Vulcan Foundry in 1886 followed the Wright design, but an 1887 order for 30 from Beyer Peacock incorporated Joy gear. It would seem that Aspinall struck a good deal with the inventor over royalty payments, for in his diary David Joy comments: ' . . . I had a fearful go at a bargain with J.A.F

Aspinall. I could never hold my own at a bargain'.[3]

A new Aspinall design was that of the 2-4-2 side tank which appeared in 1889. Some 270 of the class were ultimately constructed and their usefulness was easy to see, for during that first decade of the twentieth century they were operating more than 50 per cent of the railway's passenger mileage. Changes in detail took place over the production period; later engines differed from those produced initially in that they had longer coal bunkers, whilst others were fitted with smaller cylinders and some had Richardson balanced valves instead of unbalanced 'D' valves. Aspinall borrowed an idea from his former chief at Crewe, F. W. Webb, and fitted radial axleboxes to the front and rear axles. Because of the extensive mileage these engines were expected to run bunker-first, Aspinall designed a water pick-up apparatus which could be worked whichever way the locomotive was running. This two-way scoop could be lowered and raised in either direction by means of a vacuum-actuated piston acting through levers. A similar vacuum-operated pick-up apparatus was also provided for tender engines, but this only worked in one direction.

A member of the class, No 1008, was the first locomotive actually constructed at Horwich and this has been preserved as part of the National Collection at York. Members of the class con-

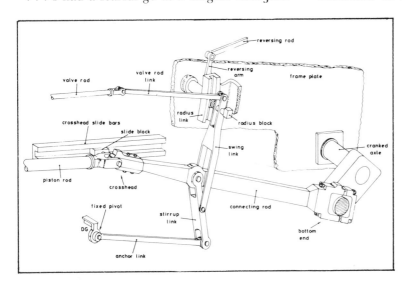

Joy valve gear.

structed during the Hughes era were provided with Belpaire boilers working at 180 psi compared with the 160 psi of the Aspinall machines. The 5 ft 8 in coupled wheels were the same diameter as those of existing 0-4-4 tanks, whilst many boiler dimensions were the same as for other classes, thus allowing for similar parts and the use of common flanging blocks. It was not complete standardization, but it was getting close to an arrangement Aspinall wanted.

Although the Wright 0-6-0 tender engines were still effective, Aspinall desired a standardized version. The design proved to be another winner, and between its introduction in 1889 and 1901 some 400 were constructed, although, as with the 2-4-2 design, variations in cylinder bore, type of valve and other minor details did exist. The wheel diameter of 5 ft 1 in made these 0-6-0s more suitable for passenger traffic than the Wright engines, and they could be found throughout the L&YR

system on both heavy goods trains and on passenger duties; to allow for the latter, several were fitted for steam heating. Hughes constructed more of the class, the final two of his 1905 order being built with Schmidt superheaters. Others with Belpaire boilers and superheaters were constructed in 1912 whilst a further five to the basic Aspinall design were built in 1918. A number of these engines lasted until the 1960s, indicating the soundness and usefulness of that original 1880s design.

Following the introduction of his 0-6-0 tender engines, Aspinall looked at the Wright 0-6-0 and decided that many of those in better condition could be converted to saddle tanks and used for shunting purposes. This work required the frames to be lengthened in order to carry the coal bunker and a saddle tank to be fitted over the boiler. The tenders thus released were used for newly constructed locomotives, especially the

Above *The 2-4-2 tank design of 1889: No 10762 in LMS days.* (D. K. Jones collection)

Right *Aspinall's water scoops, one-way for tender engines and two-way for tanks.*

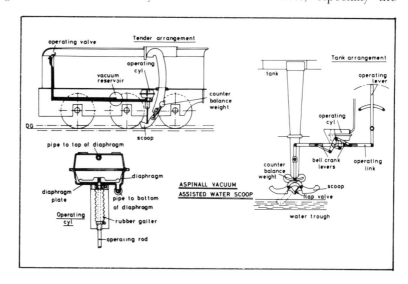

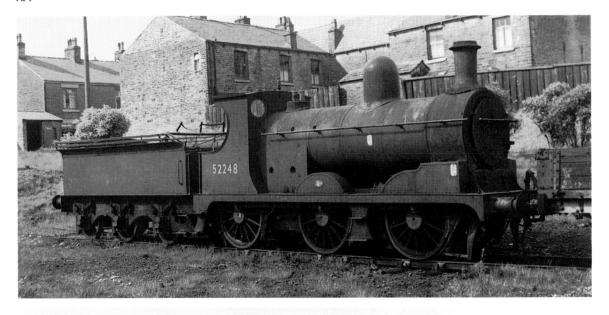

Top *An Aspinall 0-6-0 built in 1894, surviving as BR No 52248 in 1962. (D. K. Jones collection)*

Above *Round-top and Belpaire boiler versions of Aspinall 0-6-0 locomotives. No 62 was built in 1894 and No 1019 in 1889, reboilered in 1911. (National Railway Museum, York)*

Left *BR No 51408 at Bolton in 1960, an 0-6-0 saddle tank reconstructed from a Wright 0-6-0 tender. (D. K. Jones collection)*

Above right *'Atlantic' No 1424, built in 1902 and fitted with the Aspinall superheater; the ash hopper pipe is visible behind the smokebox. (National Railway Museum, York)*

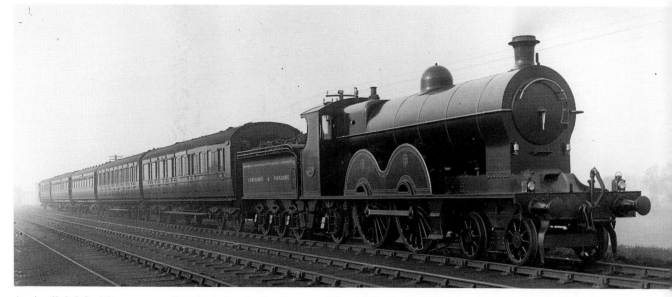

Aspinall 0-6-0s.[4] Some were fitted to the Aspinall-designed 4-4-0s which began to appear in 1891. These were improved versions of the earlier but essentially Wright-designed 4-4-0s, and both varieties were constructed during the early 1890s. Aspinall's engines had 7 ft 3 in diameter driving wheels and were intended for fast passenger services from Manchester to Liverpool, Southport, Blackpool and Leeds. The bogie was of the swing-link type and several other Aspinall features were incorporated. Although the large-diameter driving wheels may appear unsuitable for working the severely graded L&YR lines, especially that to Leeds, they were powerful locomotives capable of hauling 220-ton loads at average speeds of 42.8 miles per hour.[5]

Aspinall considered that a high centre of gravity was required for steady riding and was consequently less damaging to the track. He mentioned his theory when presenting a paper entitled 'Express Locomotives' to the International Railway Congress in London during 1895. His view was that the higher the centre of gravity, the more vertical would be the force on the outer rail on curves, and as springs acted vertically the shock loading effect would be less. With a low centre of gravity the overturning force became nearer to a side thrust and greater would be the loading on the side of the rail. Side oscillations would be greater because the springs were set to dampen vertical forces, not side forces. He did, however, caution his audience about the effects of a high centre of gravity when cornering on track with incorrect superelevation.[6]

The high-pitched boiler of Aspinall's 'Atlantic' (4-4-2)- type locomotives which appeared in 1899 showed that he had faith in his own pronouncements and was prepared to back them with design. The centre of gravity of these locomotives was 5ft 6 in above the rail and caused concern to some regular passengers more used to a low-set boiler. Some went so far as to ask Aspinall if the locomotives were safe, but he was very certain of his facts and laid before them evidence as to his reasoning.[7] If that did not utterly convince the sceptical travellers, the actual riding of the locomotive must have done.

As with the 4-4-0s, a swing link bogie was fitted and several other features which had been tried on different 4-4-0s were also incorporated. In 1896 the Institution of Mechanical Engineers had sponsored trials with steam jacketing as a means of reducing cylinder losses and, naturally, Aspinall took the lead. One of his 4-4-0s was fitted with 17 ½ inch diameter steam-jacketed cylinders to test the effect, whilst others of the class were given features such as long-travel valves, centre bearings or extended smokeboxes. Not all such modifications came during Aspinall's period as CME, but the 4-4-0s proved invaluable as mobile test-beds.

As a result of the steam jacketing trials, the initial 20 4-4-2s were fitted with steam jackets, the steam supply being at boiler pressure and the exhaust passing to the injector on the right-hand-side of the locomotive. The Belpaire boiler was the largest of its day and it had a peculiar arrangement of an extended smokebox, or perhaps more

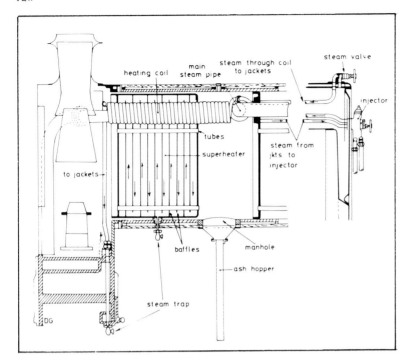

correctly a recessed boiler-front tubeplate. The idea behind the arrangement is uncertain, but it may have been to reduce spark throwing, as a large-volume smokebox was considered to be useful in achieving that end. The last locomotive of that initial batch of 4-4-2s had its tubeplate recessed by a further 3 feet and a form of superheater fitted in the space made available. Gas passed through tubes in this unit and the steam circulated around these tubes before passing to the cylinders. In practical terms it was difficult to clean and did not prove to be the success hoped for as insufficient superheat temperature was achieved. After the initial locomotive, five more were similarly fitted and four were still running with the device in 1914 when Aspinall mentioned their indifferent performance during discussion of Fowler's paper on superheating.[8]

In the space between the front tubeplate and the superheater was an ash hopper which allowed accumulated ash to be discharged on to the track. Richardson balanced slide valves were fitted to the original 20 and to the second batch of 20, but these tended to leak and Hoy began to replace them with outside admission piston valves in 1901. The steam reversing gear was also replaced by vertical screw reversers commencing at the same time. Despite these problems, the 'Atlantics' were a success, their large-capacity boilers being

well able to maintain steam for the 19 in x 26 in cylinders. They advanced British locomotive design not only in power and performance but also in the features they incorporated. Not all were widely adopted, but all were worthwhile experiments.

Aspinall's final steam design was an 0-8-0 coal locomotive, although this actually appeared after he ceased to be CME; in fact, construction did not commence until Hoy had succeeded him in that office. Several features were common to other classes, thus continuing the standardization policy, but there was no slavish adherence to such a policy — if change was considered necessary, new parts were designed. The two 20 inch diameter inside cylinders were the largest put in a L&YR locomotive to that date, whilst the boiler was different in size from any previously constructed. Of the Belpaire type and similar to that of the 4-4-2 locomotives, with the same tube length and barrel diameter, there was no recessed smokebox and the firebox was not so deep. It was that boiler which caused problems and resulted in the introduction of a novel form of firebox.

A boiler explosion on one of these engines during 1901 was attributed to defective stays, and Hoy set about redesigning in order to minimize future risk. Stays are a necessary evil because they provide strength but are subject to defects which can result in subsequent explosion. The defective stay may only be recognized after such an explosion, so they can give rise to a sense of false security. Marine boilers had long given up the use of furnace stays through the introduction of corrugated cylindrical furnaces, and extension of the idea to locomotive practice had been attempted a number of times previously. Webb had introduced a corrugated steel firebox during the late 1880s, the use of steel being to save on the expense of copper, and corrugations to increase strength.[9] Ramsbottom had also made use of a corrugated furnace on shunting engines some years earlier.[10]

This is no place to go into a mathematical discussion as to the strength of the corrugated furnaces, but they are stronger than plain cylindrical types and therefore do not require any stays. Hoy's design of corrugated firebox was fitted to locomotive No 392 in 1902 and the following year to a further 20 new engines. A 7/8 inch thick steel tubeplate with steel tubes was originally fitted, but leakage soon became evident and the tubeplate thickness was reduced to 5/8 inch to correct the defect but without much success. Later, copper ends were fitted to the steel tubes, but leakage was not stopped until the steel tubeplate was replaced by a 1 inch thick copper tubeplate.

After about five years in service, cracks developed at the tubeplate edges whilst furnaces developed a tendency to become oval. Jacking back into shape was a temporary solution, but the

priming to which these boilers were prone could not be overcome. Circulation was also very poor and, although it was reported that they steamed well, it did take a longer time than normal for them to reach pressure following the lighting of the fire. Hughes compared them unfavourably

Above right *Horwich erecting shop. Aspinall 0-8-0 coal engine No 392 is suspended from the crane.* (G. Charles collection)

Right *Different L&YR boiler and firebox arrangements.*

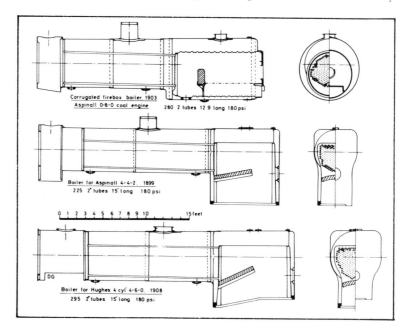

Corrugated firebox boiler, 1903
Aspinall 0-8-0 coal engine   280 2" tubes 12 9 long 180 psi

Boiler for Aspinall 4-4-2, 1899
225 2" tubes 15' long 180 psi

0 1 2 3 4 5 6 7 8 9 10   15 feet

Boiler for Hughes 4 cyl 4-6-0, 1908
295 2" tubes 15' long 180 psi

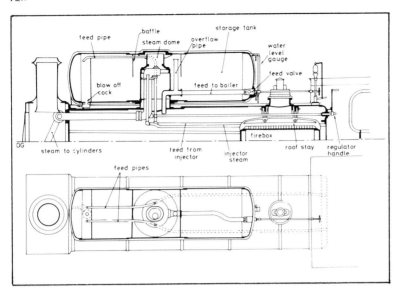

with stayed firebox boilers[11] and later replaced them with the Belpaire variety.

The only Lancashire & Yorkshire design Hoy actually originated was a 2-6-2 radial tank for branch line services on heavily graded routes around Manchester. The rather short coupled wheelbase of 6 ft 2 in + 6 ft 2 in gave trouble on curves, and the flanges on the inside coupled wheels had to be removed. The coupled wheels were of 5 ft 8 in in diameter and maximum axle loading was 18 tons. As with Aspinall locomotives, the boiler was pitched high, its centre-line being 9 feet above rail level. Seats were provided for driver and fireman and a wooden platform was fitted above the metal footplate; for locomotives of the period these were comforts indeed. A two-way vacuum-operated water scoop, similar to the Aspinall type, was also fitted.[12]

It may appear that Hoy was not very active during his short term as CME, and if new locomotive designs are basis for making such judgement then that is certainly true. However, he did actively engage himself in modifications and the testing of ideas, especially those aimed at improving economy. A 2-4-2 radial tank locomotive with a round-top boiler was fitted with a Druit Halpin thermal storage tank in 1902, Hughes fitting five others with similar devices three years later.

This arrangement consisted of a tank situated above the boiler with steam and water connections to the boiler. The boiler's steam dome was situated in the tank and steam would be collected in the normal manner; however feed from the injector would go to the storage tank above the boiler where its temperature would be raised to that of the boiler water. In order to maintain the boiler water level, the fireman would open a valve which allowed the hot water to drain from the tank into the boiler by means of gravity, boiler and tank being at the same pressure. A gauge glass allowed water level in the tank to be monitored, but maintaining this was not as critical as that of the boiler as there was no furnace crown which could be exposed. During periods of hard working on severe gradients and where stopping was frequent, the locomotives fitted with these tanks showed a distinct saving of water and coal. This was because hot feed water could be supplied from the tank whilst the locomotive was working hard and heat added to the cold water in the tank whilst the locomotive was stopped. On easier sections of the line the advantages were not so evident, and were outweighed by problems of sediment.[13] This resulted in the devices being removed after six years of service.

With the introduction of electric traction on the Liverpool to Southport line, a different approach to engineering was required. Much of the actual electrical engineering work was contracted out, but Aspinall and Hoy still took an interest. Hoy's bogie design for the power cars used on that line was mentioned in chapter 2, and these cars continued in service for a great many years. Each train set consisted of four cars, two first and two third class, the third class cars, positioned at the ends of the sets, having the power bogies. The 600-volt electricity supply was collected from a third rail and fed to the two 150-hp motors on each bogie, giving a total of 1,200 hp.

Although the train current was supplied at 600 volts dc, it was distributed from the power station sited near Formby at 7,500 volts, three-phase ac, then transformed at substations situated at strategic points along the line. This arrangement reduced production and distribution losses. Four 600kw rotary converters, each basically comprising an ac motor driving a dc generator, were situated at the substations together with three air-cooled static transformers. Current was collected from a third live rail positioned in the six-foot way between the two running tracks, and in order to ensure a good return circuit a similar rail was positioned between each set of rails and connected to those running rails. Pick-up and return were achieved by means of vertical contact shoes.[14]

When the Manchester-Bury line was electrified, a 1,200-volt dc system was chosen and it was thought that vertical contact shoes would create problems when rails became dirty or coated with water or ice. Aspinall designed a fully protected side-contact pick-up arrangement which avoided the need for horizontal surface contacts. The pick-up gear was secured between the axleboxes of the motor bogies, a spring exerting a force of 25 lbs in order to keep the pick-up bar in contact with the side of the live rail.[15]

George Hughes had an interest in electrification but he was also concerned with the effective use of steam on branch lines. Early in the twentieth century, steam rail-motors became fashionable and several different designs were produced. Hughes decided to give them a trial and in 1904 he ordered two from Kerr, Stuart and Co, these being to a design of T.H.Riches, CME of the Taff Vale Railway. They were rather unusual in that they had two very short transverse boiler units positioned on either side of a common firebox, but they did perform effective work and served to convince Hughes that there was something in the idea. He did, however, believe that he could produce a better design for L&YR routes.

The Hughes rail-motors were like the Taff Vale variety in that they consisted of a separate four-wheeled power unit to which was connected the passenger car by means of a pivot pin, but there was considerable difference between the power units. The Horwich units were like conventional locomotives but smaller; in fact, the boiler made use of standard flanged plates and fittings, thus reducing the cost of manufacture. The two 12 in x 16 in outside cylinders had Walschaerts valve gear and each engine unit could operate in isolation from its passenger car, such as when they were

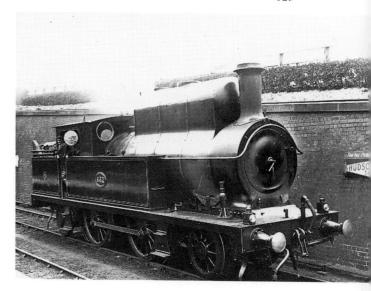

returned to Horwich for repair, the passenger car being left propped up at the engine end. These rail-motors could be operated from either end by means of control lines, whilst an electric bell system allowed for communication between driver

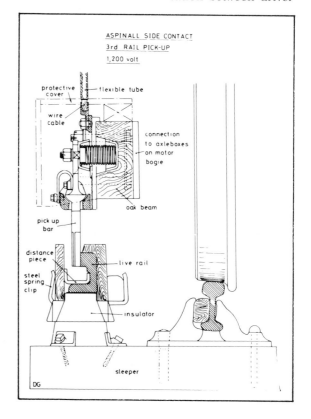

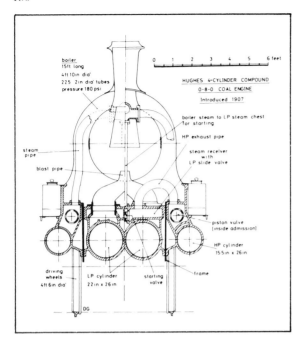

and fireman, the latter having to stay on the footplate.[16]

George Hughes continued production of Aspinall and Hoy designed locomotives for some time after he became CME, but only so long as they were required to fill specific needs. He quickly set about modifying existing designs to suit changing circumstances and instituted work on a number of new designs, although not all were actually produced. A number of existing locomotives were modified in order to test the claimed advantages of compounding and superheating. Hughes required evidence of an advantage before he would commit himself to full production, and different ideas had to be tried before the most suitable was selected. He was a good and innovative engineer but also a careful one who relied on experimentation of his own to provide the answers.

Hughes's views on compounding were firm and decidely against the use of the principle for express passenger locomotives. He had concluded that there would be little loss due to condensation in a cylinder where the piston speed was high, and this belief was probably confirmed from experience with Hoy's experimental compound 4-4-0. Compounding still had advantages, however, and Hughes was determined on a trial, so he rebuilt No 1452, an Aspinall 0–8–0, as a four-cylinder compound with two 15^{1}/$_{2}$-inch high-pressure outside cylinders and two 22-inch

low-pressure inside cylinders, all with a 26-inch stroke. Inside admission piston valves were fitted for the HP cylinder and balanced Richardson 'D' valves for the LP. Adjacent inside and outside cranks were at 90 degrees to each other, so a single set of inside Joy gear could be used for two cylinders. Steam pressure was retained at the 180 psi of the original design.

In July 1906 Hughes reported that the trials were satisfactory and obtained permission to construct 20 new compounds. In fact, ten were compound and ten simple, Hughes probably wishing to carry out realistic comparative trials with new engines. Details of comparative running were actually given by the CME in his paper 'Compounding and Superheating'.[17] When he presented that paper in 1910, the compounds had been running for over two years and a considerable amount of data was available, but Hughes stated that he believed a further three years' results would be needed before true figures for coal and maintenance costs could be determined. At that time. however, he was prepared to state that compounds on average consumed 9¾ per cent less coal per ton mile than the simples. Maintenance costs were about the same for compounds and simples but they were still relatively new engines and during later years repair costs of the compounds might be expected to rise. The fact that no further compounds were constructed for the L&YR seems to indicate that Hughes did not in fact find the initial savings to be worthwhile after prolonged tests.

An interesting feature of the compounds was the starting valve which was patented by Hughes. With the reversing lever in full forward or full back gear, a small starting valve, actuated by the reversing shaft, allowed steam at full pressure to enter the LP steam chest; thus the locomotive would be started as a simple. When the cut-off was reduced, this starting valve would stop live steam from passing directly to the LP chest and the engine then operated as a compound. The starting valve consisted basically of two small slide valves placed back-to-back, and it worked in an auxiliary chamber cast into the LP cylinder block. No special arrangements were made for the HP cylinder when working simple, steam pressure being on both sides of the piston thus essentially putting them in equilibrium.[18]

This design was both elegant and simple, requiring no special attention from the driver when changing from simple to compound operation or vice versa; the driver just did his job and the skill of the designer made the decisions for him. So simple and effective was the design that it

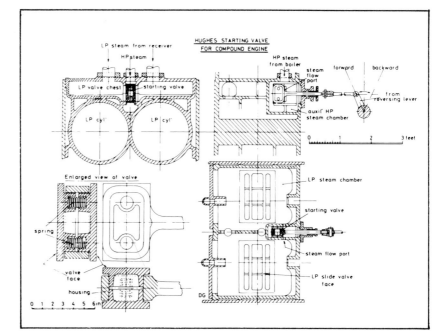

Far left *Hughes four-cylinder compound 0-8-0 coal engine.*

Right *Hughes compound starting valve.*

Below right *Piston-type starting valve as fitted to the 4-6-0 compound.*

was repeated in modified form several years later when one of the Hughes-designed 4-6-0s was converted to a compound by Fowler shortly after he became CME of the LMS. The only difference was the use of a piston starting valve instead of a pair of flat valves, so it remained very much a Hughes design. Again the driver made no decision as to compound or simple working, simple operation becoming automatic when cut-off was within 5 per cent of full gear.[19]

Whilst carrying out his compounding trials, the advantages of superheating were also investigated by Hughes. Two 0-6-0s under construction at the end of 1906 were fitted with Schmidt superheaters and Hughes proceeded to gather operating data in his usual rigorous way. Modifications for the superheated engines included 20-inch diameter cylinders instead of 18-inches, larger steam ports and increased valve lap. Boiler modifications were required in order to allow the fitting of the superheater, and these reduced the steam generation surface area, but grate area and steam pressure remained the same at 18¾ sq ft and 180 psi respectively. Results illustrated the advantages of superheating and Hughes was quickly convinced.

Other locomotives, including five of the 4-4-0s with 7 ft 3 in driving wheels and all 20 of the 2-4-2 tank engines ordered in 1910, were given superheaters. These latter locomotives were a development of the Aspinall 2-4-2 tanks but had Belpaire

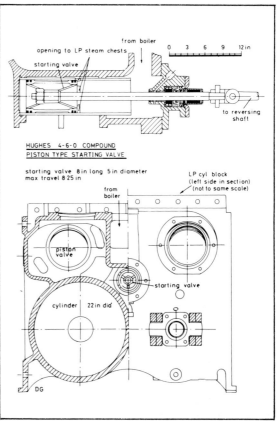

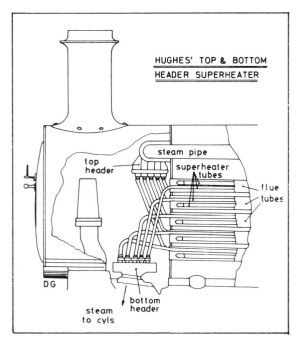

HUGHES' TOP & BOTTOM
HEADER SUPERHEATER

steam pipe

top
header

superheater
tubes

flue
tubes

DG

steam
to cyls

bottom
header

L&YR, but not before other forms of superheater had been tried. Robinson superheaters were tested together with a Hughes-designed plug-type superheater, but both of these, as well as the Schmidt form, were found wanting against the top and bottom type.[20] It is possible that the payment of royalties on the Schmidt and Robinson types had some influence on the decision, but Hughes was an engineer concerned with results and overall savings rather than the simple matter of initial cost.

During the Hughes era a number of new designs were introduced as well as modified versions of existing designs. This is not a book about locomotives but engineers, so they will not all be mentioned. It should, however, be recognized that Hughes was active in upgrading the locomotive stock in order to meet traffic demands, and he did so very successfully. Where possible, standard parts were used and most locomotives had superheaters once these had shown themselves to produce increased economy.

An exception were the five 0-8-2 tanks designed for heavy shunting and banking duties. This type of operation was very much 'start-and-stop', thus superheating was considered to be of no benefit. These 1908-built engines had the largest boilers built by the L&YR to that date, and their 21 1/2-inch diameter cylinders were the larged fitted to any British simple locomotive. In order to ease movement around curves, the wheels on the middle two driving axles were made flangeless and were given wide tyres.[21] In general, the class of engine used non-standard parts but this shows Hughes's willingness to deviate from a pattern should necessity dictate.

One design which proved to be unsuccessful, at least in its original form, was the four-cylinder 4-6-0. This was introduced in 1908 in order to

boilers and several other new features apart from the superheaters. As a result of the performance of these new 2-4-2 tanks, a number of the earlier Aspinall engines were rebuilt to the latter pattern and given superheaters. Six of these received Schmidt superheaters, but 20 were given the Horwich-designed 'top and bottom' superheater, Hughes considering that this had many advantages over the Schmidt type.

The top and bottom superheater, as the name implies, had headers at the top and bottom of the smokebox with superheater elements joining these headers. This design, with 20 or 28 elements, subsequently became standard for the

deal with increased train weights and accelerated services on the trans-Pennine routes. Hughes wanted an engine which embodied rapid acceleration, good hauling power and the ability to negotiate fairly tight curves. The design actually produced has frequently been compared unfavourably with other express locomotives of the companies which were grouped to form the LMS, and in many respects the adverse critism was justified. It has to be borne in mind, however, that the design was for service on the sharply curved and heavily graded L&YR routes which required rapid acceleration from frequent stops. The locomotives were not designed for operation over the London & North Western's West Coast line nor over Midland Railway lines. Like can only truly be compared with like.

In fact, however, they did not come up to the standard set by Hughes, being rather sluggish performers and often short of steam. Surprisingly they were not fitted with superheaters, but it is doubtful if that would have improved performance to a good level. In order to allow for working on tight curves, the wheelbase was kept as short as possible by placing the inside cylinders well in advance of the bogie centre. Flexibility was allowed by giving a small amount of lateral play to the trailing coupled wheels, whilst the coupling rods were provided with ball-and-socket joints which gave vertical and lateral movement.

It is certain that Hughes would have wished more time to produce an ideal design, but traffic demands dictated the need for the locomotives. In producing the design, he also had to compromise in order to achieve relative simplicity and keep within existing workshop practices for maintenance purposes. He did consider using the Yarrow-Schlick-Tweedy system for balancing, this being common for large marine reciprocating

engines, but that would have required costly modifications to the crankshaft. Adjacent cylinders could not have been at 180 degrees to each other and separate valve gear would have been needed for each cylinder. Hughes had decided upon simplicity and that meant that a single set of inside Joy valve gear had to operate both sets of valves on that side of the locomotive. Good balance was essential in order to minimize hammer-blow, the weight of the locomotive being high due to the very large boiler provided to meet the demands of the 16 in x 26 in cylinders.[22]

Details of these locomotives, which were generally considered poor performers, have been included to show the thought which went into their design. Hughes approached the problem in a scientific way and the energy expended deserved better results. Some of the problems were ironed out; the fitting of an air duct below the trailing axle improved air flow to the boiler and hence improved steaming, but the 4-6-0s remained inefficient as far as coal consumption was concerned.

With the end of the First World War, Hughes was able to modify the 4-6-0s into the machines they should have been in the first place. Modification was effectively redesign. Although the boiler diameter remained the same, the working side was changed by the fitting of a 28-element top and bottom superheater. Walschaerts valve gear with inside admission piston valves was provided for each cylinder, whilst steam passageways were opened up and made more direct. Fifteen of the original 20 4-6-0s were rebuilt and a further 35 built new to the same design.

Although better in performance and efficiency than the originals, they were still not as good as might have been expected. Leakage of steam past the piston valves resulted from wear at the ball-

Above left *Hughes 'top and bottom' superheater.*

Left *The 4-6-0 locomotives as originally built. Nos 1514 and 1525 at Rainford with the Royal Train, July 1913.* (National Railway Museum, York)

Right *Superheated Hughes 4-6-0; LMS No 10442 (L&YR No 1671) at Blackpool in September 1938.* (D. K. Jones collection)

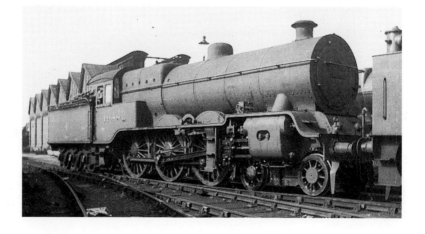

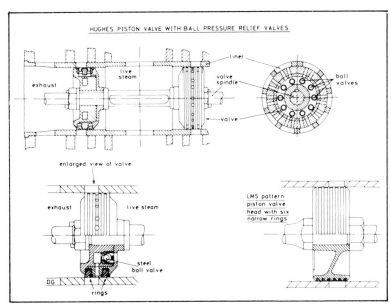

HUGHES PISTON VALVE WITH BALL PRESSURE RELIEF VALVES

enlarged view of valve

Left *Piston valves with ball pressure relief valves as fitted to the superheated 4-6-0s.*

Below *A Hughes 4-6-4 tank engine in Horwich erecting shop.* (G. Charles collection)

Below right *Hughes 'Crab' 2-6-0 BR No 42789 at Ayr during 1965.* (D. K. Jones collection)

pattern pressure relief valves within the piston valve heads. When these were replaced by LMS-pattern valve heads with narrow rings, coal consumption was reduced.[23] Hughes had fitted the ball valves in order to reduce the pumping effect of the piston valves and also to minimize valve chest wear when the steam was shut off. With steam shut off the balls fell from their seats allowing connection between the live steam and exhaust sides of the piston valve. This was an example of a clever solution to a problem which could have been overcome in a less complex way.

E. S. Cox says that these redesigned 4-6-0s had very good pulling power at lower speeds, but at sustained higher speeds they were much inferior to the LNWR 'Claughton' Class 4-6-0s.[24] This

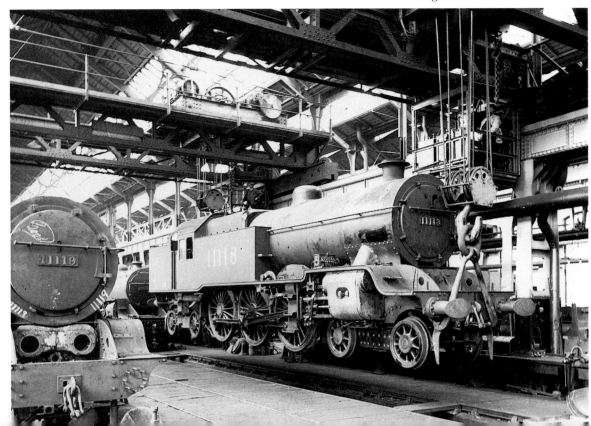

would seem reasonable as the Horwich locos were not designed for sustained high-speed running — they were originally constructed for L&YR service between Lancashire and Yorkshire, and Hughes had wanted good acceleration, not sustained high speed, such as on the West Coast Main Line. Admittedly the rebuilt Hughes 4-6-0s were not absolutely successful in meeting the initial design requirements, but it is somewhat unfair to burden them with being poor at something for which they were not originally designed.

A 4-6-4 tank locomotive was essentially the final locomotive designed for the L&YR although the first did not appear until after the grouping. They were essentially required to handle the fast suburban traffic and so release the 4-6-0s for express work, but much of the work was already covered by 2-4-2 tanks and the need for these larger locomotives was difficult to determine. In the end only ten were built instead of the 30 intended, but they did perform useful service, had a considerable reserve of power and rode well in both directions.

The Hughes 2-6-0 was not a product of the L&YR but came about after the formation of the LMS. However, being the final Hughes design it is worth a mention in this chapter. So successful was this 2-6-0 that it became the only standard locomotive of the initial LMS design scheme not to derive from Midland practice, and it lasted well into the British Railways era. Although several modifications were made to the design after Hughes left office, credit must go to him for producing what was a first class mixed traffic locomotive. Long travel, long lap valves were fitted, the first on the LMS, and these gave a degree of performance and economy which was unique to the group during its formative years.

In order to allow the locomotives access to Midland routes with their rather restrictive loading gauge, Hughes inclined the cylinders by an unusually large amount, giving them something of an ungainly appearance and earning for them the nickname 'Crab'. In all, 245 engines of the class were constructed for use throughout the LMS system, five being given Lenz poppet valve gear in 1931. This improved efficiency in terms of coal consumption compared with unmodified members of the class, and that was already good compared with the Hughes 4-6-0s and 4-6-4s. Maintenance costs for the 'Crabs' were also much lower than these other classes and Hughes had, obviously, arrived at an excellent design.[25]

It is interesting to speculate how LMS locomotive affairs would have developed had Hughes remained in charge with the freedom of action which Stanier enjoyed. However, as with life itself, locomotive history can be a succession of 'ifs' and 'buts'.

7. Locomotives of the London & North Western Railway

It took some time for Ramsbottom to firmly establish himself as sole Locomotive Engineer to the LNWR, so there was no definite point at which the introduction of Ramsbottom-designed locomotives commenced. Shortly after he moved to Crewe, the 0-6-0 'DX' engine was introduced, and that makes a convenient point at which to start. In fact, Ramsbottom was not as prolific a locomotive designer as he was an inventor, so not very many classes can be attributed to him. During his years in office he did, however, rebuild many earlier designs, and the most famous of these rebuilds is *Cornwall*. This locomotive, subsequently rebuilt again by Webb, fortunately survives, although in nothing like the form devised by Trevithick.

The 'DX' locomotives were exceptional for their day and it is often forgotten that the design was introduced in 1858. Over the next 14 years no fewer than 943 were constructed, 86 being for the Lancashire & Yorkshire Railway. When introduced it was still policy to name all LNWR engines, and the first 'DX' was called *Hardman*. Many of Ramsbottom's inventions were fitted including the duplex safety valve and a displacement lubricator, but several other completely new features were also added. For the first time a locomotive was provided with a screw reverser, and the suspension springs were held by hooked hangers, features which became standard practice but which Ramsbottom devised.

The smokebox sloped forwards at the bottom, the door having its hinge arranged horizontally and lifting vertically, a practice which remained on LNWR locomotives for many years. The 'DX' boiler proved to be very effective and was put on a number of rebuilt locomotives, including Crewe-type 2-2-2s.

The most celebrated of Ramsbottom's locomotive designs must be the 2-2-2 'Problem' Class. No 531 *Lady of the Lake* was displayed at the 1862 International Exhibition in London, being awarded a bronze medal, and its fame was such that the whole class became known as the 'Lady of the Lake' Class. Introduced in 1859, the 'Problem' Class engines established themselves on the fastest trains and gave the railway a reputation for fast and punctual service. Two outside 16 in x 24 in cylinders taking steam from the boiler at a pressure of 120 psi turned the 7 ft 6 in driving wheels, whilst a Giffard injector, one of the earliest applications in British locomotive practice, supplied water to the boiler. A brick arch was employed in the firebox, air supply being regulated by means of dampers. In the smokebox was a hopper for collecting ash, thus minimizing the risk of overheating due to the ignition of this ash. Other usual Ramsbottom features like piston rings and a screw reverser were provided, but a novel introduction was that of the water pick-up

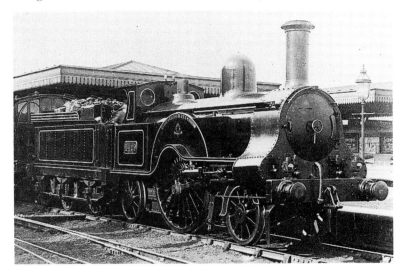

Rebuilt 'Problem' Class No 1429 Alfred Paget.

scoop described in chapter 3.[1] Over the years Webb rebuilt many of the class, some a number of times, and in that rebuilt form they lasted into the twentieth century.

In 1863 a 2-4-0 design with 6-foot driving wheels was introduced for passenger train working, the first LNWR engines to have coupled driving wheels. As was usual, the class name 'Samson' was taken from the name of the first member of the class and, as was to be the case with many Ramsbottom locomotives, Webb rebuilt them in later years. This illustrates a number of points which are worthy of consideration. The fact that they could be considered worthy of rebuilding, in some cases several times, indicates the basic soundness of the Ramsbottom-designed loco-motives. That Webb should rebuild in many cases rather than construct new designs is indicative of his thoughtful engineering approach and funda-mental economy of operation. Why go to the expense of constructing from new when an equally good engine could be obtained for lower cost by upgrading existing stock? One of the essentials of the rebuilds was a new boiler which would operate at higher pressure, and over the years Webb gradually increased working pressure, thus increasing economy of operation. Another class to be subsequently rebuilt was the 'Newton' Class introduced during 1866. Of 2-4-0 form with 6 ft 6 in driving wheels, they were intended for the main line between Lancaster and Carlisle, the 'Problem' Class engines experiencing some diffi-culty with the gradients on that section.

When Webb succeeded Ramsbottom as CME the change was not abrupt, basically because Webb, a former Chief Draughtsman and Works Manager, had been involved with the design and construction of many Ramsbottom engines. He had his own ideas but was happy with the loco-motive situation and appreciated that the designs which then existed could be adapted to suit future operations. Much of the early rebuilding work comprised of nothing more than the fitting of a cab and new chimney. A fine gesture after his appointment was to name the first new loco-motive of the 'Newton' Class *John Ramsbottom* after his former chief.

Webb has enjoyed a greater notoriety than other British Locomotive Engineers because of his adherence to compounding. Much of what has been written about the compounds is pure conjecture and based upon the flimsiest of evi-dence or no evidence at all. Even writers of estab-lished reputation have chosen to castigate the man and his engineering skills without taking care to research the facts. There is a phrase very much appropriate to contemporary journalism, 'Never let the facts get in the way of a good story', and that seems to have been the approach of a number of authors. Any objective writing which concerns F.W. Webb must, inevitably, waste valu-able space refuting such arguments before going on to deal with the real situation. That, unfortu-nately, has to be the case here.

Some authors who have written so definitively about Webb and his compounds were not born when those locomotives were operating, whilst others must have been but young children at the time. Nobody born after 1895 can really claim to have experienced and appreciated the perfor-mance of Webb's compounds. Conclusions drawn here are based upon contemporary writ-ings, engineering knowledge and logical thought.

Before dealing with the compounds, however, it is worth considering the fact that Webb was responsible for a great deal more. His contribu-tion to the development of Crewe Works and to engineering in general has already been dis-cussed. As far as locomotives are concerned the compounds amounted to barely 200 machines, whilst during Webb's time as CME Crewe built nearly 4,000 engines. These are just figures to illustrate the scale of things; compounds were but a small part of Webb's locomotive world, but over the years they have been used as a means of vilifying him.

Upon taking over from Ramsbottom, Webb continued the basic locomotive policy but did make changes to suit new operating conditions. The '17-inch Coal Engine' was a development of the Ramsbottom 'Special Tank', which in turn was based upon the 'DX' engine design. This class proved to be very useful for goods haulage, and the design was also inexpensive to produce. Ahrons considers them to have been the cheap-est and simplest locomotives ever made in Britain[2], although such a statement should be qualified, for their size and power. In 1881, ten years after their introduction, Webb produced a tank version and this also proved to be very effec-tive. These engines were useful for local passen-ger traffic as well as goods work, but it was probably their success on the latter trains which caused Webb, in 1885, to make the statement that he thought the day for tender engines, except for express work, was gone.[3] At the same time he also said that he was preparing designs for a com-pound version of the goods tank engine, but that never materialized.

The '18-inch Express Goods', or 'Cauliflower' Class, appeared in 1880 and the locomotives'

Above *'Cauliflower' No 1269 as built.* *(LNWR official)*

Left *'Cauliflower' No 28417 as rebuilt with a Belpaire boiler.* (D. K. Jones collection)

long-term performance probably caused Webb to change his mind on the widespread adoption of tank locomotives, although a tank version did appear towards the end of the century. More powerful than the earlier 0-6-0 engines, this class was intended for express goods work, hence the need for larger cylinders. A large boiler was also required, and the same type as fitted to the 'Precedent' passenger class was provided. With so many locomotives in these classes, this gave a degree of parts standardization as well as the manufacturing standardization which was already in use for the likes of flanging blocks, cast steel wheels and other details.

An introduction which was to become a standard feature for many LNWR engines was that of Joy valve gear. The first of the class, No 2365, was fitted with the gear and exhibited at Barrow in 1880 when the Institution of Mechanical Engineers held its summer meeting there. At that meeting David Joy presented a paper about his valve gear and Webb took part in the discussion. Webb stated that he thought well enough of Joy's gear to 'ask his directors to have an engine built

to try the experiment'.[4] It is a commonly held belief that Webb never asked anybody, he just told them. Could it be that he was much mellower during those early years, or was he just speaking out of character? Perhaps he was even on friendly terms with the Directors at that time. It is evident that Webb was impressed by the gear and possibly more so by the fact that he reached agreement with Joy regarding royalty payments, for he was not a man to pay money needlessly.

In the discussion Webb went on to give details of the engine and mentioned the use of 'trick' ports in order to increase the steam flow area through the valve. By making use of such a feature, and from the discussion of the matter, it is evident that Webb thoroughly understood the need for an adequate steam flow area between valve and cylinder. The use of the Joy valve gear offered him advantages in terms of construction, as no eccentrics were required. Thus increased bearing surfaces were possible at the bottom ends and crossheads, whilst a central axlebox could be provided. The simpler arrangement between the frames compared with link motion valve gear also gave more space for examination and cleaning. Such accessibility, together with the generally more simple nature of gear, persuaded Webb to make more general use of it; it was not simply cost, for some other valve gears did not require the payment of royalties.

Joy gear was not, however, used to the exclusion of all other forms, and in later years Stephenson and Allen valve gears were fitted in different classes of locomotives. This has also been used as a means of illustrating Webb's confusion and illogical thinking, but it is simplistic to believe that a single form of valve gear should be the standard throughout a locomotive fleet. There are advantages and disadvantages of each type of gear from constructional as well as operational points of view; no particular form suits all conditions. Webb had his reasons for choosing a certain form of gear for each class, and it cannot be argued that he was necessarily wrong in that choice.

At the end of his discussion of Joy's paper, Webb raised a matter which is very illuminating in terms of his views on the standardization of locomotive construction. He felt that engineers should consider the adoption of uniform dimensions for engine parts in the same way as had been done for screw threads. That, he concluded, would make it easier for English private firms when in competition with other manufacturers for overseas orders. Such a view, expressed in 1880, shows considerable foresight.

Webb was nothing if not inventive, and if a problem arose he attempted to find a solution of his own rather than adopt those of others. In some cases the better policy might have been to simply follow other people, but an individualist must explore his own ideas. Faith in the compound locomotive illustrates one aspect of Webb's individuality, and others might be seen in his extensive use of steel for boiler construction together with the development of corrugated and water-bottomed fireboxes.

For general shunting duties, Webb designed a rather unusual 0-4-0 locomotive, five of which were built in 1880 and a further five in 1882. They became known as the 2 ft 6 in shunters, although their driving wheels were actually of 2 ft 8 in diameter, and several minor variations distinguished individual members of the class. Driver and fireman were positioned at opposite ends of the boiler, which looked very strange as no definite chimney could be seen. One was provided, but the surrounding dome obscured it, giving a most strange appearance. The purpose of the dome in such a position was to save heat, this further being achieved by the fact that the smokebox was completely surrounded by water. These engines were employed at several LNWR locations with one, No 3017, being subsequently fitted with a bell and canopy for shunting in the Liverpool dock system. This engine was equipped for oil burning and a deflector plate was fitted above the chimney to prevent smoke from directly striking the girders of the Overhead Railway.[5]

By contrast, Webb's simple-expansion passenger engines were quite conventional, the 'Precursor' Class 2-4-0s of 1874 being based upon the Ramsbottom 'Newtons'. In the same year Webb also introduced the 'Precedent' Class, identical in a mechanical sense but for driving wheel size and boiler. The 'Precursors' had 5 ft 6 in driving wheels and a boiler identical to that fitted to the 17-inch goods engines. The 'Precedents' had

Webb 'Precedent' Hardwicke in company with one of his 'Coal Tanks' at Dinting.

Left *'Whitworth' Class No 739*
Sutherland. (G. Charles collection)

Right *'Precedent'* No 955 Charles
Dickens.

6 ft 6 in driving wheels and a boiler with a larger
firebox. The 'Precursors', with their smaller driving wheels, were designed for operation on the
line between Crewe and Carlisle, whilst the
'Precedents' had been constructed to operate
south of Crewe to London. In February 1875,
when discussing a paper at the 'Civils', Webb told
the audience that by May of that year he hoped to
have all express trains on that line hauled by
engines of these classes. From performance
results of the 'Precursors' he had formed the
opinion that an engine with four small wheels was
best adapted for working heavy express traffic.[6]

Over the following years modifications to the
designs were made including the use of higher
pressure boilers, 150 psi instead of 140 psi, and
thicker frame plates on what became known as
the 'Improved Precedent' or 'Large Jumbo'.
Officially classed as rebuilds of 'Newton' Class
locomotives, the 'Large Jumbo' engines were
built continuously in batches until 1901.
Rebuilding of the 'Samson' Class introduced the
'Whitworth' Class, which was but another variation on the basic Webb 2-4-0 type with 6-foot driving wheels. For these express engine classes Webb
made use of Allan straight link valve gear which
he must have considered to be more suitable than
Joy gear for the type of running involved.

Most famous 'Precedent' was *Charles Dickens*
which operated the service between Manchester
and London over many years and was specially
rostered in order to accumulate a considerable
weekly mileage. This gave opportunity for publicity which Webb was not slow to seize. In 1891 *The
Manchester Guardian* published a letter from Webb
mentioning that the engine, built in 1880, had
covered one million miles, and in 1902 he had a
similar letter published in that newspaper when
the engine had completed two million miles. A
more intriguing letter, detailing the exploits of
the locomotive, appeared in *The Railway Magazine*
during September 1902, and this was signed
'*Charles Dickens*, LNWR engine No 955'. There is
no evidence that Webb actually wrote the letter,
but in view of his keen interest in publicity it is
highly unlikely that he was not involved in some
way.

Another famous Webb 2-4-0 simple was
Hardwicke, an 'Improved Precedent'. Involvement in the 1895 'Race to the North' afforded
this engine and her sisters railway immortality
and, fortunately for *Hardwicke*, survival. Details of
these runs through the night have been offered
by many authors and appeared in the contemporary railway press, so repetition is unnecessary.
Compounds were frequently assigned to the section between London and Crewe, but a 'Large
Jumbo' would generally be provided for the run
north to Carlisle. *Hardwicke* and her sisters put in
excellent performances over the mountains but
loads were generally on the light side. That, however, does not detract from the performance;
Mallard, after all, was going down hill with a very
light load when she set the world speed record
for steam traction.

These fast runs have been used as means of
comparing the Webb simple engines with his
compounds, but such comparison is not reasonable. Compounds were not built to haul light
loads nor was very fast running part of their
design criteria, although improvements on what
was actually achieved could have been possible
had steam passageways been less restrictive. The
very nature of compound locomotive design
does not allow it to compete on equal terms with
the simple expansion engine, size for size and
weight for weight. Other factors such as coal and
water consumption, as well as initial and mainte-

nance costs, come into the equation.

Webb wished to make comparisons but wanted to gather as much definite information as he could, and to that end in 1894 he constructed a dynamometer car. By later standards it was rather crude and basic, but it did function, allowing him to obtain information as to drawbar pull and speed. Construction of this car illustrates another aspect of the Webb character, a thirst for knowledge as to how his locomotives performed. It has been said, without any evidence, that Webb was

unaware that his compounds were so poor because everybody was afraid to give him bad news due to his raging temper. It is also alleged that he never rode on his engines to find out for himself. C.S. Lake was certainly reluctant to inform Webb of the starting difficulties experienced by the compound hauling the train on which he travelled to Crewe for his interview with the engineer.[7] That was out of respect for an elderly friend rather than fear, but others in the traffic department would certainly have taken

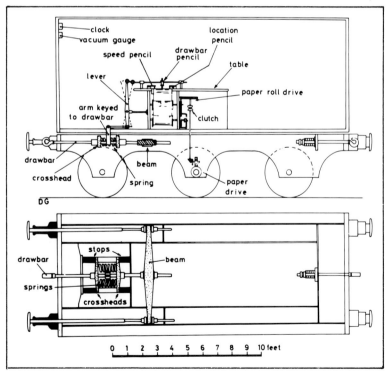

Arrangement of Webb's dynamometer car.

delight in such revelations if there was so much antagonism as popular legend indicates.

Webb decided to employ compounding because he considered that such a system was the only one which could allow for the development of sufficient power from a particular size of locomotive. That was what he told an audience at a 'Civils' meeting in 1889, but he also went on to mention other reasons for the adoption of compounding.

During his first ten years as CME, Webb developed larger and stronger simple expansion locomotives in order to meet traffic demands, but by 1880 he considered that the arrangement as used on the LNWR had reached its limit. Increasing the diameter of inside cylinders would mean a reduction of crank web thickness or of bearing length. Neither of these options nor the use of outside frames did he wish to contemplate, so the idea of a three-cylinder compound with two outside HP cylinders and a single inside LP cylinder seemed reasonable. This arrangement he had proposed in 1879 when discussing a paper at the 'Mechanicals'.[8] His reasoning for the adoption of a two-axle drive without coupling rods was also based upon logic.

Steels of the period were generally not of the same high standard as was available later. although that from Crewe was better than most, and it was not unknown for coupling rods to fail in service. By avoiding their use, such failure could be avoided and less maintenance was required. Divided drive and the absence of coupling rods also made for simpler crankshafts, again reducing the risk of failure. Costing also became an important factor, and Webb was firmly convinced that operating costs would be lower with compounds than for simple expansion engines. In 1889 he could claim a saving of 600 tons of coal per year due to the use of compound locomotives, and that more than offset the slightly higher building cost. Webb used figures to back his claims but, no doubt, sceptics will argue that he used figures selectively and was not informed about any poor performances of his compounds. There is no answer to that except to say that Webb was aware of defects and willing to mention the solutions he adopted.

Webb acknowledged that the three-cylinder compounds were 'sluggish' when running downhill because of 'the big cylinder pumping against the smaller cylinders'. To avoid this problem he decided to fit automatic snifting valves. Over the years since 1872 until that time (1889) trains speeds had increased by almost 18½ per cent and they had also increased in weight, but the com-

pounds were able to take the trains and double-heading had almost been eliminated; at that date it amounted to only 0.65 per cent of passenger mileage. These figures were obviously given to put the Webb compounds in good light, but they were presented to an audience of engineers, including W. Adams, J. Holden, W. Stroudley, T.W. Worsdell and J.A.F. Aspinall, and could have been torn to shreds had there been any doubt as to authenticity.[9]

Webb had other reasons for adopting compounding, one of which concerned his drivers. He experienced the greatest difficulty in getting them to operate at full regulator and control the power by means of cut-off because the drivers believed that such practice resulted in hot bearings. There was evidence to support that claim and Webb believed that compounding would allow for more efficient use of steam and avoid the hot bearings.[10] These are all arguments used by Webb to support his case for compounding and there were few contemporary engineers who did not agree with the basic claims. There were defects in design, and again Webb has acknowledged those of the earlier classes: 'It was well known that when the first engines were put upon the road there were some failures..., faults of construction due as much to the errors of the drawing office as to anything'.[11] If he publicly acknowledged these defects somebody must have mentioned them to him, and so he cannot have been always kept in the dark about the alleged poor performance of his locomotives.

It is not the intention to detail each of Webb's compound classes in terms of construction and performance, the subject requiring a book of its own. Points will be considered only as far as they concern Webb's skill, or lack of it, as an engineer, this not being a thesis on locomotive design and performance.

Following an initial trial with a converted engine, Webb introduced the three-cylinder 'Experiment' Class in 1882, separate sets of Joy valve gear being used for inside and outside cylinders. The inside LP cylinder was the largest which could be fitted between the frames, 26 inches in diameter, and the outside HP cylinders were made 11½ inches in diameter in order to provide sufficient power to start a train; when starting, only the HP cylinders received steam. Over the years there has been considerable discussion as to the ideal ratio between LP and HP cylinder volumes and few authorities ever seem to agree. The 'Experiments' had a ratio of 2.56:1, but for later compound classes Webb selected different values, the reasons probably being the require-

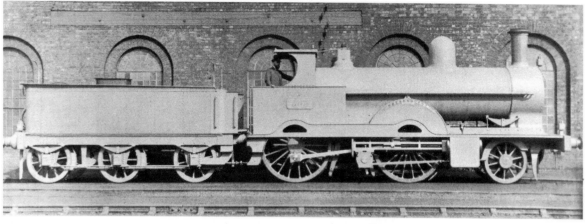

Three-cylinder compound Dreadnought *with Webb on the footplate.* (LNWR official)

ments of starting power, standard-sized parts or even construction, rather than theoretical niceties.

After a period of trial running with the 'Experiment' Class engines, Webb decided upon an enlarged version in order to take account of the increasing weight and speed of passenger trains. In an Institution of Mechanical Engineers paper presented at a meeting in Liège during July 1883, Webb gave details of the new locomotive and again emphasized the objectives he had in mind when designing the 'Experiments'. Economy of fuel consumption was the purpose of compounding, and the avoidance of coupled wheels gave added advantages. Two pairs of driving wheels allowed for greater adhesive weight than was possible with only one, but avoided excessive track loading. That could also have been obtained by using coupled wheels, but Webb considered that there would be less of a grinding action when passing around curves if the driving wheels were uncoupled, and he further believed that wheels on different driving axles could be of different diameters. They never were with any of his compounds but he did, obviously, consider the idea.

Dreadnought and her sisters had larger diameter HP cylinders than the 'Experiments', 13 inches compared with 11½ inches, the LP remaining the same at 26 inches. This gave a more favourable ratio between high- and low-pressure cylinder volumes. In addition, Webb increased the port area from 21 sq in to 36 sq in in order to give increased freedom of exhaust. From this is it obvious that he fully understood the problems afflicting the 'Experiments' and was taking steps to counter them. In order to supply steam to the

larger cylinder, a bigger boiler was required and this also operated at increased pressure compared with the original class of compounds, 175 psi instead of 150 psi.[12]

For the leading wheels Webb devised his own form of radial axlebox which allowed for lateral movement of 1¼ inches on each side of the centre-line. This axlebox proved to be a great success

Webb's radial axlebox.

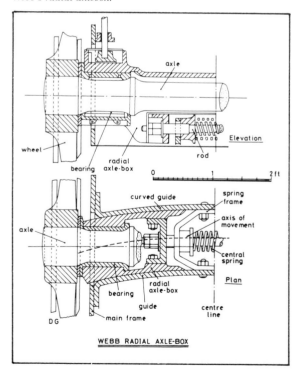

Left *'Teutonic' Class compound No 1306* Ionic.

Below left *Webb's slip eccentric.*

and was adopted for LNWR carriage stock as well as locomotives, and also by other railways. One of the 'Dreadnoughts', *Marchioness of Stafford,* was sent to the International Inventions Exhibition held in London during April 1885, winning for Webb a gold medal in the railway plant section. At the end of 1888 a very favourable article concerning the compounds appeared in *The Engineer.* No author was given credit, but whoever wrote the

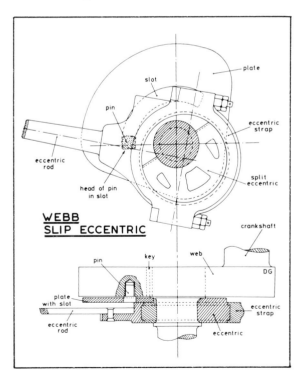

WEBB
SLIP ECCENTRIC

article knew the machines in considerable detail. Details of several runs by *Marchioness of Stafford* were given and the average overall coal consumption for the entire 40-strong class since introduction was stated to be 36.5 lbs per mile. The writer concluded by expressing the opinion that the engines were a success which ' . . . reflects the greatest credit on Mr Webb, not only for his ingenuity as an inventor and his skill as a designer, but for his energy and perseverance in working against a good deal of opposition, and a sufficiently noisy expression of doubt as to the excellence of the most thoroughgoing change in locomotive engine construction that has been effected since the *Rocket* superseded the *Puffing Billy.'* 13

In 1889 the 'Teutonic' Class of three-cylinder compounds was developed, and again this was a variation on the previous class. The driving wheel diameter was increased from 6 feet to 7 feet but the basic design was much the same as the 'Dreadnoughts'. Since that class was introduced a modification had been made to them in that a bypass valve was fitted which allowed steam from the HP cylinders to be directed to exhaust rather than going to the LP cylinder. This made for easier starting as it had been found that under certain conditions steam at the LP cylinder exerted an opposing effect to the HP cylinders. When the engine was running the driver could close the valve and compound working would begin. Webb simplified the valve mechanism by removing the Joy gear which operated the inside LP cylinder valve and in its place providing a slip eccentric arrangement. The eccentric took up the correct position for operating in whatever direction the crankshaft was turning, this being achieved by

Right *Sectional drawing of 2-2-2-2 No 3292* Greater Britain.

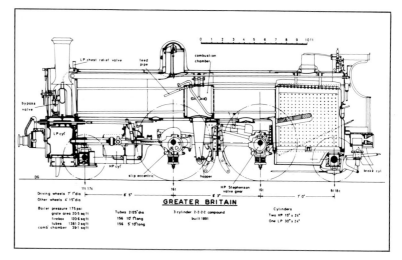

GREATER BRITAIN

Driving wheels 7' 1"dia
Other wheels 4' 1½"dia

Boiler pressure 175 psi
 grate area 20·5 sq ft
 firebox 120·6 sq ft
 tubes 1381·2 sq ft
comb' chamber 39·1 sq ft

Tubes 2·125"dia
156 10' 1"long
156 5' 10"long

3 cylinder 2-2-2-2 compound
built 1891

Cylinders
Two HP 15" x 24"
One LP 30" x 24"

means of a pin connected to the crank web and sliding in a slotted plate attached to the eccentric. The arrangement was ingenious and it did work, but there was no way of altering the cut-off for the LP cylinder which was set at maximum.

Use of slip eccentrics did allow a myth to develop with respect to a strange phenomenon where wheels driven by the HP cylinders rotated in one direction whilst those driven by the LP cylinder turned in the opposite direction. The use of the slip eccentric could allow this to happen but a number of conditions would need to be satisfied at the same time and occurrences were certainly less frequent than legend supposes. If an engine had backed on to its train, the inside slip eccentric would remain in reverse gear after the outside HP valve gear had been set for forward running. At the same time, the LP valve must have been open to the receiver so that steam from the HP could be directed to the LP cylinder and the bypass valve had to be stuck in the closed position so that steam from the HP had to go to the LP and not directly to exhaust. Theoretically such an incidence was possible and in practice might have taken place, but if it did a driver should have immediately shut off steam to prevent continued slipping.

Writings of the twentieth century abound with stories of Webb three-cylinder compounds attempting to pull away from a station with sets of driving wheels turning frantically in opposite directions. Although these locomotives did exhibit starting difficulties, contemporary journals barely mention the fact whilst incidents of wheels turning in opposite directions are conspicuous by their absence. In a series of articles dealing with Webb compounds, Charles Rous-

Marten, who made many trips behind them, does not even mention the matter. He admits that the 'Dreadnoughts' were sluggish starters but could not recall more than two or three cases of definite problems during his many journeys.[14] With respect to the 'Teutonics', he considered them to be the most successful of the three-cylinder compounds and were excellent in their performance.[15] If contemporary media and well-respected railway writers make no mention, then such incidents are likely to have been less common than recent 'authorities' would have people believe.

For working heavy fast passenger traffic to Carlisle, Webb introduced the 'Greater Britain' Class in 1891. Again this was a three-cylinder compound, but the HP cylinders were of 15 inches diameter and the LP 30 inches, all having a 24-inch stroke. Stephenson valve gear was applied to the outside cylinders and a slip eccentric to the inside. In order to allow the fitting of the longer boiler, a 2-2-2-2 wheel arrangement had to be provided, the driving wheels still being uncoupled. The boiler itself was novel in that it had two sections of tubes separated by a combustion chamber. It is highly unlikely that this chamber actually promoted combustion for the flame would have been extinguished during passage through the first section of tubes. The exact reason for its use is difficult to determine, but it did allow for a large effective tube length to be obtained without the problem of manufacturing long tubes. A steam soot blower was also provided within the chamber, thus allowing tubes to be cleaned more effectively than would have been the case with single length tubes. A hopper from the chamber allowed ash to be discharged on to the track.[16]

In 1894 a variation of this class was introduced, the only basic difference being the fitting of 6 ft 3 in instead of 7 ft 1 in driving wheels. The idea behind this was to allow for better hauling power on gradients, but the 'John Hick' Class does not appear to have been particularly successful at that. This may have been due to the fact that train weights and speeds were being increased regularly and the strange 'equal to 17' rule made operational life difficult. This arbitrary rule took no account of the state of the engine, gradient, weather conditions or many other factors, but simply dictated that a pilot engine had to be taken when the size of train exceeded a particular value. This naturally caused many strange situa-

tions and some trains were operated with an extra engine which was more of a hindrance than a help. Operating costs increased because two locomotives had to be used in many situations when one would have been capable of hauling the train. The rule certainly irritated Webb as is evident from his remarks during the discussion of Aspinall's paper on train resistance.[17] Both of these 2-2-2-2 classes suffered from an operating inconvenience due to the length of their footplate. In order to allow for turning on existing turntables, the locomotive length was set, but the use of the extended boiler resulted in a footplate only 3 feet long.

A phrase used by Rous-Marten has been misinterpreted, accidentally or deliberately, and used to cast doubt on the ability of the 'John Hick' Class. When discussing what the compounds had done, Rous Marten stated that he could not comment on the 'John Hicks' because he had never been fortunate enough to travel behind one unassisted by a pilot engine.[18] This has been seized upon as gospel that the class always had to be assisted as the engines could not haul loads by themselves. No such statement was made — the author simply stated that his experience was limited. The 'equal to 17' rule was indiscriminate, so when the 'John Hicks' were employed on heavy passenger trains, for which they were designed, a pilot had to be taken whether it was needed or not.

In 1897 Webb changed to four-cylinder compounding with coupled driving wheels, even before the last of the 'John Hicks' Class was constructed. Again the design was to meet increasing traffic demands, so nobody could accuse Webb of not trying. Two practically identical engines were constructed, one, *Black Prince*, a compound and the other, *Iron Duke*, a simple. This allowed Webb to test the effectiveness, and the constructional

Left Greater Britain *with Webb on the footplate.* (LNWR official)

Below left *Sectional drawing of the 'Jubilee' Class 4-4-0 compound.*

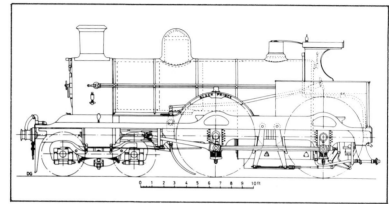

Top right *4-4-0 four-cylinder compound No 1502* Black Prince.

Middle right *Drawing of* Black Prince.

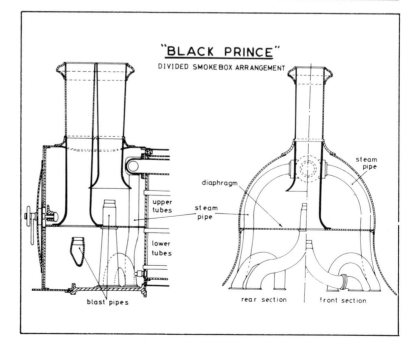

Right *The divided smokebox and double chimney fitted to* Black Prince.

expense, of compounding, but he again came down firmly in its favour and subsequently rebuilt *Iron Duke*, both engines becoming part of the 'Jubilee' Class. The HP cylinders were of 15-inch diameter and the LP 20½ inches, the stroke being 24 inches; all cylinders were connected to the forward coupled axle. The boiler pressure was increased to 200 psi allowing for increased potential power development. The boiler, driving wheelbase and driving wheel diameter of these 4-4-0s were the same as for the 'Teutonics', and at

9 ft 8 in the coupling rods were amongst the longest then used in Britain.

Webb did not like bogies and designed his own arrangement which he classed as a double radial truck. It provided the support required and must have been effective, for both Whale and Cooke made use of it on designs produced during their periods in office. The use of four cylinders allowed Webb to employ only two sets of Joy valve gear, which drove the inside LP slide valves directly and operated adjacent outside HP piston

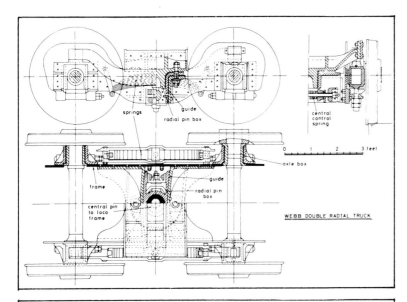

Left *Webb double radial truck.*

Left *Valve gear fitted to the four-cylinder compounds.*

Top right *An LNWR publicity photograph showing compound 0-8-0 No 50 and the material used in its construction. (LNWR official)*

valves by means of rocking levers. All cylinders were notched up simultaneously and the valve arragement was considerably simplified allowing space for a large central axle bearing as well as the usual side bearings.[19]

Initially Webb provided *Black Prince* with a double chimney and a divided smokebox as a means for improving the draught. A diaphragm allowed the upper and lower tubes to connect with separate sections of the smokebox which in turn had their own blast pipes. Theoretically the arrangement should have provided a more even suction effect through the tubes, but this does not appear to have been the case in practice and the experiment was soon discontinued.

The 'Alfred the Great' Class appeared in 1901 and were identical except for larger boiler and HP cylinders; the latter were subsequently reduced to the same diameter as those of the 'Jubilees'. A final modification was to provide independent valve gear for the outside cylinders and that was set in hand just before Webb retired.

Although many different compound classes were introduced by Webb, most did not differ radically from their predecessors, changes in boiler, wheel diameter or cylinder size being the exception. These changes came about to meet new operating circumstances and were evolutionary, which is why most classes only comprised relatively few locomotives compared with simple expansion designs. During 1901 Rous-Marten wrote two articles for *The Railway Magazine* entitled 'What Mr Webb's Compounds Have Done', and in these he related his own experiences.[20] He was not, however, as scathing as some less experienced commentators and wrote most favourably of the compounds in general. Performance, and prejudice, are very personal matters and a number of people at the time must have seen things differently, especially the operating department, for Whale wanted nothing to do with the compounds when he became CME.

Webb eventually applied compounding to goods engines; he had intended to do this from the start but time did not allow. An eight-coupled coal engine was introduced in 1892 and the following year a three-cylinder compound version was produced. As with the passenger engines several stages of development took place, and subsequently a four-cylinder version entered service. It is generally overlooked that Webb was responsible for the introduction of the 0-8-0 goods type which became something of a LNWR standard. His final design was the 4-6-0 four-cylinder compound which was intended for mixed traffic and fast goods services. Only two were actually completed before Webb retired, but a further 28 were constructed whilst Whale was CME.

Although generally considered as failures, they must be looked at in the light of events at the time. Had he remained, Webb would certainly have looked at the performance of the initial batch of ten before constructing a further 20, which is what he did with the passenger classes. With Whale in charge, compounding was very much out of favour and these engines are not likely to have received the workshop consideration they would have received under Webb. If they were bad engines it is strange that nothing was done to rectify matters, and surprising that the last of them was not scrapped until 1920.

As Superintendent of the running department, Whale had to deal with the difficulties resulting from the 'equal to 17' rule and the inability of the compounds to give that little extra when required. In many respects that was the main problem with the compounds; they could not be flogged in order to make up lost time. Design for economy of operation did not allow a reserve of power, and each class of compounds seems to have been constructed to the requirements of that time rather than for possible future needs. Certainly that would have been a reasonable philosophy to adopt had railway operations been fairly static, but that was not the case, and Webb does not appear to have appreciated the fact. There were engineering faults with the compounds, but that applied to most locomotives classes everywhere and modifications after a period of service would generally sort them out. In modifying subsequent classes Webb took notice of operating difficulties, but he never allowed himself the luxury of over-designing any class so that it had something in reserve for future changes.

Whale, however, did recognize the operating difficulties and wanted no part of compounding. Reserve power could be obtained from a simple expansion engine with large enough cylinders and a big enough boiler, so as soon as he became CME he instructed the drawing office to prepare drawings for a large 4-4-0. The drawing office, under J.N. Jackson, the Chief Draughtsman, and T.E. Sackville, his Locomotive Assistant, must have relished the freedom from the straitjacket imposed by Webb. Certainly all design work will have been carried out by that team to Whale's general specification, for the new CME was by no means an experienced locomotive design engineer. The speed with which the 4-4-0 'Precursor' was produced, the first being turned out in March 1904, less than a year after Whale took over, suggest that some design work was already in hand. Many detail parts were carried over from the Webb era and the excellent facilities which had been arranged at the works allowed for rapid construction.

The 'Precursors' were certainly a success as far as operating performance was concerned, coal consumption being something of a secondary consideration. They were not, however, used on the heavy gradients over Shap; a more powerful machine was needed for that section. In essence, the 4-6-0 'Experiment' Class of 1905 were an enlarged version, with 6 ft 3 in driving wheels instead of 6 ft 9 in. Differences in grate and fire depth have already been considered in chapter 3 and need not be discussed again, but it is strange

that such a difference should have been allowed if Whale was requiring footplate crews to handle both classes effectively. One of the criticisms levelled at the Webb compound classes was that they required slightly different footplate techniques; Whale was imposing the same problems.

Despite this, both classes were effective when introduced and Whale had trial trips made in order to test them. During April 1904 the first 'Precursor', No 513, ran trials between Rugby and Crewe during which indicator cards were obtained, the results being published. With a total train weight, including the Webb dynamometer car, in excess of 470 tons, average speeds of 54.5 miles per hour were obtained whilst the locomotive developed over 730 ihp at maximum output.[21]

Following Whale's retirement, J.N. Jackson provided an article for *The Railway Magazine* dealing with the locomotives produced during Whale's term in office.[22] This made mention of the fact that 'Precursors' experienced difficulty in keeping time whilst operating trains between Crewe and Carlisle, so it is evident that they were tried on this line and found wanting. The article also gave details of the tank engines and goods classes constructed during that period and paid special attention to the rail-motor. A proposal for the construction of an experimental car came from the traffic rather than Whale, and he probably had little to do with the project apart from to authorize the drawings and construction. The design differed from the Horwich arrangement in that the locomotive section was contained within the carriage, giving the impression of a self-propelled coach. It could, however, be separated from the coach when repair was required.[23]

From the tone of the article it is evident that Whale did not take an active part in the design work; simple phrases like 'Mr Whale tried' and 'Mr Whale built' indicate courtesy rather than actual fact. Had there been more active involvement it would certainly have been mentioned. The CME would in any event have been too busy with other matters to involve himself with detail design unless that was one of his prime interests. Webb was interested in design and the details of engineering construction; Whale was not, his passions lay in operation, and others could be relied upon to produce designs.

C. J. B. Cooke's major claim to locomotive fame was the introduction of superheating to LNWR locomotive stock. If he had done nothing else during his tenure, that step would have earned him his salary. Elsewhere other railways were reaping the benefits of superheated steam, and

Top *A Whale 'Precursor' as LMS No 5289* Leviathan (G. Charles collection)

Above *'George the Fifth' Class; LMS No 25328,* John Rennie.

Right *'Prince of Wales' Class; LMS No 25694 at Polmadie in 1923.* (D. K. Jones collection)

Left *'Claughton' No 1097* Private W. Wood VC. (LNWR official)

Below left *A 'Claughton' rebuilt with a Belpaire boiler and Caprotti valve gear; LMS No 5927.* (G. Charles collection)

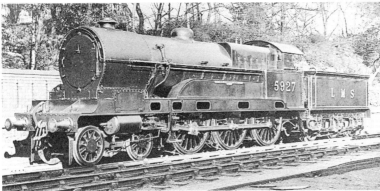

Below *Whale's dynamometer car behind an 0-8-0 on a test freight train.* (LNWR official)

Bottom *A development of the Cooke 0-8-0 'G1' superheated design of 1912; LMS '7F' No 49245 with Belpaire firebox and 'G2' boiler introduced in 1936.* (D. K. Jones collection)

Crewe came rather late on the scene, but Cooke does appear to have been a cautious engineer. During 1909 trials were arranged with locomotives from the Caledonian, Great Northern, and London, Brighton & South Coast Railways. Performance of the superheated Brighton tank engine resulted in immediate consideration being given to that practice.

A superheated version of the 'Precursor' was developed using Schmidt superheaters, Cooke having decided that adoption of that form offered many advantages. Not least amongst these was the fact that if anything went wrong, somebody else could be blamed, and to that end the Schmidt company was given a free hand in the design.[24] Only one superheated 4-4-0, No 2663 *George the Fifth*, was constructed initially, but other saturated engines were built at the same time; Cooke obviously had difficulty convincing other people as to the advantages of superheated steam. Construction of the saturated engines did allow the advantages of superheating alone to be tested, for No 2663 incorporated a number of other modifications compared with the 'Precursors', including piston valves. These were to a Schmidt design and incorporated 'trick ports' similar to those fitted on slide valves, but they leaked excessively and Cooke later abandoned them.

During its first few months of operation, *George the Fifth* showed coal savings of 26.7 per cent whilst working the Euston to Crewe section, and 25.77 per cent on the Preston to Carlisle line.[25] That convinced reluctant Directors, and money was soon forthcoming for the construction of more 'George the Fifth' Class engines. Permission was also obtained for a two-cylinder superheated 4-6-0 along the same lines as the Whale 'Experiment', this being the 'Prince of Wales' Class, which also proved that the superheated engine was far superior to the saturated version. It is likely that Cooke did not wish to build this class and was more interested in a four-cylinder 4-6-0, but his plans were thwarted by a rather conservative Civil Engineer. The higher static axle-loading of the four-cylinder engine was mitigated by the absence of hammer-blow, but the Civil Engineer could not, or would not, concede the point and Cooke had to settle for the 'Prince of Wales'. He would not, however, give up and the Crewe drawing office was set to work producing a four-cylinder design which would satisfy the axle-loading restrictions.

The resulting 'Claughton' design was, because of this artificial restriction, less of a locomotive than it might have been, for much of the weight was saved by having a smaller diameter boiler than intended. In later years, replacement of the boilers made the 'Claughtons' into better locomotives. But despite these initial limitations, *Sir Gilbert Claughton*, the first member of the class, and the subsequent engines allowed for heavier trains and accelerated services.

During later years the performance of the 'Claughtons' left much to be desired in that it was uneven. They were capable of fast running and did put in many fine performances, but consistency was not a word which could be applied. In addition, coal consumption tended to be abnormally high. These at least were the views of E. S. Cox who was involved with the engines during the post-grouping period.[26] Subsequent tests with larger boilers and different valves, including Caprotti valves in some cases, showed that improvements were possible, but none which would make the engines superior to the Stanier '5X' Class 4-6-0. For their time, however, the 'Claughtons' were a significant advance in LNWR locomotive stock.

Cox was more impressed with the 'Prince of Wales' Class engines, considering them to be exceptional performers for their size and capable of taking a considerable amount of overload. This class was based upon an earlier one and included new features, but that is the essence of good design, making use of existing sound practice and incorporating those features which are likely to lead to advance. Although Cooke receives the credit as CME, the drawing office under Jackson did the work and maintained a continuity, even from the days of Webb, for many of his ideas were incorporated in modified form. Had he not organized the workshops so effectively, construction would certainly have taken longer and been more expensive.

One type of Crewe locomotive which owed its introduction to Webb was the 0-8-0 goods engine. This underwent a number of changes following its introduction as a compound in 1893, but remained very much the same format as devised by Webb apart from the change to simple expansion and the provision of superheaters. The final 'G2' Class of 1921 could trace its ancestry back to Webb's 'A' Class, an uprated version, the 'G2a', with higher pressure boiler, stronger motion and improved braking, being introduced during 1935. New locomotives were constructed, but others of earlier types were also rebuilt. Unfortunately freight engines tend to attract less attention, but the history of many classes is more interesting than their passenger counterparts.

8. Locomotives of the Midland Railway

Many of the early Midland locomotives came from contractors and Kirtley had very little to do with the design, but eventually matters at Derby settled down and a pattern became established. Outside builders still constructed many of the engines, but generally to specified designs. In 1856 Derby produced its first locomotive to a Kirtley design and that was a 2-4-0 for express goods work. At that time the Midland was essentially a goods railway and strong efforts were made to ensure satisfactory hauling power.

In terms of design, Kirtley appears to have had strong preferences and used six wheels in various combinations almost to the exclusion of everything else. Up to the 1850s most locomotives constructed for operation in Britain were of the six-wheeled variety and many lines were laid down to suit that form. It has already been mentioned that Midland lines tended to have more severe curves than elsewhere, thus limiting scope for the use of engines having a long wheelbase. Throughout the Kirtley years that presented no real problem, and power could be provided within that restriction to meet demand. In fact, as far as goods engines were concerned there was always adequate space for a large boiler.

Kirtley did have a preference when it came to engine frames, and although he discarded sandwich frames in 1852 he appears to have had a particular liking for the outside arrangement. This applied to engines built at Derby and by contractors, and towards the latter part of his period in office a distinct preference for curved top frames can be observed. Undoubtedly the major introduction of the Kirtley era was the Markham system of coal burning. Locomotive style did not change but efficiency did. Throughout Kirtley's reign, train loads increased and more powerful locomotives were produced to meet the demand. Many of these still came from outside, as Derby Works did not expand sufficiently to supply the needs of the railway. Unlike at Crewe, there never seems to have been any intention for the Midland to be self-sufficient in locomotive construction.

Boiler pressure increased to 140 psi in the 1860s, welding of the longitudinal boiler seam replacing the use of rivets and lap joints. Trials indicated that this form of construction required less repair, but its use was discontinued some years laters.[1] Large cylinders, up to 17 inches in diameter by a 24 inch stroke, allowed considerable power to be developed from relatively small locomotives, size becoming something of a limit-ing factor. From 1860 onwards, the wheelbase for all six-wheeled Midland engines, apart from 2-2-2s, was 8 ft + 8 ft 6 in. In a number of cases springing for the coupled wheels on 2-4-0 locomotives also made use of compensating levers to account for indifferent track conditions. Flexibility with 2-4-0 engines was obtained by providing outside bearings for the leading axle and allowing these axleboxes $1/2$ inch lateral play in the horns on either side of the centre-line.[2]

This was all part of good design practice which allowed the Midland to operate its services effectively. The locomotives may not have been outstanding in terms of high speed or hauling capability, but they did do the job for which they were designed; the Midland had no need for any other sort of engine. Longevity was a feature of Midland-designed locomotives and many of Kirtley's engines lasted through the Johnson era, although several rebuilds took place; if operating circumstances did not change there was little need in changing the basic locomotive form or arrangement. One aspect of Kirtley design which could have usefully been altered was the cab or, more accurately, lack of a cab. Even as late as 1870, when other designers were providing some basic protection for footplate crew, Kirtley was only fitting simple weatherboards to his locomotives. He was not alone in that, the GWR being even further behind with the introduction of such facilities, but in most other respects Kirtley was a very caring man and the seeming lack of thought for footplate crew does appear to be out of character. It is possible that his early career as a fireman and driver coloured his view and left him with the impression that the comforts of a cab were not required by hardy footplatemen.

When Johnson took control he was faced with the task of providing more locomotives to meet increasing traffic demands, the late 1870s marking a growth period for Midland operations. Older locomotives could be scrapped, but many of the Kirtley engines were still useful and new boilers could provide an effective way of extending their life. Johnson developed a number of standard-type boilers, a matter made somewhat easier due to the limited size and wheel arrangement of Midland engines. New locomotive designs were also produced, especially for passenger traffic, and the Johnson style became recognized; his engines were considered to be amongst the most visually attractive ever to appear in Britain. Sufficient has been written about

Midland locomotives, and those of Johnson in particular, to make repetition unnecessary; a multiple volume review by Essery and Jenkinson covers the development in great detail.

From a technical point of view, the Johnson engines were useful but contained few innovative ideas which could be considered of major significance in locomotive development. Johnson was a steady engineer who worked effectively within the restrictions imposed upon him, and provided adequate locomotives to meet requirements. Some new ideas were, however, tried and were proved successful. The use of piston valves has already been mentioned, as has the development of a compound locomotive using the Smith system. Johnson's initial reluctance to embrace compounding indicates his cautious approach, but increasing demands for power had to be met within the restrictive load conditions of the track. His Institution of Mechanical Engineers

Presidential Address of 1898 indicates many of his views on design, including the belief that long lap valves offered considerable advantages, and the need for ensuring that failure of any individual part whilst on the road would not lead to a major accident.

This address is important as an aid to determining Johnson's attitude to locomotive design, for he made no other utterances on the subject. With respect to the future of locomotive engineering he did express the opinion that electricity would be a most important agent in the hands of railway engineers.[3] The lines of a Johnson-designed electric locomotive are interesting to imagine.

The Midland under Johnson was to the fore in the introduction of continuous brakes. This essentially applied to passenger stock, but locomotives had to be equipped to power such brakes, so the Locomotive Superintendent needed to be aware of developments.

Right Midland Class '1' 0-6-0 built at Derby in 1864 as No 197, and renumbered 573 in 1866. It was rebuilt again in 1881, 1896 and 1901, and was photographed circa 1904. (P. C. Dewhurst collection, NRM, York)

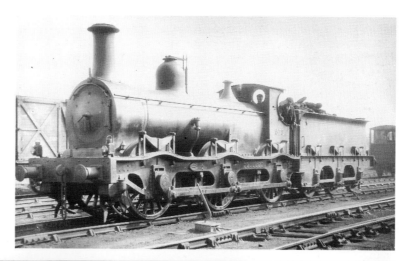

Below 2-4-0 No 151, built at Derby in 1874, at St Pancras circa 1895. This was a Johnson version of an original Kirtley design, with outside bearings on leading axle. (G. Tod collection, NRM, York)

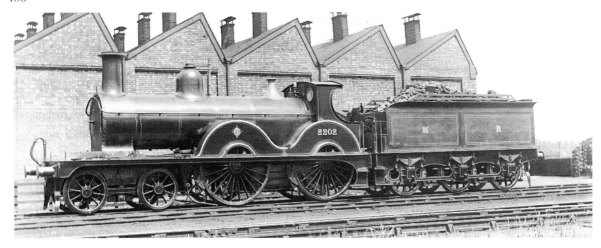

Extensive use was made of the Westinghouse air brake following its excellent performance in the Newark brake trials of 1875, and Johnson worked with T.G. Clayton, Carriage & Wagon Superintendent, to ensure that all locomotives required to work the air-braked stock were correctly fitted. Other braking systems were tried, but the Westinghouse system appears to have been superior to any other until 1877, when disagreement developed. This involved money, and need not be discussed here, but the outcome was that the Midland moved to a vacuum brake system on the lines of that development by R.D. Sanders. In later years Johnson had his team devise a Midland form of combined automatic steam and vacuum brake, steam braking for the engine and tender and vacuum braking for the coaching stock.[4]

With respect to locomotive design, Johnson moved away from the Kirtley 2-4-0 arrangement by introducing a bogie to give support and guidance at the front end, and for many years all Johnson passenger engines were of 4-4-0 form. The first of this type was the '1312' Class introduced during 1876, and others of similar form but with larger driving wheels soon followed. Driving wheels of 7-foot diameter proved to be very popular for fast running, but smaller diameter wheels and different sized cylinders were used depending upon the speed and tractive effort requirements. It is one of the '1738' Class built in 1885-6, No 1757 *Beatrice*, which was awarded a Gold medal at the 1887 Saltaire Exhibition. This engine was of course no more attractive than other members of the class, or other 4-4-0s for that matter, but had been specially prepared for the exhibition.

At the turn of the century, styling changed and new 4-4-0s were less attractive visually, but from a power and engineering point of view they had something extra to offer. In the meantime, Johnson turned his attention to single driving wheels and several 4-2-2 classes were introduced while 4-4-0s were also being designed. This might indicate a reluctance to settle on one type, but there was an advantage to be gained from the use of that arrangement — a large diameter driving wheel could be fitted. Restrictions on wheel-base prevented the use of coupled wheels of a diameter in excess of 7 feet, but large-diameter driving wheels allowed for high-speed running, hence the advantage of a 4-2-2 form.

Single driving wheels had fallen out of favour as trains became heavier due to the problem of slipping which resulted in delay. Johnson had issued a directive which resulted in the withdrawal of the remaining Kirtley single-wheelers, but one remained at Leicester where it served as stand-by stationary boiler for the pumping engines. The District Locomotive Superintendent at Leicester was Robert Weatherburn who in later years claimed some of the credit for the reintroduction of single wheelers to the Midland. At a time of locomotive shortage, and against Johnson's instruction, he had the old Kirtley single-wheeler prepared for service but added a gravity sanding system. The locomotive worked well for several months but Johnson became aware of its running and took notice. He sent for Weatherburn and admonished him for failing to carry out instructions, but then requested full details of the locomotive's running.[5]

Johnson did not immediately follow this up with a single-wheeler design, nor did he consider gravity sanding to be the ideal solution. In 1885 a form of air sanding had been developed by Francis Holt, Works Manager at Derby, and this had been tested on a 2-4-0 temporarily converted into a single by the removal of its coupling rods. Trials over the Settle-Carlisle route were a success, but the Westinghouse company complained that by taking air from the braking system there could be a reduction in brake effectiveness. At that time the Midland was engaged in a dispute with Westinghouse, so steam was substituted for air and a much more effective sanding system developed.[6]

The first Johnson single-wheeler was introduced in 1887 and others followed at a steady, if slow, rate over the following 12 years. The driving wheel diameter varied from 7 ft 4½ in for the initial batch to 7 ft 9½ in for the final ten engines. There were other detail differences including an increase in cylinder diameter and boiler size, but there was a similarity in external appearance. Like the 4-4-0s, the entire range of Johnson singles could be considered as elegant machines. Johnson may not have had the initial idea of using a single-wheeler with sanding gear, nor was he responsible for the development of air or steam sanding, but like any good engineer, he did not need to be ingenious or original himself but had to be capable of recognizing and making use of ingenuity and originality.

The Belpaire-boilered Class '3' 4-4-0 engines introduced in 1900 were a major departure from previous Johnson styling, but they also introduced significant engineering changes to Midland locomotive practice. Engineering improvement was the point of the exercise as larger and more powerful locomotives were demanded for the newly introduced corridor trains running over the Settle-Carlisle line. The most radical engineering and visual change was in the Belpaire boiler which not only provided adequate steam for a trip over that gruelling route but it moved Midland style firmly out of the mid-Victorian era. Over the following five years, 80 of these new locomotives were built and they were collectively known as 'Belpaires' even though there were minor design differences between some batches.

Johnson's final passenger design was the compound 4-4-0, the introduction of which was mentioned in chapter 5. Use of the Smith system of compounding was adopted with Deeley making the suggestion that it should be tried. This move towards compounding was taken in order to obtain more power from a locomotive little larger than a 'Belpaire' Class '3'. At 20 tons 12 cwt their maximum axle-loading under working conditions was some 2 tons greater than that of the 'Belpaire' engines, but the wheelbase was not that much larger. This complied with the restrictions imposed by the Civil Engineer but, as already mentioned, Deeley stated that a larger boiler would have been more useful but the increased weight on the wheels was not allowed.[7] More driving wheels would have allowed a reduced axle-loading, but again wheelbase restrictions prevented such a scheme. Subsequent plans for three coupled driving axles or even Deeley's four-cylinder compound were not permitted because of those restrictions.

The compounds as produced were good engines and might have been better had Johnson, Deeley and Fowler been allowed more freedom in terms of size and weight. Work within tight limits does, however, tax the skills of the designer and those engineers were able to squeeze plenty of power out of a relatively small engine. The fact

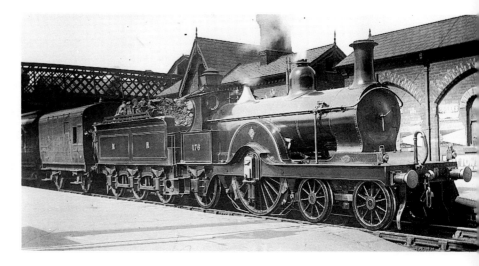

Above left *Johnson 4-4-0 no 2202 at Bedford circa 1902* (J. Adams collection, NRM, York)

Right *Johnson 4-2-2 No 176 at Bedford circa 1904.* (J. Adams collection, NRM, York)

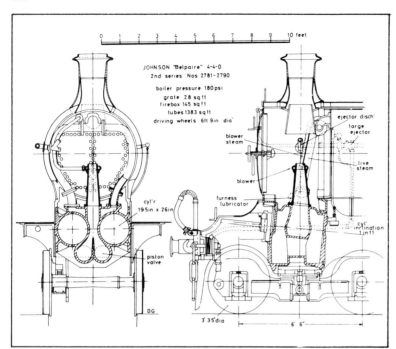

JOHNSON "Belpaire" 4-4-0
2nd series Nos 2781-2790

boiler pressure 180psi
grate 28 sq ft
firebox 145 sq ft
tubes 1383 sq ft
driving wheels 6ft 9in dia'

that the design lasted so well is in some respects due to its initial effectiveness, but also partly due to the Midland's small engine policy. Over the years several modifications were made to the basic design, including the fitting of a better regulator and superheating, but the design remained fundamentally that introduced by Johnson.

Initial trials carried out by Johnson with No 2631 over the Settle-Carlisle line in 1902 were comprehensive and showed how powerful and efficient the design could be. Full results were published in the journal *Engineering*[8] and need not be repeated here. It is, however, necessary to state that this sort of performance was not a regular feature of daily operation and during the 1920s express passenger locomotives on other lines were much more powerful and efficient. As 4-4-0s there is little doubt that they were good and met the demands of the traffic department, but it is also true that a more powerful 4-6-0 could have been developed had the abovementioned restrictions not applied. A 4-6-0, or even 2-8-0, compound as proposed by Fowler is likely to have served the LMS very well indeed.

The compound 4-4-0 engines lasted well because they were effective on the Midland, and on the Midland lines of the LMS. It is not really the compounding system which was at fault, it is the size and weight restrictions. There was a wealth of compound operating experience on the

Midland and footplate crews could handle the locomotives comfortably. Had that expertise been tapped, as it was in France, compounding could certainly have been put to much better use on the railways in Britain. Footplate crew inexperience did not help the operation of Webb's compounds, although he frequently attempted to make the controls easier. Operation of the Midland compounds has been extensively covered by O.S. Nock in his monograph, and the reader is referred to that work for further information.

Both Deeley and Fowler modified Johnson locomotives and incorporated features which enhanced performance. Superheating as fitted during Fowler's time certainly changed good engines into very good engines as it had done on other railways. New boilers working at higher pressures achieved less spectacular improvements in performance, but the basic small engine remained. Deeley was a keen experimenter and wished to reduce the number of variables as far as possible whenever making comparisons. Compounds could not really be compared with the Johnson 'Belpaires' as the former were Class '4' and the latter Class '3'. A series of two-cylinder simple engines of Class '4' was devised and set to operate services similar to the compounds. These '990' series engines were good but not as good as the compounds, nor was the comparison 'like

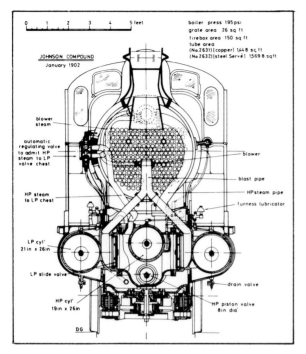

JOHNSON COMPOUND
January 1902

boiler press 195psi
grate area 26 sq ft
firebox area 150 sq ft
tube area
(No.2631) (copper) 1,448 sq ft
(No.2632) (steel Servé) 1,569.8 sq ft

blower
steam

automatic
regulating valve
to admit HP
steam to LP
valve chest

blower

blast pipe

HP steam pipe

furness lubricator

HP steam
to LP chest

LP cyl'
21in x 26in

LP slide valve

drain valve

HP cyl'
19in x 26in

HP piston valve
8in dia

DG

with like', as the simples had smaller driving wheels and a different form of valve gear. That gear was to Deeley's own invention, with the drive being taken from the crosshead of the opposite cylinder.[9] It was novel but no advance on other forms of valve gear and was not repeated.

As far as goods engines were concerned, the Midland remained firmly attached to the 0-6-0 format whether of the tank or tender variety. There were exceptions for particular duties, but the 0-6-0 hauled most goods traffic on the Midland system. One exception was the 0-4-4 tank engine used by Kirtley and Johnson for suburban services, some of these even being provided with condensing arrangements for working in tunnels. Deeley also adopted a trailing bogie for his 0-6-4 tanks of 1907, these also being designed for suburban services. A feature was the tank which extended to the front of the smokebox, and it gives some idea as to what the superstructure of the Deeley 2-4-4-2 compound would have looked like.

Tender goods engines, apart from the American 2-6-0s, were all of the 0-6-0 form and that suited the Midland throughout its existence. Passenger engines always receive attention, but for most railways it was the goods traffic which earned the real money and the Midland was no exception. Over the years from Kirtley to Fowler there was a gradual evolution, with the most dramatic single

change being the introduction of superheating. Boiler design altered due to benefits derived from passenger locomotive operation, higher pressures and Belpaire boilers being introduced to goods engines long after they became standard features of passenger engines. That was the way elsewhere, and the Midland was no different.

This evolution ended with the introduction in 1911 of the Class '4' standard goods, more usually referred to as the '4F'. Only two engines, both with superheaters, were constructed at that time, and these were initially designated as Class '3'. Further orders were not completed until 1917, but quantity production quickly followed. As goods and mixed traffic engines they served the Midland, LMS and British Railways until the final days of steam. Their size suited Midland lines, but their abilities suited the extended railway system in Britain. That was good locomotive engineering for which Fowler has not been given due credit.

A major exception to the 0-6-0 rule for goods engines was the 2-8-0 designed specifically for operation on the steeply graded Somerset & Dorset line. With its heavy gradients this route differed from the remainder of the Midland, and specialist locomotives were called for but very rarely built. The Somerset & Dorset had its own Locomotive Superintendent, but he was subordinate to the CME at Derby and had to request motive power and major repair facilities. However, he did have the responsibility of ensuring that traffic demands on the route could be met. This usually meant calling for standard Derby products and modifying them as necessary to meet particular requirements. Such modifications were of a minor nature and the locomotives were essentially Derby standards.

There was an ever present need for strong goods engines on the line and this became very apparent just after the turn of the century. The then Locomotive Superintendent, A.W. Whittaker, requested new locomotives and Derby responded with the offer of a choice of two 0-8-0 designs. There was, however, a problem, as the Midland's partner in the S&D Joint Railway, the London & South Western Railway, refused to allow an eight-coupled locomotive on the line unless a considerable amount of money was spent on the strengthening of bridges. Savings from the use of larger locomotives would not cover this additional cost, so Whittaker could not have his new engines.[10] This incident illustrates that Derby was not as reticent in locomotive matters as is presumed. The locomotive department was prepared to produce designs for specific purposes, but restrictions imposed by the Midland management

Fowler '4F' 43906, the final form of the Midland 0-6-0 tender goods locomotive. (D. K. Jones collection)

or other railway managements curbed any enthusiasm which might have been generated.

Although larger locomotives were offered to Whittaker, the designs still made use of undersized bearings as found on other Derby machines; the lowest common denominator of Midland design still applied for specialist locomotives away from standard Midland routes. That was a major failing in Derby practice and one which none of the CMEs tackled.

When F. Ryan succeeded Whittaker in 1911 he looked at the proposition again and decided that a weight reduction of 6 tons on the coupled wheels would practically eliminate any need for bridge work. This weight reduction would be achieved by the use of a leading pony truck, whilst the problem imposed by turning upon the rather short S&D turntables was overcome by fitting tender cabs; locomotives could then be worked tender first without inconvenience to the footplate crew. It is certain that Ryan did have influence on the design, but many of the features were standard Derby practice, including the boiler which was the same as that fitted to the 4-4-0 compounds. Modifications were made to the boiler due to the different smokebox of the 2-8-0, but it

was still basically a standard type. The superheating arrangement, based on the Schmidt pattern, was also standard, but the cylinders differed radically from anything else on the Midland in that they had to be sharply inclined at 1 in 12 to give clearance at platforms. Outside Walschaerts valve gear was also new to Derby and in many other respects the 2-8-0 could be considered as a non-standard.

Six of these Class '7F' engines were ordered to replace eight older locomotives and the first entered service in March 1914. Trials showed that the design had been a success and one of the class was 'borrowed' in order to work coal trains between Toton and Brent. Problems with the inadequate axleboxes soon became apparent, but in general S&D locomotive No 85 performed well and the '7F' design was taken as the basis for a similar standard Midland version with a maximum axle-loading of 17½ tons. This was rejected by the Civil Engineer, so an opportunity for the Midland to have a large useful freight engine was lost.[11]

Two basic facets of Derby locomotive design are demonstrated by this incident, and both were due to deficiencies in the permanent way. Short bear-

The Somerset & Dorset '7F'; preserved No 53808.

ings had to be used due to the flexibility of frames needed to compensate for the track, and bridge restrictions were totally unrealistic for any railway operating in the twentieth century. The Board had an opportunity to rectify matters, but appears to have chosen not to do so. Johnson, Deeley, and Fowler had to work within these restrictions and, to a great extent, they did so admirably. Midland locomotives may not have been the best in Britain but they were probably the best the Midland management had any right to expect.

A final Midland locomotive worthy of mention is the 0-10-0 Lickey banker introduced in 1920. As a 'one off' it does not fall into any form of standard category but serves to illustrate the potential of the Derby design team. The original intention had been to construct an 0-10-0 tank locomotive, but axle-loading restrictions again prevented that and the maximum axle-loading came out at 15½ tons, well below that of the '7Fs'. The use of four cylinders was novel to Derby, but their arrangement presented difficulties as the design called for them to all be in line and driving the middle axle. Steep inclination at 1 in 7 was needed for clearance to the smokebox to allow steam chests to be fitted above. A rather complicated arrange-

ment of steam lines was thus required to overcome the problem, but at least it must have given the design team something different to consider.

This section dealing with Midland locomotives has been shorter than the chapters concerning the locomotives of the other railways. This is for two reasons, one of which being the extensive coverage given to this railway's fleet in the series by Jenkinson and Essery, which makes repetition unnecessary. The other is that this book is about locomotive engineers, and chapters on locomotives have only been included in order to deal with their work. The Midland had an extensive locomotive fleet during its history but from an engineering aspect there were few major innovations. There was a degree of continuity in the products of the CMEs which was not found on the other lines under consideration, and that was an advantage, but in some respects it was also a disadvantage when bad practice was perpetuated. Nonetheless, Midland locomotive engineers, working within the restrictions of the railway, produced locomotives which lasted for many years after those restrictions were lifted.

9. Locomotives of the LMS

As with the preceding three chapters, no attempt will be made here to give a complete account of the locomotives of this company. It is, however, essential to deal with some locomotives in order to assess the contribution of the engineers concerned. Sir Henry Fowler's contribution with respect to Midland locomotives was dealt with in the previous chapter but some important changes came about during his years in charge of the LMS locomotive department.

It was inevitable that on the formation of the LMS one of the constituent companies would dominate locomotive affairs, and the fact that the Midland came to do so has long been a matter of controversy, and some regret. That is now history and it is not the intention here to open old wounds and discuss the relative advantages of Derby, Crewe or Horwich practice. The reputation of Henry Fowler has suffered as a result of the actions of others who dictated matters which influenced the design and type of locomotives built during the early years of LMS existence. Strong and forceful personalities on the operating side resulted in the locomotive department having to dance to an outside tune and produce locomotives to a design other people wanted but which were not actually needed. The operating side was, in effect, too close to the situation to appreciate the advantages of change; what had proved to be effective in the past would suit the future, despite the fact that improvements were possible. There can be some sympathy with that point of view; after all, the operating side had trains to run and only wanted to ensure that it was able to do so. Niceties of design did not come into it, nor did efficiency of performance so long as the service was operated.

Midland routes suited small locomotives and these had been able to run the required service in the past, so why not on the larger LMS? Some form of standardization was essential during those formative years in order to minimize manufacturing and maintenance costs, and to standardize on the basis of one of the existing fleets was logical; a completely new set of standard classes would have only confused matters. The simple fact is that because of its small engine policy, Midland locomotives were able to travel to most parts of the LMS system whereas the general stock of L&YR or LNWR locomotives could not be employed as efficiently on Midland metals. Midland locomotives were, in effect, the lowest common denominator, which is not to imply that they were necessarily inferior in all cases.

Fowler had to contend with this situation but he did not like it. He was in favour of compounding and attempted to develop larger locomotives in order to meet the demands of the mid-1920s, but circumstances conspired against him. Hughes had been engaged upon the design of a four-cylinder 4-6-2 in 1924 as a development of the 4-6-0, but the operating department did not want it. When Fowler took over he also had aspirations in that direction and developed schemes for a 4-6-0 version of the standard compound. By the end of 1925 plans for compound 4-6-2 and 2-8-2 engines were in hand. As a step towards this the Hughes 4-6-0 no 10456 had been converted to a

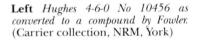

Left *Hughes 4-6-0 No 10456 as converted to a compound by Fowler.* (Carrier collection, NRM, York)

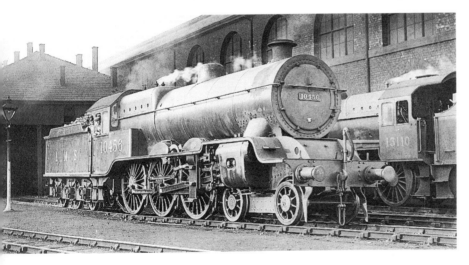

Right *'Royal Scot' No 6119 Lancashire Fusilier.* (D. K. Jones collection)

compound, with a starting valve similar to that fitted to the Hughes compound 0-8-0s, but of piston form. The engine showed savings over the simple form and must have given Fowler confidence in his aim to develop a larger compound. Work on the compound 4-6-2 actually commenced with sections of frames being cut and even cylinder castings made, but then the order was given to stop.[1]

The operating department had other ideas and wanted a locomotive based upon the GWR 'Castle' class, *Launceston Castle* having demonstrated the abilities of a thoroughly modern design of locomotive when she ran trials between Euston and Carlisle during September 1926. Over the heads of those in the locomotive department, operating people approached higher management and Fowler had to comply with a decision to stop work on the compound. He took that setback well and did not seem to complain nor took his obvious frustration out on members of his staff; certainly nobody ever made adverse comments in subsequent accounts of the period. His fellow engineers never heard him complain and when dealing with the topic he simply stated the facts without any hint of animosity. Opening the discussion of a paper concerning American three-cylinder compounds in 1927, he told the gathering without further explanation that he had had to abandon the idea of constructing what would have been the first high-pressure compound locomotive built in Britain, the intended pressure being 220 psi.[2]

Abandonment of the compound resulted in the development of the 'Royal Scot' Class, about which much has already been written. With time short for an introduction of the proposed three-

cylinder 4-6-0 into service, the contract for construction of 50 'Royal Scots' went to the North British Locomotive Company. Over the years debate has continued as to the extent of LMS influence on the design but the explanation offered by E.S. Cox[3] is probably closest to reality. Design work was carried out by North British using a number of standard Derby features. It can be concluded, therefore, that the 'Royal Scots' were essentially North British-designed locomotives with specific parts made to suit current LMS practice. The bearings for the coupled axleboxes were to the Midland pattern, being manganese bronze with brass and white metal inserts. However, they were much larger than standard Midland practice and also had oil supplied by mechanical means.

Bearings caused many problems when the standard short bearings of Midland practice were adopted for LMS-built locomotives, as they did with Midland engines when they were set to work throughout the LMS. Deeley had stated that short bearings were part of Midland locomotive design practice because flexibility of frames and wheels was required in order to allow engines to negotiate sharp curves without difficulty; under such circumstances wide bearings would run hot.[4]

Use of inadequately sized bearings could therefore be justified for Midland locomotives on that basis, but there was really no excuse for perpetuating the practice when running experience with the Horwich 2-6-0 had demonstrated the superiority of larger bearings. This inconsistency is difficult to understand, and emphasizes that standardization can be detrimental as well as advantageous.

Coal trains between Toton and Brent had been

handled by double-headed 0-6-0 locomotives and the need for a larger more powerful engine which could on its own haul the trains was something of a priority. However, curvature of Midland track was a limiting factor so an updated version of the earlier Hughes-proposed 2-10-0 could not be given consideration. A Garratt was eventually considered to be the most suitable design. The 2-6-2 + 2-6-2 scheme proposed was again not acceptable, and there the matter rested.

After Fowler became CME, Beyer was approached again but for a 2-6-0 + 0-6-2, this being the arrangement upon which Horwich was working at the time of the earlier approach. Anderson, then Superintendent of Motive Power and formerly Fowler's Chief Draughtsman in Midland Railway days, seems to have taken the lead this time, but he ignored the more advantageous items of the Horwich scheme including long-lap valves and large bearings. Beyer, Peacock had considerable experience of Garratt construction and could easily have produced the right type of machine for the job.

Antiquated Derby practice had no place on locomotives for the late 1920s but Anderson appears to have insisted upon these details amongst others, possibly as a result of his days as Chief Draughtsman and a belief that what was produced then was still perfectly valid. The three locomotives delivered in 1927 were able to do the work as required, but because of these defects there was no improvement in fuel consumption and the axlebox bearings wore rapidly. When 30 more Garratts were ordered in 1930 these mistakes were not corrected and the only improvements were in the provision of double exhaust valves and a rotary coal bunker to minimize dust.[5]

There seems to have been some sort of schizophrenia present at Derby during those dark days of the late 1920s, for some locomotive designs did incorporate improvements, in particular with respect to bearings and valve gear, whilst others remained firmly entrenched in Midland tradition. The Class '2' 4-4-0 and Class '3' 2-6-2 tanks of 1928 and 1930 respectively incorporated short-travel valves and small bearings, whilst the 'Royal Scots' and 2-6-4 tanks which entered service in 1927 were provided with adequate bearings and long-travel valves. These latter designs had more than proved the advantages of such features and no logic dictated a return to former practice. Fowler was in charge as CME but, although he was progressive and favoured the development of new larger locomotives, he will have exercised little influence on detail design; his main interest lay elsewhere. Certainly nobody

else appears to have taken a lead in ensuring consistency, so matters drifted into a form of productive chaos.

Fowler must take some responsibility, but it is evident that he was not master in his own house. Interference by Directors, higher management and heads of other departments should not have been allowed. Only the easygoing nature of Fowler allowed him to tolerate the situation, for it is certain that other more demonstrative CMEs would have taken matters differently. Whether that would have helped the LMS or made the situation even worse is purely speculative, but with powerful advocates of different railway systems fighting for control of the company's heart, and probably its soul, any CME would have found the situation troublesome at that time. Perhaps a descent to the depths was essential for a rebirth.

It has to be said, however, that some good did come from Derby during that time and there was the embryo of a useful design team. As a locomotive for specific purposes, the 2-6-4 tank could not really be faulted and it formed the basis for subsequent development by Stanier, Fairburn and on into British Railways days. That the same drawing office could produce this triumph and at practically the same time continue to develop locomotives with known defects is little short of amazing. Small teams may have been assigned to particular projects, but there should have been some leadership from above, and even if the CME took no active interest in the details of design the Chief Draughtsman must have been aware of the situation. The writings of E.S. Cox, who was at Derby during this time, shed little light on the situation except to confirm that nobody appeared to be in overall command of design, and that there was no definite policy.

The 'Royal Scots' whatever their parentage, proved to be just what the LMS wanted for its West Coast route. A slightly smaller and less powerful locomotive of the same basic type would suit other routes, and some bright individual at Derby sems to have had the idea of combining the enlarged 'Claughton' boiler with 'Royal Scot' cylinders and chassis. Two 'Claughtons' were nominally rebuilt to produce what became known as the 'Patriot' Class, but when others of the same type were later constructed there was little of the original 'Claughton' involved. The 'Patriots', or 'Baby Scots', were not particularly better in performance than the improved 'Claughtons', but over the years improved reliability and lower repair costs justified their construction.[6] Who was actually responsible for the conversion idea is unknown, but as CME Fowler took the credit. He

'Patriot' No 45550 at Edge Hill, Liverpool in 1960. (D. K. Jones collection)

also took the credit for the 'Royal Scots' and their performance, but rather embarrassingly had to correct performance figures when Gresley proved that the LMS (formerly L&YR) dynamometer car was defective.

During his contribution to the discussion of L.H. Fry's paper concerning an American three-cylinder compound locomotive, Fowler took pains to mention the results of dynamometer car runs with the first 'Royal Scot', No 6100. These results were also compared with those from trials with standard and modified 'Claughtons' as well as 4-4-0 compound locomotives. As might be expected, the 'Royal Scot' proved to be most economical in terms of coal and water consumption per drawbar horsepower, values being 2.66 lbs and 22.3 lbs respectively. When Collett presented his results of similar trials with *Caldicot Castle* in 1924, the figure of 2.83 lbs of coal per drawbar horsepower[7] was greeted with a degree of disbelief, but the 'Royal Scot', it seemed, was even better. Fowler was happy but still held to his view as to the superiority of compounding, stating that he personally thought that better coal consumption results might have been obtained with a compound, possibly working at a still higher pressure. He did, however, admit that the single expansion engine had an advantage in the simplicity of its mechanism.[8]

During the early part of 1928 Gresley borrowed the LMS dynamometer car in order to test the accuracy of the corresponding former North Eastern Railway vehicle. At least that is what he told the people at Derby, but it is equally as conceivable that he suspected the figures claimed for

No 6100 and wished to check on the accuracy of the testing gear used. Whatever the reason, he proved that the LMS car was in error due to friction at worn linkage support rollers. Corrected figures gave the 'Royal Scot' a coal consumption of 3.5 lbs per drawbar horsepower which was more to Gresley's liking as it was about the same as that for his 'Pacifics'.[9] Gresley had already proved the GWR dynamometer car to be defective in 1914,[10] and is likely to have held a suspicion regarding the accuracy of locomotive test results produced elsewhere.

Although the 'Royal Scots' were a success, Fowler still had a passion for compounding especially if high pressure was used. Several locomotive builders were experimenting with high-pressure compound systems and that developed by the Schmidt company in conjunction with the German locomotive builders Henschel attracted Fowler's attention. He obtained permission to construct a locomotive using this principle with the traction part based on a 'Royal Scot' chassis. North British built the locomotive, with the Superheater Company, the British associate of the Schmidt company, dealing with the boiler arrangements. How actively Fowler involved himself with the locomotive is not known, but the ingenuity, and complexity of the design must have intrigued him. When discussing Gresley's paper 'High Pressure Locomotives' in 1931, he did acknowledge that he had adopted the Schmidt-Henschel arrangement, thus implying responsibility for construction.[11]

The system design owed nothing to Fowler or anybody at Derby but is worth considering if only

166

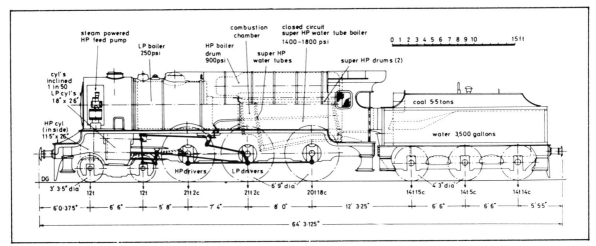

Above *Diagram of the LMS compound* Fury.

Left Fury *in steam.*

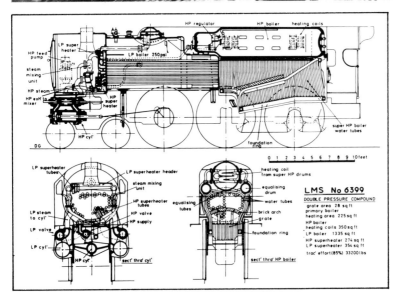

Left *Section veiw of the compound locomotive* Fury.

to indicate the sort of thing which attracted the CME. The steam generating side operated at three separate pressures with the super-high-pressure side being of water tube form operating on a completely closed system. The firebox was formed by water tubes which connected with a foundation ring at the bottom and two equalizing drums at their upper ends. These drums were connected by equalizing tubes which formed the roof of the firebox. The equalizing drums connected with coil tubes positioned inside the high pressure steam drum, these coils acting as heating elements to generate steam in that drum. The totally enclosed super-high-pressure system was filled with distilled water and as temperature increased so did pressure, thus this part of the system would vary in pressure between 1,400 psi and 1,800 psi depending upon the rate of firing. Being totally enclosed and with no means of filling during normal operation the fireman did not need to pay any attention to the level in the super-HP system.

The 900 psi high-pressure side, heated by hot water circulating from the super-high-pressure system, did have a water level which had to be maintained, water being supplied from the low-pressure boiler by means of a pump. The low-pressure boiler operated at 250 psi and received heat from combustion gases passing through tubes like any normal locomotive boiler. Steam generated more quickly in the HP drum than in the LP section, so a bypass arrangement allowed HP steam to be directed to the LP side to avoid waste and promote low-pressure steam generation.

In operation the regulator handle worked high- and low-pressure sides simultaneously. High-pressure steam was directed to the HP cylinder after flowing through the HP superheater elements positioned in the lower flue tubes. Exhausting from the HP cylinder, this steam entered a mixing chamber where it combined with low-pressure steam at 250 psi which had previously passed through low-pressure superheater elements positioned in the upper flues. From the mixing chamber the steam flowed to the two outer LP cylinders and then to exhaust up the chimney.[12] Theoretically the arrangement should have provided a vast improvement on conventional locomotives, but it was extremely complex and not really suited to railway operation.

After only a few days of trial running during February 1930, one of the super-HP tubes failed, causing the fire to blow out the firebox door resulting in injury to some of those on the footplate, and the death of the representative of the Superheater Company. Analysis indicated that the rupture was due to metal failure resulting from too high a temperature, probably caused by inadequate circulation of water in the tube. *Fury,* as the locomotive was called, did not run again until 1932 when further trials were undertaken, but nothing could get the locomotive to perform properly for any length of time. Shortly afterwards it was rebuilt in the conventional form with a Stanier taper boiler, effectively becoming the prototype rebuilt 'Royal Scot'.

During discussion of Gresley's paper, Fowler made no mention of the failure nor, diplomatically, did Gresley, Beames or R. C. Bond. Only one individual raised the point of the LMS machine and that was to simply comment that all 120 gallons in the super-HP system had been blown out in about 3 seconds.

The arrival of Stanier marked a distinct change of course, but it was not accomplished without some problems. The new chief from Swindon insisted on certain practices with a distinctly GWR flavour without really assessing if they would actually suit locomotive operations on LMS routes. When difficulties became evident, he was man enough to allow modifications to be made and courageous enough to admit his mistake.

As already discussed, the real benefit produced by Stanier's arrival was the formation of an effective design team to whom credit for the designs must really go. However, as CME Stanier received the credit and locomotives produced during his period in office have all been referred to as Stanier's.

Large taper boilers characterized Stanier locomotives and the fitting of a typical GWR safety valve bonnet to the first 2-6-0 had already been mentioned. Long-travel valves also became standard, but they were operated by outside Walschaerts gear, not the inside gear favoured by Swindon. The 40 2-6-0s were built at Crewe during 1933 and 1934 but, although they were a success, no repeat order was ever made. A reason for that may have been the outstanding success of the 4-6-0 Class '5' locomotives, subsequently known as the 'Black Fives'.

The history of the 'Black Fives' is so well known that repetition is not required save to say that they must have been the most successful mixed traffic class of locomotive ever built in Britain. As with other Stanier locomotives introduced during the 1933-5 period, they were fitted with domeless low superheat boilers but they performed well from the start whilst some of the early designs failed rather badly. Their rugged simplicity allowed for thrashing when required, but they could be main-

tained readily even with basic equipment in the most primitive of workshops. Economy of operation and that relative ease of maintenance made them popular everywhere, and production continued in BR days until 1951. Ivatt modified the final batches, but their longevity illustrates how basically effective the design was. 'Black Fives' provided the benchmark against which other locomotives could be judged.

Soon after he arrived, Stanier was given permission to construct three 'Pacifics', and the design team was set to work. Several members of the team must have been involved with the earlier Hughes and Fowler projects for 'Pacifics' locomotives, and a number of the schemes worked out initially will have been based upon these. Three-and four-cylinder versions were considered before the latter was chosen, the final scheme owing much to the GWR 'King' Class as far as the front end was concerned, except that four independent sets of valve gear were used.[13]

First of the class, No 6200 *The Princess Royal*, was turned out in the middle of 1933 and the second, No 6201 *Princess Elizabeth*, a few months later.

However no work was undertaken on the third locomotive for which approval had been given, leaving the initial pair to prove the effectiveness of the design. That they did to a great extent, but there were a number of points which required attention and many, but by no means all, related to the boiler and its fittings. The steaming capability of the boiler was not all it might have been but that related to the superheat arrangement rather than the steam generating part. The regulator valve was a departure from normal LMS practice in that it was fitted in the superheater header, but it suffered from distortion and became difficult to keep steam-tight. The bogie axleboxes and slide bars had a tendency to run hot, necessitating frequent visits to the works for attention. The inside big-end bearing ran hot and on at least one occasion disintegrated in service. These locomotives were prestige machines and had to be kept running; instructions thus went out that they were only to be sent to the works under exceptional circumstances.[14]

Eventually the problems were resolved and a further nine locomotives were ordered for delivery in 1935. The 'Lizzies' took their place on LMS express services performing exceptionally well on the heaviest trains. Smoke deflectors were never required and would probably have spoilt their appearance, which was improved when high-sided tenders replaced the low type fitted to the initial two locomotives.

The 'Turbomotive', the unofficial name given to No 6202, was unique in British locomotive practice and it is surprising that Stanier took the bold step to construct such a machine so early during his period in office. The construction and early operating years of this locomotive have been detailed in a paper by R.C. Bond[15] and will not be repeated here. Certainly turbine propulsion deserved investigation and the service results seem to have justified the experiment from an engineering point of view. An engineering experiment was probably how Stanier saw construction, for a single non-standard locomotive of such different form could never have fitted successfully into an express locomotive link. From Stanier's contribution to the discussion of Bond's paper, it is evident that he was impressed by the idea of a turbine-powered locomotive, but he was well aware of the limitations as far as the operating department was concerned. For a long time the 'Turbomotive' was based at Liverpool and was worked by 20 sets of men in turn, thus limiting the amount of experience any crew could gain and so restricting continuity. As a 'one-off', repair costs were high and during the war keeping large groups of standard locomotives at work had greater priority. Despite the problems, Stanier did feel that the experiment had been a success, but he was probably looking at it from an engineering rather than commercial point.

A notable failure during the early Stanier years was the 4-6-0 'Jubilee' Class which was intended as a modern version of the 'Patriot', although engines of that class were still being constructed when design work on the 'Jubilees' commenced during 1933. This new three-cylinder locomotive was essentially a development of the earlier Fowler engine, and unfavourable comparisons were made upon its entry into service. At the time, low-degree superheat was still favoured and the boiler design went along the same route as that of the 2-6-0 and the first 'Pacifics'.

As soon as the initial members of the class were in service, problems became evident, and that was a serious matter as no less than 90 had been ordered. Placed on the Euston to Birmingham service, the first locomotives proved to be inferior to those they were replacing in that they could not produce steam at the rate demanded. This, obviously, was due to the boiler, but an almost identical boiler was fitted to the 'Black Fives' and they did not suffer steam generating problems to anywhere near the same extent. The boiler was indeed defective, but it was aggravated by the draughting arrangement which was causing the major difficulty. Blast pipe and chimney dimensions had been based upon a formula developed at Swindon, but that was for two-cylinder not three-cylinder engines. The three cylinders of the 'Jubilee' gave six exhaust beats per cycle, but the 'Black Fives' gave only four, which suited the draughting arrangements.

The boiler was fitted with the low-temperature superheater favoured by Swindon, and that low steam temperature itself reduced thermal efficiency. In addition, the tube surface area per unit of grate area was low compared with standard

Top left *Numerically the first 'Black Five', No 5000, now preserved.*

Above left *Stanier 'Princess Royal' 'Pacific' No 46205* Princess Victoria *at Rugby in 1962.* (D. K. Jones collection)

Right *'Jubilee' No 5601 in 1934 prior to naming.* (D. K. Jones collection)

LMS practice, and this impaired the actual ability of the boiler to convert water into steam. Hot gases were simply flowing through the tubes to the smokebox. Attempts at correction were not immediately successful, but the matter was urgent as other locomotives of the class were still under construction and a solution had to be found. Increasing the superheater area by fitting additional elements was fairly easy, although extra flue tubes also had to be provided.

It was considered that for a well-designed boiler, the free tube area (ie the area looking on the ends of the tubes) should be 15 per cent of the grate area; the 'Jubilee' boilers originally had a free tube area of 13 per cent of the grate area. An increase in this value may be brought about by fitting a larger number of small diameter tubes or by increasing the diameter of the tubes. The latter step was initially taken and actually made matters worse because it restricted the tube surface area, thus allowing a considerable portion of the hot gases simply to pass through the tubes without giving up much heat. Eventually it was decided to reduce the tube diameter and increase the number, thus giving a larger tube heat transfer surface area. A larger 24-element superheater was subsequently fitted and the final step was to reduce the blast pipe diameter in order to give the correct smokebox effect.[16]

With these alterations the performance of the 'Jubilees' changed out of all recognition and they became the locomotives they were intended to be. This boiler became the basis for a Stanier standard and all LMS locomotives were to benefit. Rebuilding with a Stanier boiler improved many classes including the 'Royal Scots' and the 'Patriots', and effectively extended their useful lives. These changes to the boiler have been mentioned in order to indicate the critical nature of boiler design. It is not simply a matter of fitting tubes between two tubeplates. Tube length, tube diameter, total surface area, grate area, draughting arrangements, and many other factors must be considered when designing a boiler. The Stanier team eventually got it right but it illustrates that boiler design must suit prevailing conditions; there is no such thing as a good universal boiler.

With the boiler organized, other Stanier locomotives could be developed to suit requirements. The new CME had an unwritten brief to modernize the LMS locomotive fleet, thus enabling it to deal with current and predicted demands without the problems of the past re-emerging. Stanier seems to have decided early on that the best policy was one of scrap and build; however, not all of the old designs were cast aside, some were simply updated with new boilers, cylinders, and fittings. Amongst that group was the 2-6-2 tank based upon the 1930 Fowler design. That earlier version was considered to be a poor machine and very much under-boilered; unfortunately the Stanier version followed the same lines and was also under-boilered, despite the fact that the new taper boiler was fitted.

By contrast, the 2-6-4 tank, which also followed an earlier Fowler type, was a notable success. A three-cylinder version was introduced in 1934 especially for services on the Southend line, but experience showed that the Fowler two-cylinder form was equally capable. As the three-cylinder type was heavier, more expensive and required additional maintenance, Stanier arranged for the construction of a modernized two-cylinder 2-6-4 Fowler tank. This design was basically sound and required little improvement over a period of many years. During Stanier's time 206 were constructed to add to those built during the Fowler regime, and in Fairburn's time a similar machine with slightly shorter wheelbase and detail alterations was produced. With some modifications to suit restricted loading gauge in certain areas it formed the basis of the BR standard 2-6-4 tank.

One of the most successful locomotives produced whilst Stanier was CME was the 2-8-0 engine for freight duties. The LMS had many older 0-8-0 freight locomotives but was in need of a modern type, the 2-8-0 devised by Fowler for the Somerset & Dorset Railway not being considered suitable for general adoption during the 1930s. Stanier's team at Derby worked on a new design after a 1933 order for five S & D 2-8-0s had been cancelled. The scheme devised followed the basic Stanier format and the initial batch of 12 had domeless taper boilers. Later locomotives had improved boilers and were classified '8F' compared with the '7F' of the initial batch. Over the years no fewer than 852 of these locomotives were produced, and they saw service overseas during the Second World War with many examples remaining in service on foreign railways until the 1970s and 1980s. Again the Stanier team had produced a very successful locomotive, but it required effort; that success did not come easily, but was won by hard work and careful re-design of parts which did not function in the manner intended. Credit for much of this design work should go to T.F. Coleman, the Chief Draughtsman, who was responsible for the final design work, but traditionally Stanier gets the glory because he selected and motivated the team.

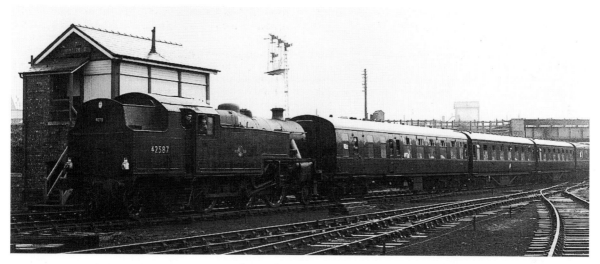

Above *Stanier version of 2-6-4 tank; No 42587 at Aintree in 1960.* (D. K. Jones collection)

Right *Fairburn 2-6-4 tank No 42096.* (D. K. Jones collection)

Right *Stanier '8F' No 48762.* (D. K. Jones collection)

The most spectacular of all the designs produced during Stanier's period in office must be the 'Princess Coronation' or 'Duchess' Class. Again so much had been written about these locomotives that repetition is not required but, as already mentioned, credit really goes to Coleman, as Stanier was overseas when much of the initial design work was carried out. Intended as an improved version of the 'Lizzies', the 'Duchesses', as they generally became known, were arguably the ultimate steam passenger locomotive designed and built in Britain. The LMS management wanted a streamlined train in order to compete with the LNER; neither Stanier nor the design team were enthusiastic, but they complied with the instruction. The idea of streamlining a train was not new and the LMS had assisted in experimental work aimed at devising the optimum form for such streamlining.

In 1931 the LMS Advisory Committee for Scientific Research had initiated a series of wind tunnel experiments on model trains in order to determine air resistance at speed. Tests had been carried out at the National Physical Laboratory on behalf of the LMS and LNER, who together with the Southern Railway covered the cost of the work. A model 'Royal Scot' formed the basis of the LMS train tested, and a number of arrangements for streamlining were employed, including one with a hemispherical smokebox which was similar to that fitted by Collett to his 'Castle' and 'King' streamliners. Details relating to the experiments and the results were published in a paper by F.C. Johansen, Engineering Research Officer of the LMS, during 1936[17] and they indicate how rigorously the work was carried out.

The results certainly showed that streamlining of locomotive and coaches could reduce the power required to overcome head-on wind resistance, particularly at high speeds. Savings for the model *Royal Scot* and a six-coach train were similar to those for the model *Flying Scotsman* and a similar train, but Gresley seems to have made greater publicity use of the information than Stanier. The conclusions did recommend caution about over-optimistic use of the data, especially with side winds, and emphasis was laid on the correct design of the entire train rather than just the locomotive. Although many leading engineers, including Gresley and Bulleid, took part in the discussion, the LMS attitude to streamlining could be gathered from the fact that no senior member of the CME's staff joined in.

Gresley designed his 'A4' locomotives as streamliners from the outset, but it is certain that the 'Duchesses' were designed as conventional locomotives with a streamlined casing added. Consideration of photographs of these engines taken during construction indicates that under the rather ugly casing was a beautiful machine trying to get out. Following the removal of the casing, the only changes required to convert them into 'normal' locomotives was the fitting of a different smokebox, a chimney and a casing for the outside steampipes. Certainly streamlining had advantages in terms of power saved at sustained high-speed running, but the problems it caused with maintenance were not considered to be worth that saving. A streamlined 4-6-4 passenger locomotive was even proposed, but the war intervened and it was never built. It is doubtful if the 'Duchesses' were ever tested to their full potential

Streamlined 'Pacific No 6220 under construction at Crewe. (LMS official)

Above *Non-streamlined 'Pacific' No 6250* City of Lichfield. *(LMS official)*

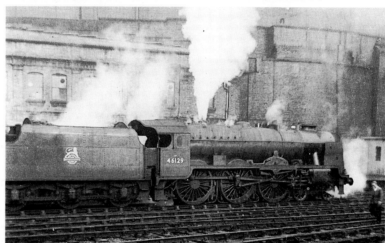

Right *Rebuilt 'Royal Scot' No 46129* The Scottish Horse. (D. K. Jones collection)

as no single fireman would have been able to feed that 50 sq ft grate over an extended period of continuous running. Indeed no train was operated which required the sustained power of which these locomotives were capable when in good order.

Fairburn's only contribution to LMS steam locomotive stock was a modified version of the Fowler/Stanier 2-6-4 tank. Again, changes were made to take account of slightly different operating requirements but the locomotive remained essentially as originally produced. A considerable weight saving resulted from the re-design and this together with the reduced coupled wheelbase, theoretically increased route availability. More extensive use of diesel shunting locomotives also came about during the short Fairburn era.

Ivatt was not keen to change the basic locomotive plan as devised during Stanier's time but he did insist upon an improvement in accessibility

for maintenance and a general increase in operating efficiency. Existing locomotives could be counted upon to maintain services when matters settled down after the war, so he made no move to force new designs on the railway. Rebuilding of the 'Royal Scots' with taper boilers was continued, this process having commenced when *Fury* was reconstructed as *British Legion* during 1935. By 1939 the 'Royal Scot' boilers were 12 years old and due for replacement, so it was considered prudent to devise a standard boiler which could be fitted to that class as well as to the 'Patriots' and 'Jubilees'. That new boiler was fitted with a double chimney and a twin-orifice blast pipe but without the complicating features of petticoats and jets as used by the Kylchap system fitted to LNER locomotives.

Two 'Jubilees' were fitted with the new boiler, which worked at 250 psi instead of 200 psi, in 1942 and the modification proved to be a success;

approval was thus obtained to convert 20 'Royal Scots'. That higher pressure certainly helped when it came to performance, for conversion turned them into exceptional locomotives for their size. The new boiler, classed as 2A, was lighter than the original, thus altering wheel and bogie loading, whilst its centre of gravity was slightly lower. These factors probably caused the tendency towards rough riding which developed following rebuilding as nothing else of significance, including the springing arrangements, was changed. Conversion was relatively slow and continued through Ivatt's stewardship and into BR days.

Only two 'Jubilees', No 5735 *Comet* and No 5736 *Phoenix*, received the type 2A boiler, but Ivatt set

about doing for the 'Patriots' what conversion had done for the 'Scots', In 1945 approval was given for the rebuilding of the class with new boilers, cylinders and certain other parts. The first eight to be built made use of the original frames but the following ten engines were given new frames. New cylinders, of 17-inch diameter instead of 18 inches, were fitted together with a new smokebox saddle. Spring suspension was altered to suit the axle loading which was greater than for the original design, and these changes raised the tractive effort to 29,950 lbs and the power classification from '5XP' to '6 P'. In accordance with Ivatt's policy, rocking grates, self-emptying ashpans and self-cleaning smokeboxes were also provided.[18]

Below *Rebuilt 'Patriot' No 45535, Sir Herbert Walker, KCB.* (D. K. Jones collection)
Bottom *Ivatt Class '4MT' No 43151 at Crewe South in 1966.* (D. K. Jones collection)

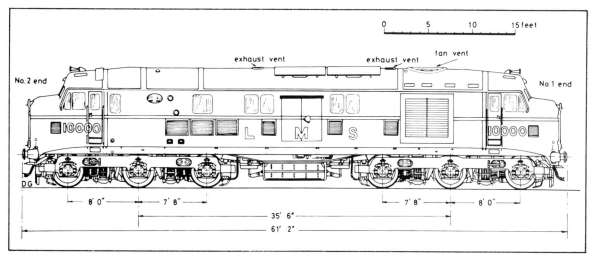

Ivatt's main-line diesel passenger locomotive, No 10000.

Only 18 of the 52 'Patriots' were rebuilt, probably because of the expense involved and the fact that with the rebuilt 'Royal Scots' there was then a large enough stock of class '6P' engines available; during BR days the power classification was increased to '7P'.

Ivatt's other steam classes have been mentioned in chapter 5 and little else really needs be stated. His Class '2' 2-6-0 appears rather antiquated compared with other post-war designs, but it was a very modern locomotive in terms of amenities for footplate crew and ease of operation. The same could also be said for the tank version, of which 130 were eventually constructed. In order to improve visibility when running in reverse, an inset bunker was provided; the tender version also had an inset bunker which looked like a coal box mounted on a water tank.

This functionality and the consideration for the footplate crew characterized the Ivatt designs, no concessions being made to appearance. His designs were attractive in a basic locomotive way but the Class '4' 2-6-0 stretched appreciation rather far in its original double chimney form. The fitting of a single chimney improved their appearance, but it is certain that Ivatt cared nothing for that. As built they were very useful engines which had good route availability, but following draughting modifications they became even better.

It is fitting to end this chapter, and the book, with mention of Ivatt's diesel-powered passenger locomotives. Although much of the electrical design work was carried out by English Electric, the design staff at Derby was actively involved, and

these locomotives can be considered as LMS machines. Ivatt was most certainly the driving force behind the project as far as the railway was concerned and the success of 10000 and 10001 in service is a tribute to his enthusiasm. Certainly diesel traction would have come about on the railways of Britain even if these locomotives had not been constructed, but it may well have been longer in arriving. English Electric, which looked upon the project as a means of gaining overseas orders, gained both orders and experience from its involvement with Ivatt.

Perhaps the most amazing thing about locomotive matters during the existence of the LMS is that very few senior people concerned with design and the workshops were brought in from outside. Stanier and Fairburn were recruited from elsewhere, but others, including Bond, Chambers, Coleman, Cox, and Riddles, were there at the grouping, albeit some still in junior positions. It was not engineering talent which the LMS lacked, nor for that matter engineering leadership, as Hughes and Fowler were both very good engineers and leaders of men. What the LMS lacked during the 1920s was *managerial* leadership and a sense of direction. Petty and self-seeking people dominated everything and caused chaos where none existed previously. They caused people to question the skill and ability of Hughes and Fowler when it was the judgement of the managers which was in doubt. Hopefully this book has cast some light on the works of these engineers and others who served the LMS and its main English constituents.

Footnote references

IME — Proceedings, Institution of Mechanical Engineers
ICE — Minutes of Proceedings, Institution of Civil Engineers
ILE — Journal, Institution of Locomotive Engineers

Chapter 1

1. *Railway Magazine*, vol 28, 1911, pp 89–93; 112–6
2. J. Marshall, *Biographical Dictionary of Railway Engineers* (David & Charles, Newton Abbot, 1978), pp 123, 127
3. E. L. Ahrons, *British Steam Railway Locomotive 1825–1925* (Locomotive Publishing Co, London, 1927), p 134
4. R. W. Rush, *The East Lancashire Railway* (Oakwood Press, 1983), p. 40–1
5. *Railway Magazine*, vol 41, 1917, p 235
6. Marshall, *Dictionary of Locomotive Engineers*, pp 22–3
7. *Railway Magazine*, vol 41, 1917, pp 236–7
8. IME, 1878, vol 29, pp 90–1
9. J. Marshall, *The Lancashire & Yorkshire Railway Vol 3* (David & Charles, Newton Abbot, 1972), pp 112–3
10. *Railway Magazine*, vol 41, 1917, p 308
11. J. Marshall, *The Lancashire & Yorkshire Railway vol 2* (David & Charles, Newton Abbot, 1970), pp 210–11
12. *Railway Times*, 3 November 1883, p 1094
13. Extract from L&YR Board Minutes, 23 June 1886; Box E1/106P, NRM, York
14. D. H. Stuart & B. Reed, *The Crewe Type*, (Profile Publications, 1971)
15. *Crewe Guardian*, 17 October 1882
16. B. Reed, *Crewe Locomotive Works & its Men* (David & Charles, Newton Abbot, 1982), pp 46–7
17. T. R. Gourish, *Mark Huish & the LNWR* (Leicester University Press, 1972), p 177
18. *The Engineer*, 12 June 1891, p 471
19. Board minutes quoted by Stuart & Reed, *The Crewe Type*, p 69
20. Reed, *Crewe Locomotive Works*, pp 218–22
21. ICE, vol 74, pt 4, 1882–83, p 285
22. 'David Joy's Diaries', *Railway Magazine*, vol 23, 1908, p 151
23. Ibid, p 228
24. *Herapaths Railway Magazine*, 12 August 1854
25. LNWR correspondence, PRO Rail 1008, piece 101
26. *Practical Mechanics' Record of the International Exhibition 1862* (Longman Green, London, 1862), p 271
27. *Railway Magazine*, vol 28, 1911, p 222
28. *Practical Mechanics' Record of the International Exhibition 1862*, pp 270–8
29. 'David Joy's Diaries', *Railway Magazine*, vol 23, 1908, p 153
30. ICE, vol 74, 1882–83, pp 285–6
31. 'Burning coal instead of coke', J. Markham, *The Engineer*, 18 January 1861, p 37

Chapter 2

1. *The Engineer*, 22 January 1937, p 109
2. 'Some Railways Old & New', J. A. F. Aspinall, IME, 1925, p 1125
3. 'Horwich Locomotive Works,' J. A. F. Aspinall, ICE vol 129, 1896–7, p 316
4. *Railway Magazine*, vol 7, December 1900, pp 484–5
5. Transactions, Liverpool Engineering Society, vol 22, 1900, p 1
6. Presidential Address, IME 1909, p 423
7. Presidential Address, ICE, vol 207, 1918, pp 4–5
8. IME, 1925, p 1142
9. *Railway Magazine*, vol 41, 1917, p 33
10. H. A. V. Bulleid, *The Aspinall Era* (Ian Allan, London, 1967), p 22
11. *The Engineer*, 22 January 1937, p 109
12. Bulleid, *The Aspinall Era*, p 67, 237, 239
13. 'Friction in Locomotive Slide Valves', J. A. F. Aspinall, ICE, vol 95, 1888–9
14. ICE, vol 129, 1896–7, p 309
15. Aspinall report to Board, quoted Bulleid, *The Aspinall Era*, pp 83–6
16. ICE, vol 129, 1897–7, pp 309–16
17. 'Friction in Locomotive Slide Valves', J. A. F. Aspinall, ICE, vol 133, 1897–8, pp 13–7, 21–4
18. IME, vol 44, 1893, pp 199–202
19. 'Train Resistance', J. A. F. Aspinall, ICE, vol 167, 1901–2, pp 155–277
20. 'Experiments on Tractive Resistance of Loaded Wagons', J. A. F. Aspinall, ICE, vol 158, 1903–4, pp 369–73
21. E. S. Cox, *Locomotive Panorama vol 1* (Ian Allan, London, 1965), p 15
22. Bulleid, *The Aspinall Era*, pp 163, 180
23. IME Presidential Address, 1909, p 424
24. Ibid, p 427
25. 'Road Locomotion', Prof Hele-Shaw, IME, 1900, pp 246–7

25. Presidential Address, ICE, 1918, p 11
27. ICE, vol 187, 1911–2, pp 211–3
28. IME, vol 135, 1937, pp 539–41
29. Journal, ICE, vol 5, 1936–7, pp 795–6
30. *The Engineer*, 22 January 1937, p 109; also University of Liverpool Senate records
31. Bulleid, *The Aspinall Era*, p 163
32. IME, 1910, pp 778–9
33. *The Engineer*, 27 May 1910, p 540
34. IME, 1900, pp 233–5
35. *The Engineer*, 30 January 1903, pp 124–5
36. IME, 1910, pp 778–9
37. 'Lighting of Railway Premises', H. Fowler, IME, 1906, pp 919–20
38. *Engineering*, 7 October 1904, pp 408–9
39. Hills & Patrick, *Beyer, Peacock & Co* (Transport Pub Co, Glossop, 1983), p 120
40. *Bolton Chronicle*, 28 May 1910, p 7
41. *Railway Magazine*, vol 33, 1913, p 104; also *The Engineer*, 2 November 1945, p 349
42. IME, 1906, p 918
43. Cox, *Locomotive Panorama vol 1*, pp 14–5; also *Railway Gazette*, 14 August 1925, p 233
44. *Railway Gazette*, 18 December 1925, p 814
45. *Railway Gazette*, 14 August 1925, p 233
46. *The Engineer*, 2 November 1945, p 349
47. 'Non-ferrous Metals in Railway Work', G. Hughes, Proc Inst of Metals, 20 September 1911
48. *Engineering*, 22 September 1911, p 393
49. Ibid, p 394
50. *The Engineer*, 14 April 1922, p 405
51. 'Suburban System of the LB&SCR', P. Dawson, ICE, vol 186, 1910–11, pp 61–6, 67–72
52. 'Railway Motor-car Traffic', Riches & Haslam, IME, 1906, pp 678–82, 686–9
53. 'Design of Rolling Stock for Smooth Rail Working', F. W. Bach, ICE, vol 180, 1909-10, pp 92–6
54. 'Horwich Locomotives', G. Hughes, IME, July 1909, pp 624, 626
55. 'Compounding & Superheating', G. Hughes, IME, March 1910, p 452
56. 'Electrical & Mechanical Equipment for All-metal Cars', G. Hughes, ICE, 1921, p 292
57. 'Horwich Locomotives', IME, July 1909, pp 612–8
58. 'Compounding & Superheating', IME, March 1910, pp 400–1
59. 'Large Locomotive Boilers', G. J. Churchward, IME, Feb 1906
60. 'A Modern Locomotive History', E. S. Cox, ILE, vol 36, 1946, pp 108–11
61. *The Engineer*, 2 November 1945, p 349

Chapter 3

1. IME, 1897, p 2136
2. ICE, vol 129, 1896–7, p 382
3. *The Engineer*, 1897, p 568
4. LNWR Documents, PRO, Rail 1008–101
5. 'Coking Crane for Supplying Locomotive Engines', J. Ramsbottom, IME, 1853, pp 122–5
6. 'An Improved Piston', J. Ramsbottom, IME, 1854, pp 70–4
7. 'An Improved Safety Valve', J. Ramsbottom, IME, 1856, p 37
8. 'Railways Old & New', J. A. F. Aspinall, IME, 25 November 1925, p 114
9. 'Supplying Water to Locomotives whilst Running', J. Ramsbottom, IME, 1861, p 43
10. 'Mechanical Ventilation of Liverpool Passenger Tunnel', J. Ramsbottom, IME, 1871, pp 22–35, 66–74
11. *Sir Henry Bessemer — An Autobiography* (*Engineering*, London, 1905), p 335
12. *Engineering*, 5 January 1866
13. *Railway Magazine*, vol 5, 1899, p 238
14. *The Engineer*, 14 June 1867, p 538
15. *James Nasmyth, Engineer — An Autobiography* (John Murray, London, 1889), pp 427–8
16. IME, vol 52, 1897, pp 236–41
17 *Railway Magazine*, vol 5, 1899, p 239
18. IME, vol 52, 1897, pp 240–1
19. ICE, 1897, p 373; also *Railway Magazine*, vol 6, February 1900, p 97
20. LNWR Chairman's letter book, PRO, Rail 1008
21. 'David Joy's Diaries', *Railway Magazine*, 1908, pp 319–20
22. *Cassiers Magazine*, vol 24, 1903, p 526
23. *Railway Magazine*, vol 6, February 1900, p 104
24. ICE, vol 81, 1884–5, p 135
25. *Railway Magazine*, vol 6, February 1900, p 106
26. IME, vol 34, 1883, pp 438–62
27. IME, 1879, p 349–51
28. IME, 1884, pp 119–21
29 ICE, vol 80, 1884–85, pp 258–9
30. ICE, vol 41, 1874–5, pp 43–5
31. ICE, vol 130, 1896–7, pp 178; also *Engineering*, 28 May 1897, pp 707, 727
32. ICE, vol 138, 1899, pp 406–11
33. *Engineering*, 9 June 1899, p 737
34. *Engineering*, 28 May 1897, p 707
35. 'Locomotive Firebox Stays', F. W. Webb, ICE, vol 150, April 1902, p 121
36. ICE, vol 155, 1903–4, pp 401–10
37. ICE, vol 81, 1884–5, p 133
38. ICE, vol 149, 1901–2, pp 112–5
39. *Cassiers Magazine*, vol 12, 1897, pp 687–94

40. *Railway Magazine*, vol 6, 1900, pp 97–107
41. *The Engineer*, 8 June 1906, p 597
42. *The Engineer*, 1 May 1896, p 451
43. *The Engineer*, 29 January 1897, p 122
44. *Railway Magazine*, May–June 1942, pp 159–60
45. ICE, vol 41, 1874–5, p 45
46. ICE, vol 167, 1901–2, p 220
46. *Railway Magazine*, May–June 1942, p 164
48. *Engineering*, 8 June 1906, p 764
49. *Railway Magazine*, Nov/Dec 1961, pp 756–62, 840–4
50. *The Engineer*, 28 November 1902, p 523
51. *The Engineer*, 10 April 1903, p 367
52. *The Engineer*, 26 June 1903, p 649
53. W. H. Chaloner, 'Francis William Webb of the L&N WR', *Transport History*, vol 1, No 2, 1968, p 117
54. *The Engineer*, 29 May 1903, p 545
55. *Crewe Chronicle*, 30 May 1903
56. *The Engineer*, 11 March 1910, p 246
57. H. A. V. Bulleid, *The Aspinall Era* (Ian Allan, London, 1967), p 22
58. W. H. Chaloner, *Social & Economic History of Crewe* (Manchester University Press, 1950), pp 157–65
59. ICE, vol 182, 1909–10, p 330
60. IME, 1910, pp 784–5
61. 'Combustion in Locomotive Fireboxes', F. J. Brislee, IME, 1908, 349–55
62. B. Reed, *Crewe Works and its Men* (David & Charles, Newton Abbot, 1982), p 134
63. Recollections of W. N. Davies, *The LNWR Recalled*, compiled E. Talbot (OPC, Poole, 1987), pp 68–9
64. Ibid, p 70
65. *Railway Gazette*, January 1909, p 12
66. *The Engineer*, 29 August 1919, p 201
67. *The Engineer*, 22 October 1920, p 397; also *Railway Magazine*, vol 25, 1909, p 24
68. *Railway Magazine*, vol 25, 1909, p 24
69. IME, May 1921, pp 538–9
70. *English Illustrated Magazine*, 1891–2, pp 377–91
71. C. J. B. Cooke, *Some Recent Developments in Locomotive Practice* (Whittaker, London, 1902)
72. C. J. B. Cooke, 'Modern Types of British Locomotives', *Cassiers Magazine*, April 1901, pp 449–68
73. Cooke, *Recent Developments in Locomotive Practice*, p 39; also *Cassiers Magazine*, April 1901, p 453
74. *Cassiers Magazine*, April 1901, p 460
75 Ibid, pp 461–2
76. 'Compounding & Superheating Horwich Locomotives', G. Hughes, IME, March 1910, pp 478–83
77. *Railway Magazine*, July/Aug 1943, pp 233–5
78. Talbot, *LNWR Recalled*, pp 71–2
79. H. C. B. Rogers, *The Last Steam Locomotive Engineer, R. A. Riddles* (Allen & Unwin, London, 1970), p 30
80. *Railway Magazine*, July/Aug 1942, pp 223–5
81. *Railway Magazine*, Nov/Dec 1943, p 341
82. 'Superheated Steam', H. Fowler, ICE, 1914, pp 109–15
83. 'Mechanical Handling of Coal', C. J. B. Cooke, ICE, 1912–23, pp 178–213
84. *Railway Magazine*, vol 1, July/Dec 1897, pp 113–22
85. Reed, *Crewe Works*, p 150
86. Rogers, *The Last Steam Locomotive Engineer*, pp 132, 152
87. *Railway Magazine*, vol 38, Jan–June 1916, p 371
88. 'A Modern Locomotive History', E. S. Cox, ILE, vol 36, 1946, pp 126–30
89. IME, March 1928, pp 245–87
90. *The Engineer*, 12 March 1948, p 259

Chapter 4

1. Patent No 12,210, 11 July 1848
2. 'On the Burning of Coal' by C. Markham, IME, 1861; also *The Engineer*, 18 January 1861, pp 37–9
3. J. Marshall, *Biographical Dictionary of Railway Engineers* (David & Charles, Newton Abbot, 1978), p 133
4. F. S. Williams, *Midland Railway — its rise and progress* (Strahan & Co, London, 1876), p 210
5. J. B. Radford, *Derby Works & Midland Locomotives* (Ian Allan, London, 1971), p 20
6. Ibid, p 21
7. 'Manufacture of Duplicate Machines & Engines', J. Fernie, ICE, 1862–3, pp 604–14
8. Williams, *Midland Railway*, p 210
9. *Cassiers Magazine*, May–Oct 1898, p 543; also IME, 1912, pp 302–3
10. *Cassiers Magazine*, May–Oct 1898, p 544
11. Presidential Address, IME, April 1898, p 164
12. *The Engineer*, 10 September 1897, p 243
13. *The Engineer*, 7 December 1909, p 623
14. *Cassiers Magazine*, May–Oct 1898, p 544
15. *Cassiers Magazine*, April 1909, p 462
16. IME, April 1898, p 169
17. 'Water Softening & Purification on the Archbutt-Deeley Process', L. Archbutt, IME, 1898, pp 446–7
18. 'Aluminium Manufacture', E. Ristori, IME, 1898, p 371
19. 'Mechanical Testing of Materials,' W. G. Peet, IME, 1898, pp 670–95

20. ICE, 1896–7, vol 130, p 197; also *Engineering*, 11 June 1897, p 798
21. *Engineering*, 11 June 1897, p 776
22. *The Engineer*, 10 August 1888, pp 110–2
23. *The Engineer*, 21 February 1892, pp 182–3
24. *Engineering*, 7 July 1899, p 11
25. *Cassiers Magazine*, May–Oct 1898, p 544; also *The Engineer*, 27 November 1903, p 524
26. ICE, vol 150, April 1902, pp 129–36
27. *Engineering*, 28 May 1897, p 707
28. *Engineering*, 4 June 1897, p 738
29. *Engineering*, 7 July 1944, p 14
30. IME, 1898, pp 404–53
31. *The Engineer*, Jan–June 1890, pp 509–11; July–Dec 1890, pp 21–2, 68, 110, 128, 153, 171
32. Archbutt & Deeley, *Lubrication and Lubricants* (Griffin & Co, London, 1900/07/12/27)
33. *The Engineer*, 10 June 1896, pp 25–6
34. *The Engineer*, 1 January 1897, pp 1–2
35. *The Engineer*, 12 February 1897, pp 157–9
36. *The Engineer*, 21 January 1921, p 78
37. *The Engineer*, 8 December 1927, pp 610–1
38. *The Engineer*, 3 July 1914, pp 7–8
39. *Engineering*, 7 July 1944, p 14
40. *Railway Magazine*, vol 14, May 1904, p 80
41. *Engineering*, 6 February 1903; pp 170–6; 27 March 1903, pp 414–5
42. *The Engineer*, 17 December 1909, p 623
43. Ibid, p 624
44. C. H. Ellis, *The Midland Railway* (Ian Allan, London, 1953), pp 133–4
45. IME, October 1898, pp 678–83
46. *The Engineer*, 25 March 1898, p 276
47. E. G. Barnes, *The Midland Main Line 1875–22* (Allen & Unwin, London, 1969), p 220
48. R. C. Bond, *A Lifetime with Locomotives* (Goose & Son, Cambridge, 1975), p 47
49. *Railway Magazine*, Sept–Oct 1942, p 287
50. E. S. Cox, *Speaking of Steam* (Ian Allan, London, 1971), p 65
51. Journal ICE, vol 11, 1939, p 617; also *Engineering*, 21 October 1938, p 484
52. Bond, *A Lifetime with Locomotives*, pp 38–9
53. ICE, vol 134, 1897–8, pp 1–65
54. Journal ICE, vol 11, 1939, p 617
55. *Engineering*, 21 October 1938, p 484
56. *Railway Gazette*, 21 August 1925, p 253
57. 'Locomotive Repairs', Sir Henry Fowler, Journal, Institute of Transport, December 1929, pp 59–89
58. *Railway Magazine*, Sept–Oct 1942, pp 287–8
59. ILE, vol 3, 1913, pp 3–15
60. Journal, Institute of Automobile Engineers, 1920, p 20
61. Ibid, pp 12–3
62. IME, 1927, p 725
63. ILE, paper 115, 1921, p 106
64. ILE, paper 177, 1924, pp 144–5
65. ICE, vol 196, 1914, pp 77–135
66. Barnes, *The Midland Main Line*, p 229
67. ICE, vol 196, 1914, pp 82–3
68. *Railway Gazette*, 21 August 1925 p 253; also *Engineering*, 21 October 1938, p 484
69. 'Lighting of Railway Premises', H. Fowler, IME, 1906, p 917
70. IME, 1927, pp 746–7
71. ILE, 1913, p 5
72. 'Trials with Vacuum Brakes for Long Freight Trains', Sir Henry Fowler and H. N. Gresley, ICE, vol 213, 1922, pp 223–93
73. 'Fractures in Locomotive Boiler Tubes', Sir Henry Fowler, Faraday Society 1921; also *Engineering*, 15 April 1921, pp 466–7
74. *Engineering*, 22 September 1922, p 374
75. *Engineering*, 19 May 1922, p 609
76. 'A Modern Locomotive History', E. S. Cox, ILE, vol 36, 1946, pp 115–8
77. Bond, *A Lifetime with Locomotives*, p 50
78. Journal, Institute of Transport, December 1929, p 69
79. *The Engineer*, 21 October 1938, p 466
80. *Engineering*, 21 October 1938, p 484

Chapter 5

1. *The Engineer*, 17 December 1909, p 623
2. *Railway Magazine*, Jan/June 1931, p 37
3. R. C. Bond, *A Lifetime with Locomotives* (Goose & Son, Cambridge 1975), pp 83, 91
4. H. C. B. Rogers, *The Last Steam Locomotive Engineer, R. A. Riddles* (Allen & Unwin, London, 1970), pp 60–1
5. *Engineering*, 31 December 1954, p 845
6. O. S. Nock, *William Stanier — a biography* (Ian Allan, London, 1964)
7. J. Bellwood & D. Jenkinson, *Gresley and Stanier* (HMSO, London, 1976, 1986)
8. *The Engineer*, 1 October 1965, p 555
9. D. Griffiths, *Locomotive Engineers of the GWR* (Patrick Stephens, Wellingborough, 1987), p 42
10. E. S. Cox, *Locomotive Panorama vol 1* (Ian Allan, London, 1965), p 100
11. Rogers, *The Last Steam Locomotive Engineer*, 72–4
12. E. J. Larkin, *Memoirs of a Railway Engineer* (Mechanical Engineering Publications, London, 1979), p 84
13. Bellwood & Jenkinson, *Gresley and Stanier*, pp 19–20

14. Cox, *Locomotive Panorama vol 1*, pp 110–2
15. Rogers, *The Last Steam Locomotive Engineer*, pp 72–3
16. Cox, *Locomotive Panorama vol 1*, p 109–11
17. ILE, vol 36, 1946, pp 231–2
18. Presidential Address, ILE, vol 133, 1936, pp 571–4
19. Rogers, *The Last Steam Locomotive Engineer*, pp 84–5
20. Presidential Address, ILE, vol 147, 1948, pp 27–31
21. Ibid, p 31
22. 'Locomotive Experimental Stations', H. N. Gresley, IME, 1934, p 43
23. Rogers, *The Last Steam Locomotive Engineer*, pp 84–5; also Cox, *Locomotive Panorama vol 1*, pp 120–1
24. Rogers, *The Last Steam Locomotive Engineer*, p 73
25. Presidential Address, IME, October, 1941, pp 50–61
26. Presidential Address, ILE, vol 133, 1936, pp 553–94
27. Presidential Address, ILE, vol 147, 1938, pp 13–35
28. O. S. Nock, *William Stanier*, p 143
29. IME, 1939, pp 13–32
30. 'G. J. Churchward, Chief Mechanical Engineer', Sir William Stanier, Transactions of the Newcomen Society, vol 30, 1960, pp 1–12
31. *The Engineer*, 1 October 1965, p 555; also *Who Was Who, vol 6*, 1961–70, p 1069
32. *The Engineer*, 19 October 1945, p 307
33. IME, 1946, p 354; also *Engineering*, 19 October 1945, p 315
34. *The Engineer*, 19 October 1945, p 307
35. 'Diesel Shunting Locomotives', C. E. Fairburn, ILE, vol 161, 1941, pp 175–225
36. 'Maintenance of Diesel Electric Shunting Locos', C. E. Fairburn, ILE, vol 179, 1944, pp 212–58
37. *The Engineer*, 27 April 1945, p 334
38. H. A. V. Bulleid, *Master Builders of Steam* (Ian Allan, London, 1983), p 183
39. 'Trend in Design of Electric Locomotives', C. E. Fairburn, Proc Inst of Electrical Engineers, vol 83, November 1938, pp 581–633
40. Cox, *Locomotive Panorama vol 1*, p 157
41. Ibid, p 150
42. Ibid, p 151
43. Bond, *A Lifetime with Locomotives*, p 157
44. *The Engineer*, 19 October 1945, pp 307–8
45. Bulleid, *Master Builders of Steam*, p 160
46. Ibid, pp 161–2
47. *Railway Gazette*, 22 June 1951, p 703
48. Bulleid, *Master Builders of Steam*, p 166
49. Rogers, *The Last Steam Locomotive Engineer*, p 54
50. Bulleid, *Master Builders of Steam*, p 171
51. Larkin, *Memoirs of a Railway Engineer*, p 92
52. Cox, *Locomotive Panorama vol 1*, p 136
53. Bond, *A Lifetime with Locomotives*, p 158
54. Bulleid, *Master Builders of Steam*, p 176
55. *Railway Gazette*, 31 January 1947, p 136
56. *Railway Gazette*, 2 January 1948, p 20
57. Centenary Lecture, IME, 12 June 1947, pp 235–6
58. Cox, *Locomotive Panorama vol 1*, p 157
59. *Railway Gazette*, 2 January 1948, pp 16–8
60. Larkin, *Memoirs of a Railway Engineer*, p 95
61. *Railway Gazette*, 2 January 1948, p 29
62. *Railway Gazette*, 20 July 1951, p 75

Chapter 6

1. 'Horwich Locomotives', G. Hughes, IME, July 1909, pp 561–2
2. 'David Joy's Diaries', *Railway Magazine*, 1908, p 319
3. Ibid, p 458
4. IME, July 1909, pp 568–9
5. Ibid, pp 567–8
6. *The Engineer*, 21 June 1895, p 536
7. 'Railways Old & New', J. A. F. Aspinall, IME, 1925, p 1134
8. ICE, vol 196, 1914, p 128
9. *The Engineer*, 8 November 1889, p 326
10. *The Engineer*, 15 August 1902, p 112
11. IME, July 1909, p 571
12. *Engineering*, 6 May 1904, pp 641–2
13. IME, July 1909, p 573
14. *Engineering*, 8 January 1904, pp 48–9
15. 'Electrical & Mechanical Equipment', G. Hughes. ICE, vol 29, 1921, p 196
16. IME, July 1909, pp 573–4
17. 'Compounding & Superheating', G. Hughes IME, March 1910, pp 399–507
18. *The Engineer*, 30 August 1907, pp 209–210
19. 'A Modern Locomotive History', E. S. Cox, ILE, vol 36, 1946, pp 118–20
20. E. Mason, *The L&Y in the 20th Century* (Ian Allan, London, 1954), pp 147–9
21. IME, July 1909, pp 574–5
22. Ibid, pp 575–83
23. ILE, vol 36, 1946, p 132
24. E. S. Cox, *Locomotive Panorama vol 1*, (Ian Allan, London, 1965), p 41
25. ILE, vol 36, 1946, p 112

Chapter 7

1. *Practical Mechanics' Journal, International Exhibition Volume 1862* (Longman, Green, London, 1862), pp 271–3
2. *British Steam Railway Locomotive 1825–1925*, E. L. Ahrons (Loco Pub Co London, 1927), p 204
3. ICE, vol 81, 1884–5, p 136
4. 'Reversing & Expansive Valve Gear', D. Joy, IME, 1880, p 432
5. *Engineering*, 21 August 1896, p 251
6. ICE, vol 41, 1874-5, pp 43–4
7. *Railway Magazine*, May–June 1942, pp 159–60
8. IME, 1879, p 350
9. ICE, vol 96, 1888–9, p 55
10. IME, 1879, p 353
11. ICE, vol 96, 188-9, p 56
12. IME, 1883, pp 438-62
13. *The Engineer*, 21 December 1888, p 511
14. *Railway Magazine*, vol 8, 1901, p 459
15. *Railway Magazine*, vol 9, 1901, p 98
16. ICE, vol 138, 1899, p 408; also *The Engineer*, 25 August 1893, pp 191-3
17. ICE, vol 167, 1901-2, p 220
18. *Railway Magazine*, vol 9, 1901, p 102
19. ICE, vol 138, 1899, p 410
20. *Railway Magazine*, vol 8, 1901, pp 454-61; vol 9, 1901, pp 97-104
21. *The Engineer*, 10 November 1905, p 456
22. *Railway Magazine*, vol 25, 1909, pp 130-8
23. *The Engineer*, 15 September 1905, p 261
24. *The George the Fifths*, W. N. Davies; *The LNWR Recalled*, compiled E. Talbot (OPC, Poole, 1987), p 120
25. ICE, vol 196, 1914, p 112

Chapter 8

1. E. L. Ahrons *British Steam Locomotives 1825-1925*, (Loco Pub Co, London, 1927), p 166
2. Ibid, p 190
3. IME, 1898, pp 149-208
4. The Engineer, 21 February 1896, pp 182-3
5. 'Leaves from the Log of a Locomotive Engineer', R. Weatherburn, *Railway Magazine*, vol 34, 1914, pp 419-20
6. Ahrons, British Steam Locomotive, p 287
7. The Engineer, 17 December 1909, p 624
8. Engineering, 6 February 1907, pp 170-6; 27 March 1903, pp 414-5
9. The Engineer, 20 September 1907, p 286
10. Somerset & Dorset Locomotive History, Bradley & Milton (David & Charles, Newton Abbot, 1973), pp 145-6
11. Ibid, pp 149-50

Chapter 9

1. 'A Modern Locomotive History', E. S. Cox, ILE, vol 36, 1946, pp 115-22; also R. C. Bond, *A Lifetime with Locomotives* (Goose & Son, Cambridge, 1975), p 50
2. 'Experimental Results with a 3-cylinder Compound Locomotive', L. H. Fry
3. E. S. Cox, *Locomotive Panorama vol 1* (Ian Allan, London, 1965), pp 50-61
4. *The Engineer*, 17 December 1909, p 623
5. Cox, *Locomotive Panorama vol 1*, pp 659-61
6. ILE, vol 36, 1946, p 138
7. 'Testing Locomotives in the GWR', C. B. Collett, World Power Conference, London, 1924, pp 884-7
8. IME, vol 113, 1927, p 957
9. Cox, *Locomotive Panorama vol 1*, pp 74-5
10. Letter from Gresley to Churchward, 7 April 1914, Box Test/Test 4, NRM, York
11. 'High Pressure Locomotives', H. N. Gresley, IME, vol 120, 1931, p 138
12. *Railway Magazine*, 1930, p 93; also IME, vol 120, 1931, pp 107-13
13. Cox, *Locomotive Panorama vol 1*, pp 106-7
14. Bond, *A Lifetime with Locomotives*, pp 106-7
15. 'Ten years Experience with Turbine Locomotive No 6202', R. C. Bond, ILE, No 191, 1946, pp 182-265
16. Cox, *Locomotive Panorama vol 1*, pp 106-7
17. 'Air Resistance of passenger Trains', F. C. Johansen, IME, vol 134, 1936, pp 91-183
18. *Railway Gazette*, 31 January 1947, p 136

Index

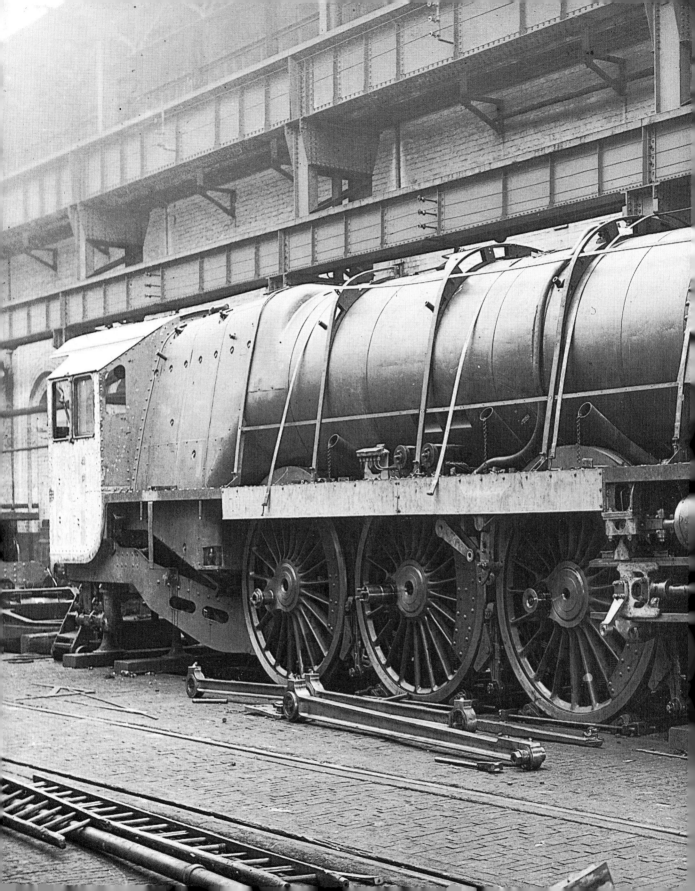